Industrial Robotics,
Machine Vision,
and Artificial Intelligence

RELATED TITLES

Industrial Robotics, Machine Vision, and Artificial Intelligence

Edited by
Ken Stonecipher

HOWARD W. SAMS & COMPANY

A Division of Macmillan, Inc.
4300 West 62nd Street
Indianapolis, Indiana 46268 USA

International Standard Book Number: 0-672-22502-6
Library of Congress Catalog Card Number: 89-60586

Acquisitions Editor: *James S. Hill*
Manuscript Editor: *J. L. Davis*
Illustrator: *T. R. Emrick*
Indexer: *Ted Laux*
Compositor: *Howard W. Sams & Company*

Printed in the United States of America

Trademarks

Contents

4   Three-Dimensional Machine Vision

R. C. Gonzalez and D. Brzakovic

7 Artificial Intelligence in Manufacturing

8   Artificial Intelligence/Expert Systems Scheduling in Manufacturing

Contributors

Shaheen Ahmad was born on April 27, 1960, in Bangladesh. He attended elementary, and junior and senior high schools in Greenwich, Southeast London, England. In 1980 he obtained an honors degree in physics from the Imperial College of Science and Technology and in 1984 he received a Ph.D. in mechanical engineering, in the area of real-time robot control with multiple processors. Since then he has been an assistant professor of electrical engineering at Purdue University. Dr. Ahmad's research interests include design of real-time robot control systems, robot-based assembly systems, and multiple manipulator coordination for industrial automation.

Dragana Brzakovic received her B.Sc. degree in electrical engineering from the University of Belgrade in 1976. She received her M.E. and Ph.D. degrees in electrical engineering at the University of Florida, Gainesville, in 1979 and 1984, respectively. Since September 1984, Dr. Brzakovic has been an assistant professor in the Department of Electrical and Computer Engineering at the University of Tennessee, Knoxville, where she teaches courses on pattern recognition, image processing, and computer vision. Her research interests include image understanding, knowledge-based pattern recognition and applied artificial intelligence, specializing in texture analysis.

Ralph C. Gonzalez received the Ph.D. degree in electrical engineering from the University of Florida, Gainesville, in 1970. Currently he is the president of Perceptics Corporation and Distinguished Service Professor of Electrical and Computer Engineering at the University of Tennessee, Knoxville. Dr. Gonzalez is a consultant to industry and government in pattern recognition, image processing, and machine learning. He is a coauthor of the books *Pattern Recognition Principles, Digital Image Processing, Syntactic Pattern Recognition: An Introduction,* and *Robotics: Control, Sensing, Vision, and Intelli-*

gence. He is also an associate editor of two technical journals and a fellow of the IEEE.

Thomas Hancock is a consultant for artificial intelligence applications of military and space projects. Formerly he was an engineer/scientist with the McDonnell-Douglas Astronautics Company, where he worked on command, control, communications, and intelligence (C^3I) systems. Previously, as a member of NASA's Jet Propulsion Laboratory, he helped develop global computing systems for NASA's Deep Space Network and the flight software on the Galileo Jupiter mission. He coauthored a book on the U.S. Air Force space shuttle operations and has published papers on artificial intelligence and space applications.

Harry G. Newman received the M.A. degree in computer science in 1975 from Sangamon State University, where he had previously obtained the M.A. degree in psychology. Currently he is the manager of Network Services, Bureau of Information and Communications Services, State of Illinois. He is also the president of Intelligroup, Inc., a consulting firm in control systems, laboratory systems, office automation, software, and data communications. Mr. Newman has taught hardware and software courses at Sangamon State University, and he has published three papers in technical journals and has three patents on electronic networks with circuits for data transmission.

Shawn Patrick started home study programming courses in 1963, while he was in junior high school. He earned a B.S. degree in mathematics and computer science from the University of Illinois, and has an M.B.A. from Sangamon State University. During his career he has been a programmer and systems analyst utilizing a variety of IBM mainframes and microcomputers. His background also includes large-scale applications systems design and data communications integration. Currently he is the assistant bureau chief of the Information Services Bureau for the Illinois State Police, where he has responsibility for one of that state's largest data communications networks.

Ken Stonecipher received an M.S. degree from Tennessee Technological University in 1973. Currently he is a systems consultant. Formerly a senior consultant to Fortune 500 companies, he has expertise in expert systems, robotics, and natural-language processing. Mr. Stonecipher has written eight articles and one book, *Industrial Robotics: A Handbook of Automated System Design.* At present he is preparing a series of articles on the selection, implementation, and development of artificial-intelligence/expert systems.

Preface

This book is a comprehensive text on the basic theory of the new technologies of industrial robotics, machine vision, and artificial intelligence. The following topics are included:

- Complex robot system components
- Machine vision system components
- Dimensioned machine vision analysis
- Sensors
- The basics of artificial intelligence
- Artificial intelligence in manufacturing
- Artificial intelligence/expert systems scheduling in manufacturing
- Glossary of terms

More importantly, the authors, who are leaders in these disciplines, discuss the impact of machine vision and artificial intelligence on industrial robotics.

The ultimate effect of this mingling of technologies is the flexible manufacturing system, or FMS. These systems are important to the future of factories because the needs of consumers will be very diverse. Manufacturers with FMSs will be able to manufacture goods in large quantities, as is being done today, and in small batches — without major modifications to the manufacturing line. The fixed automation lines that are expensive and time consuming to change are a product of the past.

The most important aspect of the FMS format is that the production machines can perform a wide variety of tasks. Industrial robots, as they are used today, can fill that need — up to a point. In the future, reliable manipulator arms that can work with hundreds of pounds of material or insert computer chips accurately into printed-circuit boards will also need to see and choose. Robots that can pick up and place objects, and see and make decisions, will be able to work with both large and small batches of products.

They will also be able to increase the quality of goods through consistent assembly processes. Above all, these machines will be able to decrease the cost of volume-produced goods with less than a 3% rejection rate.

To convert 20-year-old-plus manufacturing systems in the United States, robots must be able to adapt to existing factory requirements at a minimum cost of conversion. This cost can be greatly decreased with manipulator arms that can see the parts with which they work. These robots are able to see parts that are not consistently organized on a conveyor line. They are also able to orient themselves to a wider variety of manufacturing scenarios than has been done in the past — this factor is critical to a truly flexible system.

The final factor necessary to realize an FMS is that the robot or manipulator arm must also be able to make decisions. For example, one of the major characteristics of an FMS is the ability to combine large and small orders during the same production run. There may also be varying types of orders within the large and small batches. The robot system must be able to make decisions about reprogramming itself to accommodate the changes required in the production cycle. Artificial intelligence or, more specifically, expert systems combined with seeing robots will fill this need. They will also allow plant managers to stay informed of production cycles of robot workstations, production statistics, product quality information, system self-diagnostics, and computers coordinating the activities of the entire plant. Thus the combination of reliable and accurate robots, machine vision systems, and artificial intelligence/expert systems will be the basis of all FMSs in plants of the future.

The authors believe that the amalgamation of these technological advances will depend on the individual managers, engineers, and workers who implement them. Without an appropriate and exhaustive analysis for measuring the effectiveness of these technologies, misleading expectations could arise about the performance of these new technologies in a plant environment. Comprehensive managerial and engineering skills will never be obsolesced by technological advances. There are appropriate and inappropriate times and places for the integration of any technology. It therefore becomes more important than ever to understand the long-term goals of the corporation or organization so that the technology can best serve these goals — rather than the corporation or organization serving the technology.

The opinions expressed by the authors in this book are their own, and are not necessarily those of the organizations that employ the authors.

KEN STONECIPHER

Chapter 1

Understanding the Complex Components of Robot Systems

K. Stonecipher
Systems Consultant

1. Abstract

Without some comprehension of the complexity of robot systems it is impossible to understand the technological marriage of machine vision and artificial intelligence (AI) to robot systems.

The second section of this chapter deals with the concepts of robot end-effector interface design. In this section the discussion examines the basic elements of the end effector of a robot, such as wrist strength, compliance, overload characteristics, and breakaway design features. These are some of the design complexities of a robot wrist, which many people believe to be simple.

The third section deals with one of the most important components of any robot system: actuators. The discussion focuses on feedback components, accuracy, and the different types of actuator systems, such as hydraulic, pneumatic, and electric. The following elements of this section deal with control schemes and their importance.

The last section deals with kinematic algorithms and their importance to a robot system. It examines the design considerations of translating real-world movements, such as degrees of freedom, into mathematical formulas.

2. Robot/End-Effector Interface Design

The ability of the end effector to perform its functions is largely dependent on a number of variables. One of the most important factors in the performance of an end effector as it is selected is its ability to interface with the rest of the manipulator system. The biggest consideration in selecting a robot manipulator system is a high degree of flexibility in what it can perform at a particular workstation.

The interfacing of the manipulator and the end effector will affect the variability in the functions that the robot can perform. That is why it is necessary to look at a number of factors specifically, for example, how the manipulator system interfaces with the end effector and how these design considerations will affect the total functional performance of the manipulator.

The interface between the end effector and the manipulator must provide the end effector structurally with power to perform the functions. It must also convey data communications information for control to and from the end effector, and it must be structurally sound for the forces that are applied or transmitted to the wrist. Furthermore, it should be able to permit connections and disconnections in a consistent and quick manner. There should also be a high degree of accuracy once the end effector is connected to wrist and the manipulator to perform the repeated functions that are necessary during a production cycle. Also, the design of the interfacing between the end effector and the manipulator must be such that any sort of material in the workstation which could affect the performance of the end effector, such as oil, material, moisture, vibration, or even collisions, can be dealt with and will not affect the performance of the manipulator system.

As reported in an ICAM [Integrated Computer-Aided Manufacturing: ICAM 1980] study, the three major aspects of connection between the end effector and manipulator are strength, the wrist socket, and protection from the manipulator interfering with the end effector.

The *strength* of the wrist socket should be such that it should be able to support the weight of the end effector and also be able to withstand the inertial forces that arise from the functions being performed in that particular workstation. For example, during a pick-and-place operation, a great deal of inertia is applied to the wrist socket during a high-speed transport of a workpiece. It is necessary for the wrist socket to be able to support the weight of the end effector as well as that of the workpiece during this quick movement. Consideration should be given to loading factors in discussions with vendors in order that strength of the interface between the end effector and the manipulator can be adequately analyzed.

Compliance is the ability of the manipulator wrist sockets and end effector to accommodate certain forces or loads that may arise from the contact of the end effector with a solid object. The compliance of the wrist must be able to accommodate a wide range of end-effector interfacing so that not only can the initial production function be performed by that particular manipulator, but also a wide variety of effectors can be utilized with that same manipulator system. This is why it becomes economically advantageous to look at the most appropriate compliant interface in the wrist socket so as to accommodate a wide variety of motions and functions. Also, a good compliance system will enable the end effector to be inserted into the manipulator with a small amount of force. This enables the robot to use a number of tools as end effectors and to pick each one up as necessary in the production cycle. This factor has to do with protection considerations in regard to breakaway functions that may be necessary for protection of the robot manipulator if a collision is undergone by the end effector. Some type of breakaway protection should be built into the design of the interface between the end effector and the manipulator so that if there is any sort of collision, the entire manipulator is not damaged. The forces that may be exerted on the end effector require two conditions: (1) The mechanical action should be compliant, and (2) sensors in the wrist should signal to the workstation control computer that an error condition or exception has occurred, and to take an immediate action to deal with that contact, such as a complete stoppage of the manipulator at that particular step in the work cycle. The different types of designs that have been involved with breakaway protection for end effectors are mechanical fuses, detents, and preloaded springs.

Mechanical fuses are used because they are easily replaced and inexpensive. Fuses take the form of shearing pins that will break when there is any excessive force applied at the wrist. There may also be a small degree of "give" in the wrist prior to the breakage of some types of mechanical fuses.

Detents were first designed by John Hill of SRI International. They consist of two or more structural elements that are held in position with respect to one another by a spring-loaded mechanism. The element or elements are released by force applied to them.

Preloaded springs are the springs that act in conjunction with the wrist assembly so that any excessive force acting on it in any direction on the end effector will separate the end effector from the wrist in the breakaway action. There is a specific force range such that when that force exceeds that range, a breakaway action of the end effector is effected. Because they are resettable the preloaded springs are the most effective protection system, and the most desired mountings are between the end effectors and the wrist. Once an extraneous force has caused a breakaway action, the preloaded spring will reset itself automatically. The mechanical fuses, on the other hand, are the least desired protection system since they have to be manually reset once stress has been applied between the end effector and the wrist.

The most effective design consideration involving an overload between the wrist and the end effector is that any sort of breakaway or spring type of action should minimize the damage to the end effector and the total system. There should not be a total breakaway action in which the end effector is dropped onto the floor once excessive force is applied because of the exorbitant cost factors associated with the development of customized end effectors. Also, it should be stressed that a cabling system should not be used to prevent the end effector from falling to the floor. If the end effector is dangling from some sort of cabling system, and the manipulator is still active, then this dangling end effector cannot only damage existing material around the workstation but it also is a distinct safety hazard to any individual near the workstation. Also, if the end effector breaks away during a turning motion by the base or the manipulator, it can cause harm to personnel and material that may not even be in the direct proximity of the workstation.

Another consideration is that the end-effector breakaway should prevent damage to any other automated piece of equipment in the workstation. If an end effector becomes damaged and lodged in a particular workpiece, the breakaway action should ensure that the end effector would be sacrificed for the other types of automated equipment or fixed automation equipment such as a conveyor system. The greatest consideration here, though, is that the end effector should be sacrificed for the rest of the robot manipulator system.

The ICAM study [Integrated Computer Aided Manufacturing: ICAM 1980] mentions a test to determine the effectiveness of any sort of breakaway protection in a robot and manipulator system. The test involves displacing the end effector in each direction without rotating it and checking to ensure that it breaks away when a predetermined force limit is exceeded. In the next test the end effector is rotated slightly around an arbitrary point without allowing the center of the rotation to move. If it still breaks away after the force limit is exceeded, the end effector is fully protected. In other words, there should be certain points that have been determined in the previous analysis that are acceptable for breakaway action. In addition to these force tolerances, there should also be an action by the controller of the manipulator system to provide for the effect that the breakaway action has on the end effector. If at all possible, the end effector should be saved, but the overall functioning of the manipulator system is the chief protection priority. Again, the major concern is that no workers are injured and that no other equipment within the proximity of the workstation is damaged.

3. Actuators

The three types of actuators used in industrial robots are hydraulic, electric, pneumatic, or a combination of these.

Hydraulic Actuators

Hydraulic actuators have a simple design in regard to moving parts as compared with electric or pneumatic systems. Hydraulic actuators utilize an oil-based system to drive a cylinder which may move or actuate a component of the manipulator. There is a combination of servovalves and microprocessor control systems for this closed-loop feedback. There is also a high degree of repeatability and absolute accuracy when using hydraulic systems. This type of accuracy is closely associated with electric servomotor systems. In the early hydraulic robot design and testing, there was a problem with the actuator oscillating once it had reached the designated point. This bouncing effect, however, has been overcome through the ability to anticipate a "settling" prior to the next step in a particular function, such as the mobility of the manipulator to pick up a particular tool. Through software control a settling time can be programmed so that these types of oscillations associated with hydraulic systems can be overcome.

One of the problems associated with hydraulic systems is related to an oil-based fluid that operates the cylinder in the system. These fluids must be warmed up to operating temperature, so a "warm-up period" or "exercise" for the robot becomes necessary. This consideration should be made in regard to performance of a robot unit, especially if the robot may be operating in a plant environment where there are wide variations in temperature. These temperature variations could affect the performance of the hydraulic system due to problems with the viscosity of the oil. Another problem is that in some cases the fluid used is flammable, thus increasing the safety considerations necessary for a hazardous environment. Nonflammable fluids have been developed, but these may increase the cost factors associated with the total system.

There is also a factor of safety if a hydraulic line ruptures. It is then necessary to halt the entire system so that the line can be replaced. A line breakage may send hydraulic fluid into the workstation, which may land on and possibly damage any other machines or material being used.

Pneumatic Actuators

The second type of actuator is the pneumatic drive system. The major advantage of this system is that it does not require hydraulic fluid. With pneumatic drives, air drives a cylinder causing the actuator to operate. Control systems, through the form of feedback, control the basic manipulator.

Another advantage of the pneumatic drive system over the hydraulic system is that no extended warm-up period is necessary. Also, if there is any sort of break in the air lines of a pneumatic system, there is no leakage of liquid within the workplace. From the standpoint of safety considerations, no functional objectives having to do with the flammability of a fluid, such as in a hydraulic system, are needed with the pneumatic system.

Most applications of pneumatic drive systems are for pick-and-place types of operations. With pick-and-place operations, the actuator can act very quickly for picking a particular piece off a conveyor line and placing it in some other area.

Electric Actuators

The third type of actuator is the electric or the electric servosystem. The electric servosystem uses direct-current stepping motors with microcomputers for control and feedback in this closed-loop system. These types of robots are used very commonly in industry, but it should be noted that the electric servomotors as compared with hydraulic systems cannot handle as much load weight. The biggest advantage with electric servomotor systems is that they have a high degree of accuracy and also that they occupy a limited amount of space in the workplace. With pneumatic and hydraulic systems, extra space must be allowed for the power units associated with these manipulators. With electric servomotors, the entire system can be contained within the manipulator itself. The only associated space may be with the microprocessor controller keyboard, which may be placed some distance from the manipulator itself.

Actuator Design Considerations

The main design considerations for actuators, as shown in Fig. 1, are rigidity, positional characteristics, size and shape of the work volume, and microprocessor control.

Rigidity
The rigidity of the actuator is important because of its effect on the repeatability and accuracy of the manipulator system. Rigidity is the ability of the manipulator to hold a workpiece in one place, as in a drilling operation. If the robot does not have this type of rigidity, then the actions of, say, a particular drill may move the workpiece from where it was originally placed.

The robot should be able to adjust the rigidity of the manipulator system in order to accommodate a wide range of work loads that may be associated with a particular workplace in the future. If the robot is going from a pick-and-place function to a drilling function, it will be necessary for the support staff to adjust the mobility of the manipulator once it has to perform a drilling type of operation. Therefore it becomes necessary to be able to adjust the rigidity of the manipulator either through hardware or software or both.

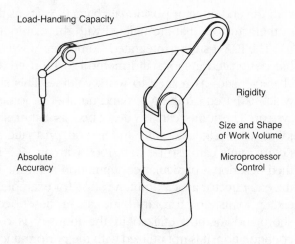

Load-Handling Capacity

Rigidity

Size and Shape
of Work Volume

Absolute
Accuracy

Microprocessor
Control

Fig. 1. Robot actuator design considerations.

Size and Shape of Work Volume

The size and shape of the work volume for the manipulator will directly affect the type of actuator that will be most effective for this particular application. Work volume generally has been described as a region which can be reached by a specific point on the wrist of the manipulator. It does not include the length associated with a particular tool on the end effector. The justification for this is that because of the functions associated with the workstation, a customized end-effector tool may be utilized. The vendor cannot anticipate the length of a customized end effector, so that the most consistent area to be considered in regard to work line measurements is the distance reached by the wrist exclusive of the end effector.

Design considerations when analyzing a workstation should be that the actuators should reach beyond the limits of the workspace to accommodate the length of the end effector that will finally be used in that system. It should also be noted that the safety factors for a particular manipulator system should be considered only after the total length of the manipulator wrist and end effector have been fully described. This full manipulator length, inclusive of the end effector, will affect the safety zone of the manipulator in its specific workstation.

The positional characteristics of the actuator combined with the manipulator will directly affect the characteristics of the arm in the workplace. The end effector and manipulator will not show the same positional characteristics as when the end effector is not placed on the manipulator. This is because of the added stresses and forces of the end effector on the total system. So it should be noted that when considering performance characteristics for the functions associated with the workplace, an analysis should be made without the end effector for each characteristic, but it should also be combined with the end-effector positional characteristics as they affect the performance of the actuators that are utilized with the manipulator.

The ICAM study [Integrated Computer Aided Manufacturing: ICAM 1980] has designated a shorthand method to be used as an aid in defining robot characteristics as related to work volume. This shorthand is a classification which is based on the types and number of joints that are in a manipulator system. The joints can be described as either sliding or prismatic. Sliding joints are designated with an "S" and prismatic are designated with a "P." Rotary joints can also be described with an "R." The shorthand utilized can then describe a particular configuration from the base of the manipulator to the end-effector attach point. A robot, for example, that has a rotary base, two sliding joints, and a rotary joint can be described as an R2SR. This type of shorthand method utilized in the industry is only for the arm and base configuration; it is not utilized with the performance characteristics of the end effector.

Microprocessor Control

The actuator is a component of a total robot control system. It is necessary to have a good understanding of the role the controller plays in this total system. The two types of systems used for motion control are open-loop and closed-loop systems. An *open-loop control system* is one in which the robot actuators are controlled by mechanical limitations or stops rather than the software control of the microcomputer controller. A *closed-loop system* is one in which the information from the actuators is provided to a particular microcomputer controller which transforms these into specific positions or points of the manipulator. The software directs a particular manipulator to perform certain functions. These points can be described using Cartesian coordinates, those points in an *xyz* system which give the robot its internal orientation as to functions it has to perform. See Fig. 2. With this orientation,

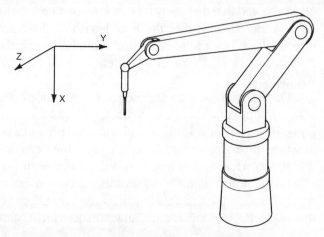

Fig. 2. Robot Cartesian coordinate orientation.

the microcomputer controller in the robot knows where the particular manipulator arm is at any point. A set of points is generated for each accessof the manipulator.

The problem with this is that the robot manipulator controller must transform the actuator feedback information in Cartesian coordinates into information in the real world. Dealing with real-world coordinates requires a higher level of computer control. With the use of a minicomputer, it becomes possible for a higher level of sophistication as to orientation of the manipulator in a work environment. The trade-off is the cost of the particular minicomputer controller, which is more expensive than a microcomputer controller with a robot. The additional computer power is necessary because of the higher level of numeric transformations that are necessary for a sophisticated robot operation. A microcomputer controller does not have the "horsepower" necessary to make all the transformations in a short time because of the volume of numerical information that is coming from the servomotor actuators. A minicomputer has an increased capacity to deal with the larger amounts of numeric information coming back from the actuators and also to store more information about the positioning of the manipulator in a real-world situation.

Actuator Performance

The performance functions that can be analyzed in regard to the actuator are its dynamic capabilities, stability, spatial resolution, control accuracy, repeatability, and compliance. It should also be noted that the performance considerations vary, depending on the type of actuator that is used, such as the servohydraulic system.

Dynamic Capabilities

The dynamic performance considerations describe how fast the manipulator can move, the ability of the manipulator to stop at a specific point, and the degree of drift that may be associated with the manipulator over an extended length of time. These dynamic properties are important because they will affect the total cycle time that a robot will find necessary to perform specific functions. Because of the physics of the manipulator structure, the desired dynamic performance characteristics of a robot are difficult to achieve. The inertia associated with a particular load and its effect on its end effectors worsens the performance of a particular manipulator. Also, the inertia and its effect on the absolute accuracy of the positioning of the particular joints are also considerations. The mass of a particular piece and the inertia associated with that piece will directly affect the performance of a manipulator. Thesewill affect the total load that the servomotor actuators will have to deal with during a rapid acceleration or deceleration.

The factor to keep in mind is that most robots work on a proportional-integral-derivative controller or a proportional-error ratio [Desforges and Dubewsky 1979]. The microprocessor controller is looking for variations of information as to the state of the shaft of the servomotor as compared to a specific number. For example, if the robot is in a stable state, the proportional-error ratio equals zero. If the robot needs to move forward a number of degrees, then the proportional-error ratio increases until an unsteady state occurs and forces the robot servomotor to advance a number of revolutions. The same is in effect for checking the performance of a servomotor. If a servomotor goes beyond the proportional-error ratio equal to zero, the controller will tell the servomotor to forward drive or back drive until it reaches a ratio of zero. With this in mind it should be noted that most controllers must be tuned for any loads up to the maximum specifications as specified by the manufacturer. It will take cooperation between the vendor and the user to define what those maximum loads and the inertial forces being placed on the servo may be. When these have been defined, the vendor will have to tune the manipulator system through interaction with the microcomputer controller to ensure that there is no overshooting of targets, especially in a pick-and-place operation where a full sweep of the robot's arm is anticipated. These types of tuning factors may trade off in the total performance or cycle time that the robot has to perform its functions. This is necessary because of the fact that, through this tuning for maximum initial loads, the speeds for acceleration and deceleration may be controlled by a number of means. This "reflected-link inertia" can be seen on the performance of a robot where the boom is extended at a rapid rate. This rapid extension of the boom plus the weight of particular tool in the end effector plus the load being grasped by the end effector will greatly affect the performance of the controller. In the past the way to deal with these high load factors has been to break up or segment an operation like this into two or more positions when the particular trajectory of the manipulator is being used at its maximum point. This has enabled the controller to maintain control of the manipulator with these high inertial factors being applied to it.

A method by which robots can be trained to do this is to incorporate what has been described as *via points* to bring the manipulator into lower-inertial modes for part of a function which may require high-inertial modes if done in one movement [Paul 1981]. Via points are points where the tool tip on the end effector or manipulator arm should pass through in an operation but briefly stops at, which will lower the inertial load factors on the manipulator system. For example, a manipulator rather than having a tool at the full reach of the boom may retract the boom and stop at a midway point between the starting and stopping point and then start up again so that the load factor does not put a great deal of pressure on the servomotors and the boom. It should be noted that the use of via points (see Fig. 3) can cause some damage to a manipulator if they are placed inappropriately. The reason is this. If a particular via point is used where there is a full-speed stop and a start in the opposite direction, a great strain will be put on the manipulator and servomotors. In some cases where a system is utilized, the strain can actually bring the manipulator to the point of rupturing the hydraulic hoses because there is no way to buffer or ease the pressure that is being applied to those hydraulic actuators.

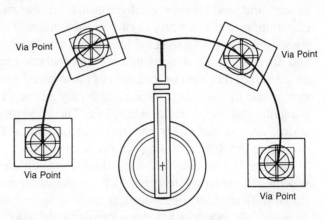

Fig. 3. Robot manipulator via points (top view).

Stability

The second major type of control is stability — the ability of the robot to avoid oscillations that may occur when utilizing a particular tool. Oscillations are simply vibrations that result from the servomotors' trying to adjust to the particular load placed on them and the controller not being able to reach a steady state and sending commands back to the servomotors to correct these operations. According to the ICAM study, oscillations are detrimental to the functions of a robot for the following reasons:

1. They impose additional wear on the mechanical and hydraulic parts of the arm.
2. They make the tool follow a different path in space during repetitions of the same movement.
3. They can increase the time needed for a tool to stop at the precise position.
4. They may cause the tool to overshoot the intended stopping position and make it collide with something.

The two types of oscillations that can occur in a particular function are dampened and undampened. Dampened operations are those which can also be called *transient oscillations*, which will eventually decay to the point where they do not exist. Undampened oscillations, when they occur in a system [Grossman 1977], will continue to grow and can damage the workstation and the robot. There are also oscillations which may occur when a particular manipulator is not in a steady-state condition. The persistent oscillations are ones where the controller again is trying to reach stabilization in sending multiple signals to servomotors to reach that stable state, but the condition is repeatedly overcorrecting or undercorrecting itself.

Please keep in mind that when designers of robots have to choose servomotor and controller systems, they try to anticipate a wide variety of load factors and end-effector configurations for the market. This results in a distribution of different types of control features which may not incorporate some of these special material loading factors in relation to different types of end effectors and functions that the manipulator may face in the real world. As a result of this, the combination of customized end effectors and functions may result in oscillation factors that may occur in the workplace or in a particular test mode in the workplace. The wide range of velocities, accelerations, and inertial loads can result in oscillation features which must be overcome through a "tuning" of the total system.

Research has also been conducted on different types of controlling schemes to overcome features such as oscillation and to maintain robot arm stability. There have been designs such as special dedicated circuitry which automatically monitors when a particular initial load velocity and sweep of the manipulator is near its maximum and will decelerate the arm when it is within specific points [Lieberman and Wesley 1977].

The joints of the manipulator may also lock when a certain function is being performed. In other words, if the base has performed its function, it may lock into position so the manipulator may move itself, or the joints of the manipulator may lock when the end effector or wrist is performing a particular function. This locking of joints is referred to as *total coincidence*. This total coincidence is the ability of the robot to dissipate off some of these inertial load factors so that it may begin moving in another direction or in the opposite direction.

A problem associated with this type of design feature is that when hydraulic actuators are used (unless there is constant pressure applied in the hydraulic lines) some of the fluids in these lines may drop the pressure to the actuator cylinders, resulting in the decay of the repeatability factors of the unit. That is why it is necessary to make sure that if a high degree of repeatability in accuracy is necessary, a comprehensive analysis is done concerning the unit's ability to deal with high load acceleration and deceleration factors.

Another example of conditions which can impair the stability of a unit is when a piece is dropped by an effector. This will cause the controller to have to deal with adjustments in the particular load factor and it may result in oscillations in a manipulator that does not have good controlling features.

Spatial Resolution
The next major area of control is spatial resolution. Spatial resolution, as

described by the ICAM report, concerns the movement of a robot arm at the tool tip. It is the function of the total microcomputer servo closed-loop system whereby the smallest increment of rotation of the servomotor is achieved. This has to do more with the smallest increment available to the microprocessor controller than the smallest unit available to the shaft of a particular servomotor or group of servomotors. It should be noted that this type of resolution again is a control factor whether it is within the microcomputer or the shaft. The end result is the smallest degree of control that the user will have when programming the particular manipulator system.

Spatial resolution is directly affected by the mechanical makeup of the particular robot manipulator system used. Even when a robot is assembled and tested, there are still mechanical inaccuracies which will affect the performance of that robot. That is why we have boom and gantry types of robots as compared with free-standing robots to do chores such as precision assembly work. In terms of spatial resolution, these controlling factors are the ability of the user to overcome the inherent causes of mechanical inaccuracies which occur in every type of robot system. No robot manipulator is 100% accurate with all end effectors and tools 100% of the time. Therefore there has to be control at the most fundamental level to overcome the physics of the problems with the mechanics of the basic unit.

When two manipulator positions differ by single increment of a specific joint, these two manipulator positions are called *adjacent*. This type of nomenclature should be used when one is working in an *xyz* Cartesian coordinate system. If a manipulator is to stay in one position to perform a series of functions, then the adjacent manipulator positions or coordinates should be determined so that the maximum cycle speed can be attained. Or if a particular manipulator is to perform a series of functions in one position then move to another position and perform these same functions, there will be adjacent coordinates which the robot planner can analyze so that he or she may be able to normalize the number of positions necessary and thereby reduce the number of command increments necessary to perform a wide variety of functions.

Because of the load factors that a long-tool end effector produces on the servomotor in the wrist of the manipulator, these spatial resolutions of the wrist-joint training can be very difficult to make. To overcome problems of control in this area, vendors have utilized what is called a low-resolution feedback transducer in the wrist joint. This transducer supplies a controller with feedback information specific only to the tool length rather than the arm length. This transducer increases the accuracy of the end effector in the wrist joint and also supplies the controller with information it may more appropriately utilize.

Another condition that will affect the performance of the manipulator system is whether a total computer control system is utilized or a hand-held trainer is utilized. With a hand-held trainer or teach pendant, the user or trainer is usually moving the robot system in small increments to get the type of accuracy necessary for the type of operation. This results in a higher number of manipulator control points that go into the system to perform that type of operation. A computerized control system has the ability to not only list all the manipulator control points in the total training session, but to also deal with center-point control which will directly affect tool point control in the training process. The computer simply assists in the total training of the system because of the fact that it will help to normalize the number of points necessary for the specific function. Without this type of control and feedback, as when a teach pendant is used, there is a higher number of incremental steps in the total teach process.

Control Accuracy

Accuracy is composed of three factors: (*a*) the resolution of the control components, (*b*) the inaccuracies of mechanical components such as linkages, gears, beam length, and deflections, and (*c*) an arbitrary point or target in a Cartesian coordinate envelope.

Accuracy is different from such terms as resolution and repeatability. See Figs. 4 and 5. Accuracy is the ability of the manipulator to differentiate between two adjacent control points in a target. Absolute accuracy is the ability of the manipulator system to come back every time to exactly the same target regardless of the adjacent control points. There will be a lower degree of accuracy as compared with repeatability when the two are described by robot vendors. The problems associated with accuracy are that the mechanical components and subcomponents of the entire manipulator system will directly affect the absolute accuracy of the total system. The inaccuracies that affect the total system are position drift and positional error. These special resolution factors will determine the degree of accuracy in a robot system.

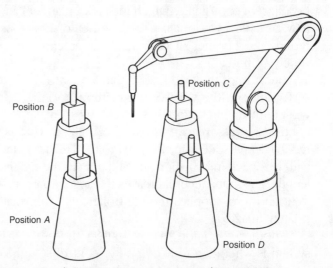

Position B

Position C

Position A

Position D

Fig. 4. Robot control accuracy/repeatability.

The physical factors or mechanical factors that affect the accuracy of a manipulator are the actual design and meshing of the gears, linkage factors, payloads that are being handled, the movements of the particular manipulator in cycle, and the actual weight of a load on the physical beam of the manipulators. *Backlash* occurs when particular factors in rotary axes, for example, can actually begin to backdrive the gears. This will affect the positional accuracy on a specific target point. With heavy payloads there is also an associated beam deflection. *Beam deflection* is the effect of gravity on the axis that may occur when a manipulator is in an extended mode. Beam deflection can also lead to resident oscillations, especially if there is no factor to deal with these heavy loads.

The accuracy of the manipulator system can be increased through the use of total computer control rather than a small teach mode with a microcomputer controller. With higher-level computer controls, such as a minicomputer, the system is able to calculate a set of coordinate joint positions to place the tool tip of the end effector in a specific position independently of factors such as beam deflection and backjoint. In other words, the computer is able to incorporate the algorithms of performance of the system and algorithms of loads and inertia and still deal with these factors and move the manipulator to a specific point requested by the trainer or user.

A microcomputer or minicomputer controller system can be trained to deal with a wider variety of shapes and load factors that may affect the performance of the manipulator. It can incorporate internally such factors as clutching mechanisms so that acceleration and deceleration of the servomotors is minimized with high load factors that may affect the positional accuracy of the system. Also, any sort of geometric analysis, such as coordinate planes, can be fed into the total microcomputer controller system so that it has more information and can calculate more geometric data as to point positioning on the particular workpiece and normalization of the steps necessary to perform a specific function. The fact is that most microcomputer controller systems give the user more flexibility to deal with more real-world environments, such as the mechanical inaccuracies of the manipulator system, and also a wider range of positional geometrics necessary for a wide range of workstations. The microcontroller is able to compensate for factors that affect the positional accuracy of the total system. This microcontroller type of enhancement through a minicomputer controller greatly aids in the performance of the total system because it can deal with larger volumes of information more quickly as compared with a microcontroller which may be internal to the manipulator. In this type of control hierarchy the minicomputer acts as a master controller, and the microcontroller in the robot acts as subcontroller.

Through the use of a microcontroller, inaccuracies that may be determined in research and development can be programmed into the total system so that a higher degree of accuracy is achieved [Sardis and Lee 1979]. These accuracy error factors are a reality of the production workspace and should be accounted for through the aid of a microcontroller.

The types of accuracy needed in a total robot system can be described as universal, minor universal, major local, and minor local. Universal accuracy considerations are factors that may occur at any accuracy point within the reach of the robot manipulator. Minor universal accuracy factors may occur from the major universal range to the point of a number of feet of accuracy within the positioning of the robot manipulator. Major local accuracy factors can be accountable through a number of feet or meters down to 1 in (2.54 cm) of positional accuracy, and minor local accuracy factors are those which occur from 1 in down to zero inches or millimeters of repeatability.* The accuracy of the target point should be the concern of the user through the analysis that has been done previously. The nomenclature is not as significant as some way of designating the positional accuracy of the manipulator.

Repeatability

Repeatability is the function whereby the robot manipulator is able to repeat or reposition itself into a position that was previously trained or commanded through instructions via the microcomputer controller. A distinction should be made between repeatability and accuracy because these two terms, while used interchangeably, do not mean the same thing. Both repeatability and accuracy will be used in evaluating the controlling system of the robot, and so the definition of each term should be thoroughly understood. See Fig. 5. The three factors that can be used to define the repeatability are resolution, mechanical components of the robot system, and target positioning.

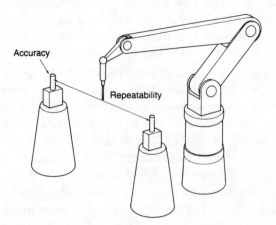

Fig. 5. Robot repeatability versus accuracy.

---

*Those that have been specifically mentioned are simply recommendations by the author.

The factors that influence the repeatability of the manipulator system are its resolution and the mechanical components of the manipulator system. Target positioning is not considered a major priority when defining repeatability. The only factor to keep in mind is the ability of the robot to return to a previously trained position. This is in contrast to accuracy or absolute accuracy, in which the ability of the manipulator to return to an arbitrary target position is extremely important. In other words, repeatability in regard to target positioning is simply trying to return to the most approximate position that has been previously trained. It is not a factor when determining the absolute accuracy of target positioning. When comparing repeatability and accuracy, the factors used to determine repeatability will always be of a greater value than absolute accuracy or accuracy when considered in the context of the resolution and the anomalies of the mechanics of the manipulator base.

The factors that affect repeatability are a result of the type of control system and the different mechanical subcomponents that make up the manipulator. The inaccuracies of the microcontroller system combined with the inaccuracies of the mechanical subcomponents affect the accuracy of the system. These factors also affect the repeatability of the system with the result that there is no absolute-accuracy positioning system for a robot 100% of the time. There is a high degree of repeatability of the gantry robot manipulator system in specific environments, but again it does not have absolute repeatability 100% of the time. For a free-standing robot the repeatability factor is lower than for robots designed for precision assembly types of functions. The precision assembly types of functions, such as with gantry robots, have a higher degree of repeatability and accuracy.

The nomenclature used to determine repeatability and absolute accuracy is to assign a factoring system such as the absolute target position and the commanded or trained target position. The difference between the absolute target position and the position where the robot manipulator comes back to the repeated position is the factor which will assist in determining the accuracy and repeatability of the total robot manipulator. This measure of repeatability has been used as a standard in certain industries to determine the accuracy and repeatability factors of a particular manipulator in a production environment. Another factor to keep in mind is that with accuracy and repeatability, there is a decaying nature of both of these factors over a long period. Consequently there are terminologies of short-term and long-term repeatability and accuracy. Again, the electrical components and the mechanical subassemblies of a manipulator system will wear out and also decay from the calibration settings over a long period. Also, with other factors such as a high degree of load and inertial forces being placed on the manipulator system, the length of short-term as compared with long-term repeatability will also be accelerated. The factors that have had an impact on both short-term and long-term repeatability, such as the difference between the absolute target position and the repeated target position, can be defined as manipulator drift. *Drift* is the outcome of the mechanical subcomponent inaccuracies and also such factors as aging, temperature factors, and loading factors on the manipulator which will affect the performance of the total manipulator system.

There are certain relationships between resolution, accuracy, and repeatability which should be noted. These have been described in the ICAM study:

1. Spatial resolution describes the smallest increment of motion that the robot can control at the tool tip.
2. Accuracy relates to the robot spatial-resolution–defined positional ability (including mechanical and accuracy) to an arbitrary fixed-target position.
3. Repeatability describes the positional error of the tool tip when it is automatically returned to a position previously programmed.
4. Repeatability will generally always be better than accuracy excluding drift.

A lot of research has been done to determine if a microcomputer or minicomputer can translate tool-point or real-world positions into joint or servomotor positions. The problem inherent with this basically good idea is that with the state of the art of robot manipulator systems, the minicomputer or microcomputer controller used to make these conversions or translations may yield inaccuracies of the total system. These inaccuracies occur because the research that has been done to date in making these translations or conversions is still being refined. Eventually there will be assistance from a minicomputer or microcomputer controller which will translate real-world positions in a workstation into the information necessary to control the joints or servomotors of the manipulator system to a high degree of positional accuracy. The ability to do this type of conversion from joint servomotor positions to the tool end-effector position and recording these positions has been called the *back solution*. The ability to convert the digitized end-effector tool position back to a set of servomotor joint positions has been termed the *arm solution*.

The actual problem in making these translations is the way that the vendors or the microcomputer coders develop the algorithms necessary to make the translations from real-world positioning to the positions of the servomotors for the joints in the manipulator. If these algorithms are not done in a comprehensive manner or if the microcomputer or minicomputer program is restricted in the use of loading-point representations of data, then this directly affects the accuracy of the manipulator system. Also, if there are any types of scaling factors involved in the system or load inertial factors, this can also affect the accuracy of the position. The most common type of problem incurred when doing this type of translation is in rounding errors whereby the microprocessor, because of its internal architecture, will begin to round off numbers in making the translations between the real-world and the servomotor joint positions. These rounding factors will affect the accuracy of the manipulator.

It should be noted that the higher the floating-point controller in making these translations, the lower the degree of error in the conversion process. If there is a high degree of numeric digit representation, such as a minimum of eight to ten places to the right of the decimal point, this will ensure a closer degree of repeatability and accuracy when making the translation process.

The other factors that will affect this translation process in regard to repeatability is to have a vendor develop the kinematic equations or algorithms used in both the arm solution and back solution process. Again, the algorithms are only as good as the design of the initial algorithm. The factors that will affect the kinematic equations or algorithms for arm solution and back solution are (1) the joint extensions and rotations, (2) the length of the arm, (3) the offset distances between successive joint axes, and (4) the axes between successive joint axes.

The factors that have been previously described can be developed in an algorithm in terms of an exact one-to-one relationship, or scaling values must be used to make those translations. In the past the industry has used what is called a linear variable-differential transformer, or LVDT. The LVDT uses sensor information, such as from an optical digital encoder on servomotors, and goes through a transformation process to come up with a precise measurement for the different factors that are affecting the kinematics of the manipulator system. There is also a calibration process which may be utilized for the transducer, which itself can be set.

There has been a tendency for the individuals that develop the arm algorithms to develop these with the least amount of code possible. The problem with this is that when any sort of conversion process may be necessary it may affect the accuracy of the manipulator system. Most vendors expect their clients to use simple tendon trainers for the positioning of the manipulator system and then to play back that type of positioning system. They also utilize a set of Cartesian coordinates in which the microcomputer controller will perform the necessary conversion factors. The problem is that there should be a broad range of kinematics equations necessary to deal with a wide range of functions to be performed in the workplace to take in account the least error factors in regard to accuracy. There should be documentation as to how the algorithms have been used in making these conversion factors and how they affect the total control of the robot system. Another factor to keep in mind is that if the basic cycle speed of the microprocessor doing these calculations is comparatively slow, then a trade-off in the number of kinematic translations that the computer has to perform will directly affect the speed of the manipulator. If there is some type of off loading or coprocessing being done to make these conversions, this can speed up the total conversion process of one processor making these kinematic translations and loading these to a master controller processor to perform the specific comments for direction of the manipulator.

Another factor that can influence the accuracy of the manipulator system has been described as singularity. *Singularity* involves the geometry of the manipulator and also the angles of the various joints that will affect the total accuracy of the system. When the axes of two different joints become closer aligned, it becomes necessary to change the end-effector positioning to perform certain functions, resulting in larger changes in the joint positioning. A matrix has been used which mathematically examines these linkage systems to determine the extent the end effector will have to move or turn in any direction per unit of motion for a particular joint. This matrix is inverse in its relationships because it describes end-effector units or rotations as they are inversely proportional to joint motion positioning. Robotics designers can get around factors such as singularity by establishing another joint as described by the Jacobian matrix. Data should be available from the vendors as to which Jacobian matrix was utilized in their robot design. These factors are critical when looking at precision types of operations because the functions of a number of joints will directly influence the end-effector positioning and repositioning in a production cycle.

As a result of singularity, the microcomputer controller is trying to deal with a specific positional accuracy. By rounding off the factors of the different joint alignments and also end-effector positioning, it tries to round off the values represented. The end defect that may happen is that the manipulator will perform these motions in a very jerky fashion. The jerky motions will not be in the manipulator armatures, but they will be in the performance of the end-effector tool. The end-effector positions and the joint servopositions being processed by the microcomputer controller, when the rounding factors are taken in effect, result in slightly amplified position commands from the microprocessor. These result in the jerky motion that is seen at the end effector.

Most robotics vendors have utilized end-effector positioning in specific workplaces with Cartesian coordinate positions. The Cartesian coordinate positioning used a set of *xy, xz,* and *yz* planes to determine the angles and orientations of the manipulator and the end effector. There is also the use of pitch, yaw, and roll about the end-effector's main axes. This combination of positioning in orientation is referred to as *Cartesian positioning.* It enables the vendors to describe a positioning system that is independent of the type of manipulator used and also will aid in making transformations between different types of systems and in a wide variety of workplaces. Vendors have used a variety of methods to assist them in problems of repeatability related to Cartesian orientation:

1. Sensors can be positioned at specific points so that there can be some form of drift compensation during the operation of the manipulator. These sensors will provide information which the controller can translate into orientation and drift correction commands.

2. Through Cartesian coordinate positioning descriptions, a set of operations can be trained on one specific workpiece and then the same coordinate orientations can be utilized on other similar workpieces in different types of positioning and orientation. These types of calculations are important when a manipulator has to deal with a wide variety of positioning and orientations of workpieces in a specific workstation.

3. In a production environment, the workpieces may be on a moving conveyor system. With a Cartesian coordinate nomenclature, it becomes possible to transform the specific (x, y, z) position to the moving positions of a conveyor system by having the controller instantaneously add those (x, y, z) orientations during the production system.

4. When utilizing a teach pendant during a manual control mode, it becomes much easier for the controller to translate these steps into smooth motions of the end-effector tool. A good computer controller is able to translate the manual positions trained by an operator into smooth, coordinating motions of the servomechanism joints and the end-effector tools.

Compliance

Compliance can be defined as the displacement of the end-effector tool relative to external forces or torques that may be applied to it. When a manipulator is said to have high compliance, it means that the end-effector tool moves a great deal in response to a small force applied to it. This manipulator can be defined as "spongy" or "springy." If the manipulator has low compliance, then the end effector will move very little and the manipulator is described as being a "stiff" system.

As a result of the different customized end-effector tools and also the different functions being performed in workplaces, compliance factors are difficult to measure. The forces and torques that can be applied to end effectors may be linear in some natures, may be arithmetical in other workplaces, and geometrical in other positions. The reaction of the end effector depends on the amount of time that a function is performed, the type of end effector that is used, the orientation of the end effector in regard to a specific function such as drilling, and any other forces that are applied to the total system [Goldhammer 1978].

Rotational changes, displacements, or movement may affect the total force performance of the system. Also, we have noted that length of time the functions are performed can affect the mechanical subcomponents and electrical subassemblies of the manipulator system. This would also have to be taken into account when trying to calculate compliance data. There are other factors in a hydraulic or pneumatic system, such as viscosity or consistency of error pressure, that would result in varying the data necessary to complete compliance factoring. The final factor that can affect compliance data is the rate at which a specific function is being performed. If, for example, one drill is rotating at a certain speed, the effect on the end-effector tool will be very different from that of a high-speed drill of the same nature applying larger torques. So it must be noted that factors such as revolutions per minute and functions such as drilling operations could change the compliance data being recorded. In short, compliance factoring is extremely difficult and should only be performed by research and development activities or by the specific vendors themselves. If the compliance factoring data is compiled by an individual who does not have a comprehensive background in mechanical and electrical engineering, it may be totally incorrect.

4. Joint-Arm Kinematics

Joint-arm kinematics can be defined as the geometry of robot arm motions with respect to fixed-reference-point coordinate systems without the impact of forces or moments that may cause motion. The importance of having a basic understanding of kinematics is that it deals with the configuration of the robot arm and the functions of the robot arm in regard to spatial coordinates. It also deals with the relationships between the joints, i.e., the position and the orientation of the robot arm in space. Many types of orientation will permit the end effector to reach a specific coordinate in space. Robot designers have to deal with the kinematics of the particular system because this will influence the flexibility and degrees of freedom of the given robot system. It is important that individuals interested in robots have a basic understanding of kinematics; if they have to do some "fine tuning" on a system or make recommendations of fine tuning to the vendor, they can then supply the proper kinematics data so that the vendor may make changes either in the algorithms of the controller on the robot arm or through specialized research and development activities. An understanding of kinematics will enable one to perform the necessary calculations of the kinematic orientations of the arm which would translate into algorithms that affect the motion and orientation of the robot arm.

Degrees of Freedom

The direct impact of an understanding of robot-arm kinematics is in the area of control and degrees of freedom. The robot arm must have a significant amount of freedom to be able to perform a wide variety of functions necessary in a workplace. It must also be able to move through these orientations in a simple fashion to minimize the time it takes to move from one coordinate point to another in a preprogrammed sequence. Not only does the robot arm or armature "links" have to be considered, but also the angle and orientation of the end effectors must be appropriate so that the robot system can perform the functions required of it.

In terms of degrees of freedom, these kinematic components shown in Fig. 6 relate to motions such as vertical, horizontal, and rotational. A robot system that had one vertical motion, one horizontal motion, and one rotational motion is said to have three degrees of freedom. Another degree of freedom would exist if the axle arm were to move in an in-and-out type of motion; this may be considered the fourth degree of freedom. Most industrial robot systems require at least six degrees of freedom of motion. Again it is important to note that we are not talking about the actual end-effector points directly, but the arm or links of the robot system.

Once the number of degrees of freedom has been designated or ascertained by the robot designer, it then becomes necessary to translate these into the kinematic orientations for that particular robot system. Most robot designers have to give their machines as much kinematic freedom as possible so that the machines will be as flexible as possible and able to handle a wide variety of functions. It is important to note that there are specific kinematic algorithms or transformations that will directly affect the performance of the robot system. That is why it becomes necessary to have a good understanding of the basic kinematics of the system so that if questions are raised as to extending the flexibility or basic kinematic algorithms of the

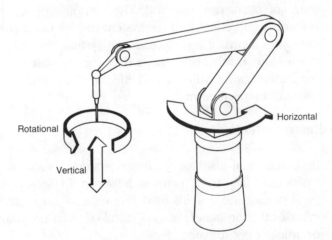

Fig. 6. Kinematic components of robot motion.

system, these questions may be formulated intelligently. As more kinematic planning goes into a particular robot system, the basic cost of the robot system increases. Therefore it becomes necessary for the robot designer to develop a kinematic plan for a particular system but not to overdesign the system so that the cost factors become too exorbitant for a commercial market.

Design Considerations

Some of the design considerations in regard to kinematics are follows.

The first consideration deals with the angular orientation of the end effector when it is in a specific workspace. When the end effector is to be used in certain work functions, the movement of the entire arm should not be necessary to perform this function. The arm links should be responsible for the gross movements of the robot system, and the end effector should be used for the fine movements of the system. An analogy would be the use of your arm and hand to pick up a pencil. Often you do not have to move your entire arm when you want to pick up the pencil; you only need to use your fingers to pick it up.

One component of the arm may be attached to a base which supports the entire system, whereas the other end or links of the robot are free to move and attach to an end effector. The motions of the particular joint in this system are relative to the specific motions of the links of the entire system and also influence the motions of the wrist and end effector. The important objective is that the arm components must bring the end-effector tool to a place where it can perform functions such as grasping. The arm subassembly may consist of three to four degrees of freedom of movement, which will position the end effector at a specific coordinate that is the workpiece. The wrist of the subassembly will consist of a type of rotary motion which can be defined in terms of pitch, yaw, and roll. The combination of these three factors will orient the end effector of the system to pick out a particular workpiece. For the components of a six-joint robot system, the arms can be defined as the positioning mechanism, the wrists can be used as a coarse orientation mechanism, and finally the end-effector subassembly can be used as the final orientation mechanism.

Coordinate Systems

In commercial use today, robot systems, such as the PUMA series by Unimation, Inc., the Cincinnati Milacron T3 Series, and the Sasea, use four basic coordinate systems to define motion: (a) Cartesian coordinates, (b) cylindrical coordinates, (c) spherical or polar coordinates, and (d) revolute or articular coordinates.

Cartesian coordinates are those which may be defined as formed by three mutually perpendicular linear axes, usually labeled as x, y, and z axes. Cylindrical coordinates are formed by two perpendicular linear axes, such as x and y axes, and one rotary axis, such as a rotation about a z axis. The spherical or polar coordinate system is one where there is one linear axis, such as an x axis, and two rotary axes, such as rotations about the y and z axes. The revolute or articulated coordinate system is one where the three axes are all rotary types of axes, such as rotation about the x, y, and z axes.

Problems of Joint-Arm Kinematics

The two types of kinematics problems are direct and inverse. The direct kinematic problem can be defined as that of positioning an orientation point of the end effector with respect to a given coordinate system through the use of joint-angle vectors, so that the initial vector is a combination, say, of joint-angle vectors B_1, B_2, B_3, B_4, B_5, and B_6. The inverse kinematic algorithm is one where the system must calculate the joint-angle vectors of a given position and orientation of the end effector with respect to a type of reference coordinate system. The independent variables that may be used in a robot system are the joint angles, and the task that is to be performed is described in a real-world coordinate system. Therefore the inverse kinematic algorithm is one which is used more frequently in computer applications. It is necessary to use a type of transformation matrix when dealing with direct and inverse kinematic problems. The transformation matrix is simply a matrix by which the microcomputer controller will translate joint vectors into the positioning of the controls that are necessary for the robotics system to perform the necessary functions on a particular spot.

One of the first types of direct kinematic transformation matrices was developed by Denavitt and Hartenberg (see Stonecipher [1985]). They described a mathematical representation through a matrix which exemplified a rigid mechanical link or armature system and the spatial geometry system that was necessary to model the robot arm in a given workspace. The primary advantage of the Denavitt-Hartenberg matrix representation is that the algorithms that can be developed through it are used universally in extracting kinematic equations for a given robot arm. The Denavitt-Hartenberg system represents position vectors in a three-dimensional space and the rotational matrix by an expanded matrix of homogeneous transformations. These transformations include the translational operations of the armature in a coordinate frame system. The end result is that through sequential transformations the end effector can be expressed through geometric models which can be related to "base coordinates" which will make up the initial orientation of the dynamics of the robot system.

It is necessary to have a good understanding of the armature links and joints and their interrelationships. A robot system is composed of rigid frames called links which are connected by revolute or prismatic joints. Refer to Fig. 7. Each joint-arm pair constitutes one degree of freedom. The joint-arm system can be numbered outward from the base of reference such that "joint 1" is the joint which is connected between the armature link and the supporting base.

A joint axis can be defined as the axis of a joint which is established at the connection point of two armature links. The joint axis can be determined by calculating the distance and angle between the adjacent links and determining the relative positions of the neighboring links in the system.

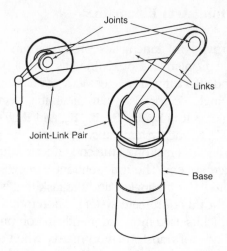

Fig. 7. Robot joint, link, and joint-arm combination.

The combination of links and joint axes and the distances and angles between adjacent links and relative positioning enables individuals to complete the kinematic configuration for a specific robot arm. It is important to observe that the link armatures come in pairs with the joint parameters determining the relative positioning between neighboring links.

The Denavitt-Hartenberg representation is a Cartesian coordinate system which establishes a Cartesian coordinate for each link at the joint axis dependent on the number of degrees of freedom desired plus the coordinates of the base system to which the arm is attached. The rotary joint can be described as having only one degree of freedom; it corresponds to the link in which it is fixed such that the rotary joint can be defined as link high joint. For example, when the joint activator is activated, the joint and link will move with respect to the link where the joint is attached. This occurs because the coordinate system representation recognizes that a particular joint system representation is directly related to the link where it is attached. The base of the robot system can be defined as a Cartesian coordinate of (x_0, y_0, z_0). As a result of this, a robot arm which has a seven-coordinate system can be defined as $(x_0, y_0, z_0; x_1, y_1, z_1; \ldots; x_6, y_6, z_6)$.

It becomes necessary to build on these algorithms and develop transformation matrices which will assist the robot arm to relate its link coordinate system to a particular coordinate frame as in a workplace when picking up or placing a workpiece, for example. The transformation matrix is composed of the following transformation algorithms:

1. Rotation of the z_{i-1} axis on angle of vector $\mathbf{B}_i$ to align the x_{i-1} axis with the x_i axis.

2. Translate the z_{i-1} axis a distance of D_i to bring the x_{i-1} and the x_i axes into coincidence.

3. Translate along the x_i axes the distance of D_i to bring the two origins into coincidence.

4. Rotate the x_i axis an angle of R_i to bring the coordinate systems into coincidence. The important thing to keep in mind here is that once the algorithms have been defined for a particular link joint, it becomes necessary then to look at algorithms which coordinate the movements of a particular joint grouping so that everything — all the links and joints — moves in a coordinated fashion. That's the objective of the particular algorithms that are performing these functions.

An inverse kinematic method can be used in terms of position and orientation of an end effector of a robot. In this case we are given the particular position and orientation of an end effector. We want to translate these into a particular position and orientation so that the robot can be placed in a specific position to grasp an object. These algorithms can be calculated into two particular phases. The first phase is to describe the position vector from the shoulder to the wrist. This will determine the positioning of the first three joints in the system. The last three joints are calculated from the position and orientation of the first three joints and the orientation desired of the end effector. In other words, it is inversely calculated rather than directly calculated as was previously shown.

Other Approaches

Two other types of approaches have been used to simulate robot kinematics and dynamics. The first is the Lagrange-Euler formulation, and the second is the Newton-Euler approach. A basic understanding of these two approaches will enable one to generalize these types of algorithms and approaches to robot kinematics to microcomputer controller design for actuators. It may become necessary to discuss options on custom design of controller actuators to accomplish functions necessary in a particular production system. Therefore it is appropriate to have a good understanding of these kinematic geometric transformations so that if it becomes necessary to suggest options when developing a microcomputer controller, these approaches can be a basis of understanding or initiation of one's own research activity.

The Lagrange-Euler Method

The Lagrange-Euler method of dynamic modeling has been described as a simple and systematic dynamic approach. It incorporates dynamic motion equations which are nonlinear and which affect external factors such as inertial loading, coupling reaction forces between joints, and gravity loading effects. The problem with this type of approach is that although it is trying to incorporate real-world factors which influence the performance of the particular manipulator system, the equation that may be formulated may not be as computationally accurate and may affect the overall system in a real-time control base. For example, it takes approximately 8 seconds to compute one move between two adjacent sets of points for a low 6-joint robot arm. It becomes very evident that although this model is trying to simulate a real-world environment, the computational time and speed limits the use of this type of formulation. Efforts have been made to increase the speed of computation by simplifying the equations and algorithms that are used. Factors such as higher inertia, however, make the use of the Lagrange-Euler modeling system and algorithm impossible because of the control and feedback requirements versus computational speed of the total robot system. In other words, the robot arm may move faster than the controlling signals can perform the particular function because the microcomputer controller is going through a large set of algorithms or tables before it sends control signals to the manipulator.

The Newton-Euler Method

The Newton-Euler vector formulation has the advantages of speed and formulation over the Lagrange-Euler methodology. It uses vector cross-referencing tables. These tables involve dynamic equations which exclude the dynamics of control devices, such as gear friction. These equations deal with each one of the armature links in a sequential fashion. In other words, the particular link of the robot system is calculated first, and then the coordinates of the next link of the robot system are calculated. This enables the system to calculate velocities, accelerations, total forces and moments exerted at the center of mass for each link. These are then determined as a forward recursive equation. The Newton-Euler vector formulation also has what is called a backward recursive formulation which determines forces and moments exerted on each link from the end effector to the manipulator base. The overall fact is that this method requires less computational time and provides a more systematic computation of forces and torques to the total system.

Other types of simulation have evolved that have tried to encompass not only the physics or dynamics of the particular armature links in end effectors but also the stresses, load factors, and inertia put on the total system. The ideal system involves a series of nonlinear differential equations which must encompass inertial loading factors, coupling algorithms between joints, and gravitational loading on the specific links. Also the formulation must involve the use of dynamic aspects which will vary with the particular joint and even the end effectors that are placed in the system. This will involve the use of highly complex trigonometric transformations. Also, there should be some sort of methodology for fine tuning these algorithms to the specific performance of the microcomputer controllers and servomotors being used in a system. Using servomechanism models in the area of dynamic control simulation often negates the coupling effects of joints used.

The RMCS and CMAC Models

The other types of models that have been proposed are the RMCS, or Resolved Motionally Control System, and the CMAC, or Cerebral Model Articulation Control.

The RMCS is an algorithm that utilizes coordinate systems based on world coordinate systems rather than robot systems. It utilizes a Jacobian matrix system and its computational algorithm. The problem again in the use of this algorithm is that because of the use of the Jacobian matrix it is extremely slow in regard to the computational time and robot-movement speed needed.

The CMAC is a table lookup method that is based on neurophysiological theory. It utilizes tables to determine control factors rather than taking control information from joints and links in the manipulator system. The problem comes from the fact that the computational speed and memory required for such tables makes the utilization of the system like this extremely cost-exorbitant. Also, these types of methodologies may neglect the use of external vectors and inertia and their impact on the dynamics of the total robot system.

The Adaptive Control Method

This method is able to maintain control performance over a wide range of motions and payloads. Once refined for the commercial market, this is the type of system that will function in a real-world environment. The adaptive control method most used is the MRAC method proposed by S. Dubowsky and D. Desforges [1979]. It utilizes differential equations as a reference model for each degree of freedom. The manipulator is controlled by its adjusting its position in regard to velocity feedback information which follows the model contained in the memory of the controlling minicomputer. The minicomputer then sends control signals which adjust positions and velocity gain and also control the accelerations and decelerations of the servomotors so that it minimizes any sort of damage to the total system. Any problems encompassed are in the area of stability analysis. With this method stability analysis becomes very difficult because of the complexities of dynamic relations between the links and joints and the end effector and real-world work situations.

The method with the most potential for research is adaptive control. Feedback control laws for equations based on desired motion trajectories can provide control on kinematic information to the total system. These incorporate the use of preplanned joint trajectories to obtain the specific equations necessary for kinematic control. They also incorporate the use of a feedback system which can update the control information about the desired trajectory. The torques that are applied to the joint actuators are kept nominal in theirtorquing speeds through the use of computed equations and feedback-information. The latter is used to constantly update and adjust the information that is used to control the kinematic system. Also there is the use of a sampling, which also provides feedback information as to the stresses and torques on the total system. This type of adaptive control significantly reduces any types of manipulator control which may be nonlinear. Also, it provides nominal forces applied to the total system but can also adequately deal with the functions that the system has to perform. The problem again with any type of high-level control system such as has been proposed in the past is computational speed as a trade-off for the overall speed of motion of the total system.

One hope for the future may be in the use of hierarchy processing systems and also through the requirement of orientation position algorithms. Through the combinations of these two different areas, we will find that the kinematics of the total robot system will be refined very much in the future. Also, the long computational times involved with the microcomputer or minicomputer controllers in the present robot systems will be overcome through the use of a hierarchy of microcomputer controllers. The latter will off-load a lot of the computational statistics and speed up these computational algorithms. These algorithms can be translated more quickly into the dynamics at the points of the manipulator system as it deals with real stresses, torques, and gravity factors.

Present research in the area of adaptive controllers is showing significant improvements in trajectory tracking under various loading conditions in the area of degree and millimeter error factors as compared with the direct positioning of a controller. For example, at a no-load condition for a specific joint, the maximum error tracking is 3.24 mm for a direct positioning controller as compared with 2.51 mm maximum error tracking for an adaptive controller. For the $\pm 10\%$ error factor at 50% of maximum load, there is approximately a 3.99-mm error tracking factor for the direct-positioning controller as compared to a 0.80 maximum error-factor trajectory tracking factor. For the adaptive controller and on maximum load for a specific joint, there is a 4.75 maximum error tracking factor as compared with a 1.35 maximum error tracking factor for an adaptive controller. It is therefore evident that adaptive controllers hold the most promise for the future. They will enable robot designers not only to have a greater degree of flexibility but will also enable robot systems, once they are in a production mode, to have a wider range of variability for fine tuning in any type of specialized function in the real-world environment.

5. Conclusions

Robot systems are very complex. We have discussed the many aspects of the requirements of a robot system from the hardware, such as the joints, links,and end effectors, to the complex algorithms that control the systems.

There will be continued research in industrial robotics. This research will aid engineers in coming closer to absolute accuracy, absolute reliability, and absolute consistency in a robot system.

One of the tools that will assist in this future research will be artificial intelligence. Artificial intelligence will be an additional tool to compensate and correct existing limitations of present robot technology. Also, artificial intelligence will assist the robot system with multitasking activities such as monitoring robot component performance for possible failure rates.

It is important that before the disciplines of robot technology and artificial intelligence merge there is a multidisciplinary approach to robot research. With this approach, the research as well as the industrial community will be able to more comprehensively improve robots for the flexible manufacturing systems of the future. Without this cross-pollinization of expertise, robot utilization will be slowed and flexible manufacturing technology will be only a term for discussion rather than implementation.

6. References

Desforges, D. T., and S. Dubewsky. "The Application of Model Referenced Adaptive Control to Robot Manipulators," *Transactions of the ASME, Journal of Dynamic Systems, Measurement, and Control,* Vol. 101, September 1979, pp. 20–22.

Goldhammer, W. H. "A Systems Approach to Robots' Use in Die Casting," *Eighth International Symposium on Industrial Robotics,* 1978, p. 131.

Grossman, D. D. "Programming of a Computer Controlled Industrial Manipulator by Guiding Through Motions," IBM Research Report RC6393, IBM T. J. Watson Research Center, March 1977.

"Integrated Computer Aided Manufacturing: ICAM," AFWAL Report, TR80-4042, Grant No. F33615-78-C-5188, September 1980, pp. 42–47.

Lieberman, L. I., and W. A. Wesley. "AUTOPASS: An Automatic Programming System for Computer Controlled Mechanical Assembly," *IBM Journal of Research and Development,* Vol. 21, No. 4, July 1977.

Paul, R. P. *Robot Manipulators—Mathematics, Programming, and Control,* Cambridge: MIT Press, 1981, pp. 143–145.

Sardis, G. N., and C. S. G. Lee. "Approximation Theory of Optimal Control for Trainable Manipulators," *IEEE Transactions on Systems, Man and Cybernetics,* Vol. SMC-9, No. 3, March 1979, pp. 94–99.

Stonecipher, K. *Industrial Robotics: A Handbook of Automated Systems Design,* Indianapolis: Hayden Press, 1985.

Chapter 2

Machine Vision System Components

H. G. Newman
Illinois State Government

1. Abstract

Robot systems must be able to sense their environment. There are two types of visual sensing systems: illuminators and light sensors. Illuminators can be single-point sources (where a laser is the present limiting case). Illumination can be general, controlled (e.g., a moving spot), striped, shaded, and polarized. Light sensors can range from the simple photodiode or phototransistor to a very high resolution camera device.

A light sensor requires a certain amount of light to effect an image, which results from the combination of illumination intensity and sensitivity of the sensor. This time-quantity of light is the integration of the light striking the photosensor during the required period. Low illumination is not generally suitable for fast-moving objects but may be satisfactory for producing images of slow-moving or stationary objects.

The information the system needs to collect is brightness, depth, color, and texture of an object. The means to accomplish this is called *machine vision*. Machine vision implies the use of cameras (commonly one or two), the necessary optical system, and an electronic interface to a computer or specialized processor.

The relationship between a camera (or cameras) and the object defines the geometry of the picture-taking process and the distances and angles that will be used in the computer programs.

Machine vision sensing has unique problems in that the computers which process the data have to obtain the information from a real, noisy, variable, physical environment.

2. The Components

The camera is one of two types: the older vidicon camera tube, somewhat the inverse of the common cathode-ray tube, and the newer, semiconductor, CCD (charge-controlled device) camera. Both have their advantages, but the CCD camera is usually preferred.

The camera lens specifications are substantially dictated by the environment, i.e., amount of light available, distance from the object, vibration, hostile chemicals, and humidity.

The interface is the electronic subsystem that passes the electronic signals from the camera to the processor. It can be anything from almost straight-through wiring (with analog-to-digital conversion) to substantial buffering and preprocessing of the information from the camera. It can start with analog information from a vidicon or digital information from the CCD. See Fig. 1. It can scale, compress, translate, and process the video information before passing it on to the processor.

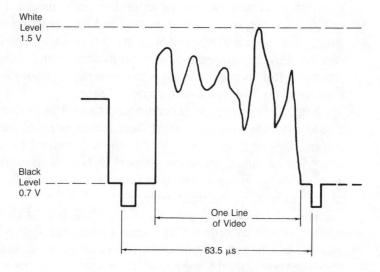

Fig. 1. A typical signal from a vidicon.

Machine vision systems do not work with continuous (analog) signals directly from a television camera but with digitized signals so that the data can be used by a digital processor for the necessary signal processing to extract the desired information.

The processor can be a general-purpose computer such as an IBM RT/PC, DEC PDP-11, or a VAX or similar microcomputer or minicomputer, or it can utilize the resources of a large mainframe system. It can be a special "dedicated" processor that does nothing but process the vision system information and then pass necessary information on to the robot controller.

3. Cameras

As previously mentioned, the machine vision system may use a vidicon camera or a CCD camera.

Vidicon Cameras

Vidicon cameras use a raster scanning system much like a standard home television set. Light is focused on a photosensitive target as illustrated in Fig. 2. The target is scanned by an electron beam to produce the video signal. The vidicon responds to light in the 350- to 700-nm range.

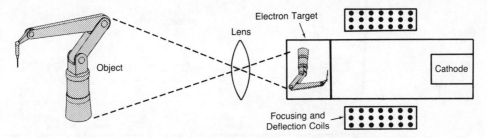

Fig. 2. Operation of the vidicon camera table.

In fact, they can scan at the same rate, 1/30th second per complete image, and the same 480 lines of horizontal scanning per frame as the standard U.S. television image. There are actually two scans, with the two interlacing each other as shown in Fig. 3. There is time for 525 lines of scanning but a 22.5-line period is used to get back to the top of the screen after the last line is scanned.

The main advantage of the vidicon camera is that it is inexpensive. Its disadvantages often far outweigh its advantages. The disadvantages are drift, distortion, persistence, burn-in, structural fragility, reliability, and power requirements.

Drift is the tendency of the electrical adjustments of the vidicon to change with time and temperature. Since the electrons that scan the tube surface are produced from an indirectly heated cathode, there has to be considerable heat generated by the filament of the tube. This means that there must be a warm-up period before the tube stabilizes.

Geometric distortion results from scanning a flat, rectangular area with an electron beam that, for ideal reproduction, should be scanning a section of a sphere. It can also result from the camera scan not being perfectly synchro-nized with the device, analog-to-digital converter, or a video receiver equiva-lent, much like a synchronous data transmission system running from clocks that vary with respect to each other. In the worst-case condition, both problems can exist along with distortion-causing irregularities in either the lens or the vidicon.

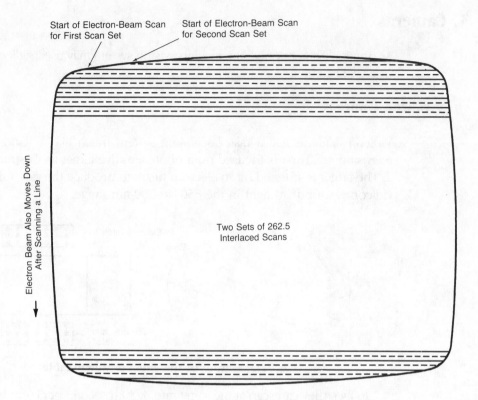

Fig. 3. Two sets of scans interlace for 525 lines of of scanning.

Persistence is the tendency for an image to remain on the phosphor surface of the vidicon. The persistence of the phosphors maintains the image long enough for a complete scan. If the light is too bright, the image persists longer and a moving image will be blurred. If there is insufficient light, the image will start to fade before the entire scan is completed.

Burn-in is the tendency for a nonmoving image to burn into the phosphor and remain there permanently. A video terminal that is left on for lengthy periods will probably retain the log-on message after the terminal is turned off.

A vidicon is made up of a filament to heat the cathode, the cathode which literally boils off electrons, several grids to control and accelerate the electrons, a photoconductive target and a wire-mesh anode to attract the electrons to the target. All of these components are small metal parts. They can stand only so much shock and will be mechanically resonant to some frequency of vibration. This is *structural fragility*. Vidicon cameras have been used in severe environments. They have been used for space exploration [Sheldon 1987] and were first used by NASA on the Ranger 7 lunar mission on July 31, 1964. It should be remembered, however, that these were not "ordinary" vidicon cameras, nor would the cost of space exploration quality vidicon cameras be acceptable to industry.

Vidicons were used before CCD cameras were commercially available. The ordinary studio and surveillance vidicon is structurally delicate. As concerns *reliability*, the MTBF (mean time between failures) of a vidicon is about 1000 hours (only 125 eight-hour shifts!).

In addition, they will always have a finite life because the filament will eventually fail and the cathode material, commonly beryllium oxide, will eventually be removed to the point that the vidicon, like other electron tubes, will become "weak." Not as many electrons will travel to the target with the original voltages applied.

The vidicon requires high voltages (commonly 900 V) to attract the electrons to the target. This means a high voltage power supply compared with the CCD tube. The vidicon also requires quite a bit more current for the filament, and therefore more power (power equals volts times amperes).

All of the above disadvantages question the practicality of using the vidicon for industrial use.

CCD Cameras

CCD cameras are often referred to as *area imaging devices* because they are not limited to the usual rectangular shape of the video display but can be any shape that their use might dictate, from a square to a line of CCD devices scanning a conveyor.

Light builds up a charge proportional to the integrated light intensity and is stored in capacitors associated with each element. Fig. 4 shows a typical CCD storage capacitor circuit and output plotted against time. A two-phase clock transfers these charges to the processing electronics much the same way as a sample-and-hold circuit does in a/d processing. The immediate processing electronics are usually amplifiers and buffers.

The advantage-disadvantage equation is just the opposite of the vidicon. There are just two primary disadvantages for most uses and quite a few advantages. The disadvantages are high initial cost and that CCD cell output can vary by about 10%. This means that some arrangement for calibrating the outputs must be done for critical applications. The calibration can be done, as so often is now the case, in hardware using adjustable resistors, or in software.

Very high resolution is obtainable. Each CCD element contributes one picture element to the final display. The smaller the CCD elements, the higher is the resolution (or finer grain in film terminology) in the final picture. If only coarse resolution is required, then a less expensive camera can be used.

The CCD camera is quite rugged. It has no small mechanical parts as a vidicon does. The CCD matrix is an integrated circuit that is like a small, thin monolith. This IC can further be securely mounted so it can be used in a very hostile environment as far as shock and vibration are concerned.

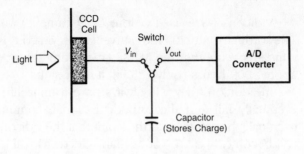

(A) Capacitor charging circuit.

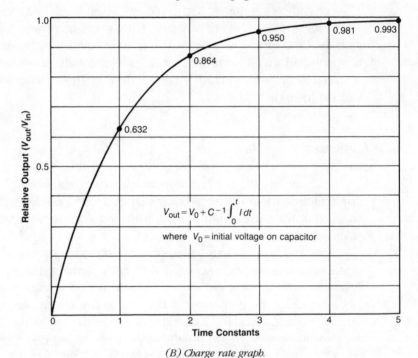

$$V_{out} = V_0 + C^{-1} \int_0^t I \, dt$$

where V_0 = initial voltage on capacitor

(B) Charge rate graph.

Fig. 4. CCD capacitor storage.

The CCD matrix has the reliability curve, of failures versus time, that any IC has. A period of "infant mortality" resulting from something less than perfect manufacturing procedures, a long period of useful life, and then gradual wearout resulting primarily from the absorption of small amounts of heat over a long period. A typical reliability curve is shown in Fig. 5.

The CCD, being a semiconductor integrated circuit, is inherently compact. Its physical size is determined by the resolution required and the number of picture elements needed. The latter will determine the $m \times n$ matrix of the IC.

Lower power than for a vidicon is required simply because a semiconductor integrated circuit is used instead of an electron tube. The typical voltages used for ICs are less than 15 V and the current is in the milliampere range or lower.

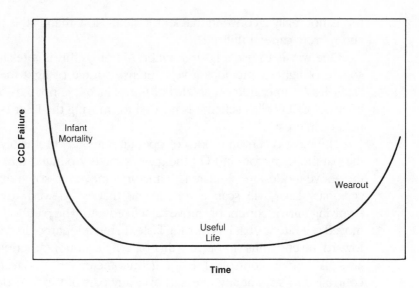

Fig. 5. Typical reliability curve for a CCD matrix.

Since the individual cells are electronically scanned, the device is inherently digital although the cells can recognize a gray scale, i.e., the continuum from white to black. So the cells are scanned as a digital device, but an analog voltage is obtained from each of them. But the interface can be simpler as each cell can immediately have its gray scale changed to a 4-bit value (for example) having 16 gray-scale levels, or a 6-bit value with 64 levels, etc. If the a/d conversion of the analog voltage output is done as close to the camera as possible, the signal-to-noise ratio is further enhanced by reducing the amount of wiring that can function as an "antenna" for radiated noise.

Linear Imaging Devices

The CCD linear array is available as a $1 \times n$ array with from 16 to 1872 elements commercially available [Rosenfield 1981]. The device can perform a single linear scan and is very useful for sensing objects that are moving relative to the camera, e.g., articles on a moving conveyor belt. Two such linear imaging devices, or LIDs, could be positioned such that one of them is doing a vertical scan over the conveyor and another is alongside the conveyor doing a profile of the object. The combination of the scan rate and the conveyor rate along with the number of CCD cells in the LID determine the resolution available. These scans can be processed in real time or buffered until it is determined that the complete object has been scanned. The effect is the same as the electrical scanning of an area imaging device except the scanning is done mechanically instead of electrically.

The advantages of the LID are the same as the CCD array has, and a large number of sizes is available. A conventional camera lens large enough to scan a conveyor belt could be of the size normally found on Mount Palomar. With the LIDs, one can have any shape "lens and camera" that is desired. Obviously this is not really a conventional lens system. How then is this potentially long and narrow camera utilized?

One way is to use a laser scanner. Although this is a relatively expensive source of light, it provides a very intense source of light that can help the "lenseless" camera detect shades of gray. Since it is not feasible to have one laser per CCD cell, a scheme is needed for moving the laser beam across the field of interest.

The most common modes of operation are (*a*) the revolving mirror, (*b*) the parabolic mirror, and (*c*) the galvanometer-operated mirror. All three of the above modes are similar. The mirror is moved in some manner so that a stationary laser will scan across a line that is "viewed" by the LID. The revolving mirror commonly moves at a fixed rate. The parabolic mirror can be moved at a rate so that it is moving faster in the midpart of its travel and slower toward the end, thus simplifying that part of its motion described by Newton's laws. A mirror controlled by a galvanometer or similar device can be controlled to scan at any rate and over any part of the field desired. It could scan the entire field linearly or sinusoidally or, for a smaller section, it could reduce the length of its scan to include just the field of interest.

Another advantage of a mirror that moves to effect a light scan is that the mirror can be controlled by the processor. The output from a machine vision system can be compared with the input that moves the mirror. Such processes have medical applications to how humans process images.

4. Interfaces

An interface, the electronic circuitry between the camera and the processor shown in the flow diagram in Fig. 6, can provide a number of functions. Commonly these are sample-and-hold amplifiers, analog-to-digital conversion, buffering, preprocessing, and timing.

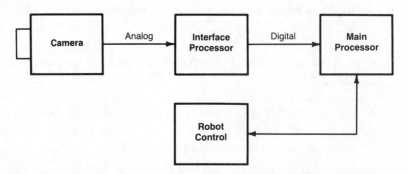

Fig. 6. Diagram of interface between the camera and the processor.

As previously mentioned, the CCD cameras build up a charge proportional to the light impinging on them. At a precise moment, when a "snapshot" must be taken, the charge has to be sent to sample-and-hold circuitry. This involves switching it to a capacitor, if it is not already connected to it, and then disconnecting the capacitor from the CCD element. This action provides the "hold" function. It is desirable that the capacitor be high quality with a low dissipation factor, which determines how fast the charge will leak off. If the charge will not stay within a required percentage of its initial value very long, then the voltage in that capacitor must be digitized that much sooner, i.e., the capacitor parameters affect the design of the electronics sampling its charge.

The analog-to-digital (a/d) converter is a device that converts a voltage into a binary value. The older (and much less expensive) a/d converters were successive-approximation devices. They made comparisons of the input voltage with internal voltage references until they got a good match, and then they output the binary value of that match. Next came the "flash" converters. They were very fast, they made all the comparisons at the same time, but were also quite expensive.

Several new architectures of a/d converters have the economic advantages of the former with speeds approaching those of the flash converters. In these devices capacitors have been substituted for the resistors in the older devices. This change produced 8-bit converters that operate in less than 200 ns [Goodenough 1986]. These devices are designed for microprocessor bus use and have three-state outputs. This means they can be electrically disconnected, and therefore do not put any load on the bus when they are not transferring information. In just 1986 alone, combinations of architectures and processes have reduced conversion time by a factor of 100.

Buffering is used to take up the slack time between the acquisition of digital data and when the processor needs it. It can also be used to receive data, e.g., from a number of camera cells, until enough data is available for parallel processing.

Buffer storage can be effected in a variety of ways. It can be in a frame buffer, an entire picture, or buffered any way the processing scheme requires. Buffering requires additional hardware, but that hardware is the sector of binary processing circuitry that is decreasing fastest in price — that is memory. Memory chips of 256 Kb are commonplace now and IBM is manufacturing a 1-Mb chip. This means, if an extra bit is included for parity checking, using seven 1-Mb integrated circuits, a 256- × 256-pixel image with 64 gray levels could be stored! Since memory is the least expensive part of the process, the designer can afford to let buffering be a key element in accomplishing faster data acquisition with minimum effect on the processor resources.

Timing is necessary for controlling the integration time of the camera(s), clocking the signals out of the image acquisition system, and synchronization of the digitizing circuitry. It is important that a common, stable timing source be available for all the components in the machine vision chain. Earlier it was mentioned how dissimilar timing sources could contribute to distortion.

Commonly, the clock (timing) signal will be provided from the computer or processor. A computer must have a clock signal internally to function. It could get its master clock signal from an outside source if necessary but if a standard, i.e., ready-made, computer is used, the interface may as well use that clock signal, provided it is stable enough. Since any computer used for signal processing would have to have a bus (the standard connections to the computer for peripherals, etc.) it is an easy enough job to measure the jitter and drift of the clock signal if the manufacturer doesn't provide that information.

The only other function normally considered for the interface system could be a signal preprocessor. For example, perhaps some of the techniques to enhance contrast by operating on adjacent-pixel gray-scale values could be done before the computer starts to process the information. If the computer is not a parallel-processing machine and it has only a limited need for parallel processing of the image data, this processing could be done before the information is passed to the computer. The Medar Company was recently reported [Redmond 1987] to be producing machine vision components, video cameras, and scanning lasers, which contain chips to preprocess images at the sensor level before being transferred to the host computer. This company has been quite successful in the automotive industry and is now planning to enter the aerospace and electronic industries.

5. Color Systems

Color adds another dimension to the visual information. The National Television Standards Committee (NTSC) specifies standard filters for color television. These are similar to Wratten 25, 47B, and 58. These filters transmit red, green, and blue wavelengths to provide the familiar *RGB* images.

Each pixel will have an *R, G* and *B* value. The processing can transform these values or change them in any appropriate manner to aid in the particular visual scheme involved. This information will obviously add 2 bits to the pixel binary value, e.g., $R = 00$, $G = 01$, $B = 10$. If 64 gray levels are needed, this will require 4 bits for the gray levels and 2 bits for the color information, for a total of 6 bits. One could then represent a color image with 64 gray levels with one 8-bit byte.

Other chromatic considerations are hue (color: blue, orange, etc.), saturation (purity or grayness of a color), and density (the overall brightness of the color). The hue, saturation, and density coordinates form a cylinder which lends itself to calculations and can be used in mathematical formulas.

6. Object Orientation

"Orientation" refers to how the object lies in the field of view. It is necessary to differentiate between absolute and relative orientation, and exterior and surface orientation. This orientation information is necessary in order to use the information collected. Otherwise, it would just be a picture.

If one is concerned with an object in a single plane, such as a disk or washer, then the orientation problem becomes trivial. But if one is trying to identify an object or compare two objects that do not fall into the above class of objects, then the process becomes more difficult. Fortunately, there is one initial clue, which is that a noncircular, symmetrical object will have a major axis (also called the axis of least inertia). To identify this axis, two points are needed to provide the slope of this line. Referring to Fig. 7, if the distance from the origin to the nearest point on the line is known, and the angle this line makes measured counterclockwise from the *xy* axis is known, then the description of this line is

$$x \sin \theta - y \cos \theta + \rho = 0 \qquad (1)$$

where θ is the angle previously referred to and ρ is the distance of the line from the origin. This is our first clue and starting point. (Consult B. K. P. Horn [1986], pp. 50–53, for the details of the mathematics involved.)

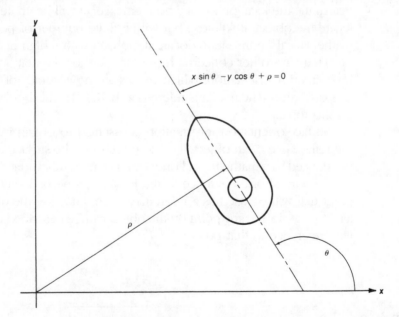

Fig. 7. Locating the major axis of an object can be found by the slope of a line through a point.

Absolute orientation may not be important when just identifying an object, but when fitting one object to another or identifying a feature on another object it becomes important. First, the coordinates, usually three dimensional, of the object must be known. Then the relationship of that object to the base coordinate system must be found. This is the absolute orientation of the object.

Relative orientation determines the transformation between coordinate systems of two cameras in order to determine the actual position of the object. Relative orientation strictly has to do with stereo optical systems. The phenomenon involved is much the same as a camera rangefinder with the distance being calculated by means of the angles between the two viewpoints and applying the familiar angle-side-angle formula of trigonometry. The problem is actually much more complicated than that since it requires the sets of coordinates to identify the camera positions uniquely, but the principle is the same. In this case, unlike the rangefinder problem, many points instead of a single point are involved.

Exterior orientation provides an object-centered view of the object that is viewed. Thus far, we have been discussing viewer-centered orientation. One is concerned with the boundaries of the object when one is, for example, controlling a mobile platform or commanding a mechanical manipulator to interact with the objects being viewed. Commonly, a minimum of four points is required for accurate exterior orientation, provided the shape of the object is already known. A curve-fitting procedure, such as least squares, is used to determine the location in minimum time, i.e., it will be an iterative process to locate the object absolutely, but with a finite number of points one can, by mathematical optimization, locate the object with a high degree of certainty.

There are other concerns related to exterior orientation, such as specifically interior orientation, which relates to the accuracy of processing, e.g., lens distortion. The reader is referred to B. K. P. Horn's book [1986] for more on this topic.

Surface-orientation information is essential to obtain information about the reflectance of an object. The description of the surface of the object can be reduced to a mathematical one. One point on this surface is considered to be the normal of the surface to the lens, i.e., a perpendicular to a specified point that will be used as a reference. Then, knowing the distance from the lens to that object, any point on the object can be described trigonometrically with reference to that point.

7. The Gray Scale

The gray scale of a sensor is the number of discrete levels of light that it can represent. After digitization, it represents the number of discrete steps from white to black that can be represented by the number of bits selected torepresent the brightness of an image. For example, if only 4 bits were used, only 16 levels of gray from and including white to black could be represented. If 6 bits were used, 64 gray levels could be used, and so on.

The gray scale can be modified, and there are two kinds of modifications. One is gray-level correction and the other is gray-scale transformation. *Gray-level correction* compensates for the nonuniformity of sensitivity of sensors in the sensor plane (e.g., the 10% variation in CCD elements). The gray level sensed by each pixel can be corrected according to the sensitivity at its location. The sensitivity of pixels can be calibrated by illuminating the pixel plane with a source of uniform brightness and then applying either electrical or mathematical adjustment.

Gray-scale transformation is often done to modify the gray level of pixels in an image to adapt to the contrast of a particular image, that is, to make the gray scale cover the range from the lightest to the darkest points of interest in the image. It can also be used to emphasize a particular region of gray levels within the image area.

Another transformation has to do with modifying the histogram of the intensity of pixels over the image or an area of interest within the image. The relative number or frequency of each level of intensity is plotted. The gray scale can then be transformed from one histogram representation to another. For example, one technique is *histogram flattening.* Histogram flattening isused to reduce the frequency of very numerous intensity values and increase the frequency of relatively sparse values. Fig. 8 illustrates an example using eight gray-scale values.

8. Image Analysis

Image analysis is usually the process of object identification. The problem of replicating the procedure humans use to identify an object, like so many robotics tasks, is a nontrivial one. Image analysis begins the process of locating and defining the various objects in the scene.

The AI process then attempts to determine what the objects are [Frenzel 1987].

Image analysis is accomplished by identifying regions and boundaries, or edges. *Edges* represent boundaries where two surfaces come together. They also identify the interface between two different surfaces or between an object and a background. An edge is also formed between two objects when one object is in front of or behind another. *Regions* are large, flat areas of an object or scene that have the same intensity value and occur between the various edges and boundary lines. Edges and regions completely define a scene.

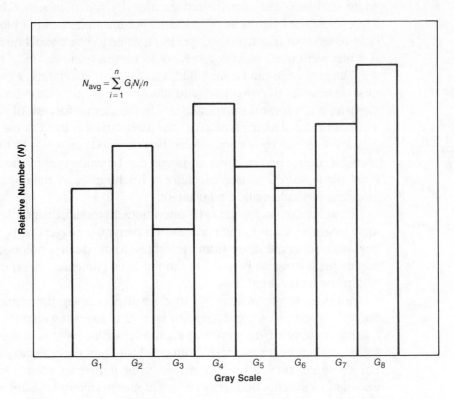

Fig. 8. Histogram flattening of eight gray-scale values.

Image analysis involves the processes of smoothing, edge detection, thresholding, pixel grouping, template matching and segmentation.

Smoothing is necessary so that surfaces, or regions, can be uniquely identified. After smoothing, adjacent pixels within a region will have equal or very close values. These may change gradually over the region due to shading, shadows, or the relation of the region's plane to the light source. Smoothing is commonly done by replacing each pixel value with a new value.

A variety of algorithms is used but the most commonly used one is to replace each pixel value with the average of those of it and its adjacent pixels. This involves the repetitive processing of groups of nine pixels.

Edge detection is the next step in image analysis after surface smoothing. The picture frame is scanned for all the binary numbers representing pixels to determine which of these pixels fall on boundaries between regions. This is done by comparing adjacent gray-scale values, which can be carried out by subtracting adjacent pixels and storing the difference values. A small difference may just be shading but a large difference can be an edge. This difference-value matrix can then have its image contrast enhanced by thresholding (discussed below), which will enhance the difference image.

One constraint on edge detection is how large (or small) a difference will be classed as an edge. In roughly textured objects it would be critical to differentiate between a texture artifact and an edge. One way to accomplish this is to analyze less than the entire frame but more than the 3- × 3-pixel array we discussed earlier. It is then easier to set thresholds on what is texture and what is an edge. This technique is called *windowing*. The size of the window is a trade-off between good noise immunity obtained with a large window and good sensitivity to definition obtained with a small window [Frenzel 1987].

When all boundaries have been determined, lines can be drawn creating a new scene with just the outlines of objects. This drawing is referred to as a *primal sketch* and can be used for object identification or determining the object's position when comparing a template of the object (referred to a particular plane) to the image of the object.

Thresholding is a procedure used to obtain a binary image such that a characteristic function $b(x, y)$ is 0 for all image points corresponding to the background and 1 for points on the object. As a result, thresholding produces a two-valued function. The thresholding function defines the binary value to be 0 where the brightness is greater than some threshold value and 1 where it is not (or vice versa)[Horn 1986], i.e., a frame that has been processed with a thresholding function will appear as a silhouette.

The whole key to thresholding is selecting the correct threshold value from the gray levels available in the frame. One way is to analyze the occurrence of gray levels in the image independent of their positions. For a continuous image a brightness distribution function can be defined. Then a number of techniques, such as histograms and spatial coherence, can be usedto determine an appropriate threshold.

Segmentation is another technique for object identification. The image is segmented, broken up into regions, each of which could correspond to the surface of an object in the environment being imaged. The problem is simple if each object in the image has the same gray level but becomes more complicated if each has a different gray level.

As the gray levels are closer together, the problem of noise levels becomes more severe. If the overall range of gray levels is N and there are R regions, then the smallest difference between adjacent regions must be less or equal to $N/(R-1)$ to be detectable as different regions and not the effect of noise. For example, if there were 64 gray levels and 17 regions, the result would be 4 and adjacent regions having a difference of 4 or less could not be uniquely determined. In that case some other technique must be used.

Texture analysis combined with the preceding paragraphs really presents a difficult problem. The result is that yet another technique is required. If texture tends to be periodic, the process can be simplified (in a sense) since Fourier analysis techniques can be used.

9. Binocular Vision Systems

Binocular vision implies the use of two cameras to provide the same function as the human eyes, that is, depth perception, stereo, or three-dimensional vision. This is not the simple task it appears to be and is typical of the sort of things the human body does easily but realizing that function in robotics is something else again.

In addition to the activities that are required of a monocular system, such as shape identification, orientation, and measurement, the distance to an object from a reference point must be established. This currently requires sufficient additional computing power that the cost/benefit ratio may not support this additional feature for many industrial applications. The problem previously discussed as affecting relative orientation would of course apply here since information is collected from two unique points.

Stereoscopic vision enables robots to find parts amid a random, irregular background. The bin-sorting application is typical of this sort of problem. Parts in a bin will lay at irregular angles and positions with respect to the camera. To a monocular vision system, without depth perception, identical parts could all look like unique objects, because of the position of their major plane with respect to the camera lens.

Like human eyesight, binocular machine vision merges two pictures into a single image, calculating depth by measuring the angular displacement of the object with respect to two cameras. That is, the closer the object, the greater the angular displacement. Until recently, the images of the two cameras could not be processed fast enough to both calculate the necessary angular displacement and do the other calculations necessary, e.g., shape identification.

Recently, several researchers [Sweeny 1986] have overcome some of the problems. Keith Nishihara, of Schlumberger Labs in Palo Alto, California, speeds up stereo vision by reducing the amount of image analysis needed to register right and left camera shots. Rather than processing full-resolution images, Nishihara's computer program finds patches of uniform light intensity in one image and merges them with identical patches in the other. The low resolution of the images prevents object identification in any detail, so Nishihara's design really does a good job only for applications requiring distance measurements.

Tomaso Poggio, a consultant for Thinking Machines, Cambridge, Massachusetts, is developing parallel-processing computer programs that provide high-resolution three dimensions by processing the two camera images simultaneously while running other vision programs for object recognition. At present, high-powered parallel-processor computers are too expensive for the average industrial use. However, the development of computers that have arrays of 32-bit, high-speed, VLSIC processors is close and will be available for such use in the near future.

A system developed by Automatic Vision, Vancouver, British Columbia, compares voltage pulse waveforms from two cameras. When viewing the same object the two cameras produce essentially identical waveforms. The processor matches up the waves between the two cameras and then calculates angular displacement by measuring the difference in phase of the two waves. This system provides high-speed depth perception along with a potential for high resolution. Since the basic system measures only the distance, additional software must be used to analyze the available high-resolution data to identify objects.

Other systems use a combination of ultrasound (a simple version is that used in Polaroid cameras) and sonar to measure distances for high resolution. If v is the velocity of sound in meters per second for the ambient air density and if a sonar signal is transmitted, reflected, and received back at the source in t seconds, then the distance in meters from the source (proximate to the camera) to the object is $d = \frac{1}{2} vt$. This principle is illustrated in Fig. 9.

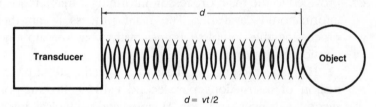

$$d = vt/2$$

Fig. 9. Finding the distance from the camera to the object.

Another technique, using two cameras, is to project patterned light. The cameras pick up the deflection pattern as well as the object detail. This system requires controlled low-level lighting, which can be a problem in industrial areas.

10. Parallel Processing

Parallel processing is the concurrent processing of either different programs or different parts of the same program. In the case of machine vision processing it commonly is different parts of the same program, with an example being successive machine vision frames. In order to operate on high-resolution matrices, representing the frames, it is necessary to either not process every frame but process every Nth sample, (b) use some algorithm to reduce the amount of data to be processed, (c) have an extremely high speed processor, or (d) have parallel processing paths. The last method is the so-called array processor, which can be a stand-alone machine, such as the

Cray array processing computer, or it can be a special processor attached to a more ordinary computer. It is also the type of supercomputer which is planned to be developed in Japan's Fifth Generation Project.

A parallel processor has the capability to execute more than one program at a time or to execute more than one part of the same program concurrently. Applied to machine vision, this means that a parallel processor could be reading the raw data from one frame into memory while it was performing some type of operation on the previous frame, such as getting ready to compare it with the frame before that. At the present, parallel processing can be done using one of the 32-bit superminicomputers and an attached array processor. The basic machine can now process information at a rate of 1 to 20 MIPS (millions of instructions per second).

To visualize this in a very simple form, suppose that binary information is coming from two cameras. The output from each of these was put into a preprocessor using high-speed versions of the 80386 or 68000 processors. This information could be processed and, using direct memory access (DMA) techniques, put into the memory of the main processor. An interrupt is provided to the main processor, informing it that a frame of binocular vision information is available. The main processor can then concentrate on processing the complete frames with whatever amount of preprocessing considered appropriate.

High-speed computers have their speed (rate of processing) specified in million of instructions per second (MIPS), floating-point operations per second (FLOPS), and, for AI applications, logical inferences per second (LIPS).

Superminicomputers now have processing speeds in the 1- to 10-MIPS range [Frenzel 1987]. The VAX 8600 operates at 2 MIPS. A mainframe computer, the IBM 3090, runs at 28 MIPS. Array processors perform mathematical operations at 10 to 100 times faster than their typical host computer. Prototype Japanese fifth generation machines have been clocked at speeds of 20,000 to 35,000 LIPS.

As an example, suppose that a 256- × 256-pixel video frame is used with 1 byte per pixel. This requires 64 KB (65,536 bytes). Each transformation of this data requires another 64 KB of memory. It also means that 128 KB are processed in whatever period the frames are being received (if every frame must be processed). If 10 frames are sampled each second, a minimum of 1.31072 MB would be processed a second. This is just data and doesn't include instructions! More data is being continuously delivered from the camera. If it is not processed, it is lost.

The options for processing the data are (a) a parallel processor that is fast enough to process the data, (b) decreasing the amount of data that must be processed by some sort of sparse matrix approach to machine vision, or (c) using a preprocessor or interface processing to reduce the amount of information that must be handled by the main processor – this would amount to a pipeline processing approach to a solution of the problem.

Very fast VLSIC (very large scale integrated circuit) 16- and 32-bit processors are available now. They will become faster still, and peripheral chips are becoming more powerful. Computers with multi-VLSIC processors will become readily available and less expensive. Multiprocessors and array processors will probably be of modular design and will be ordered in a size and power rating appropriate for the specific task.

11. Applications of Machine Vision

"Machine vision" commonly refers to the use of computer vision equipment and techniques with manufacturing processes. Although it is commonly associated with manufacturing large objects from automobiles to washing machines, it is being used in an ever growing range of applications. In addition to heavy manufacturing it is used in robotics, hazardous locations [Sheldon 1987], and for surveillance. Machine vision is used in electronics in surface-mount technology [Redmond 1987] and in a number of fields for inspection of processed material.

Machine vision is used in manufacturing either to replace people or do things people cannot normally do or should not ordinarily do [Frenzel 1987]. It is not used just to replace people for economic advantages, but because machine vision components can perform more reliably under a variety of situations some of which humans do not like. Doing highly repetitive and boring tasks, people will sooner or later make mistakes. Machines get neither tired nor bored. Machine vision can be used for repetitive work with fine detail, such as inspecting printed-circuit boards for wiring errors or wrong components. It may be used to locate the right components that are improperly placed, e.g., diodes and electrolytic capacitors that have a polarity that must be observed.

For hazardous or difficult work, such as that situated in the vicinity of radioactive material or hazardous chemicals, robot vision systems can be used without risk to their operators and can be safely decontaminated afterward.

Robot vision systems can be used to identify objects (pattern recognition) or determine their position (pattern orientation). The latter is often a requirement to achieve the former since two otherwise identical objects appear as different objects to a machine vision system if their orientation is not the same with respect to the camera.

The machine "sight" not only can be used for pattern recognition and orientation, but it can be used within a feedback loop that is manipulating the objects in some way to ensure the process is going as planned. For example, if a part is to be removed from a conveyor belt or from a bin and placed for a machining operation, the machine vision supplies information to the robot system about where the object is now and compares that information with where it should be at the end of the current operation. This acquisition and processing of information and then providing that information to the mechanical part of the robot or feedback process is one of the operations that makes a robot "intelligent." Tactile, temperature, gravitational, and other sensory emulations also contribute to the appearance of intelligence.

The acquisition of intelligent machines can be the large independent variable in the future of manufacturing in the United States. In *The Third Wave*, Alvin Toffler [1980] predicted that most heavy manufacturing will go to second-wave countries and that the United States will be a service industry country. But what would happen if service and intelligent machines are merged with manufacturing? This is something that Toffler doesn't consider and it makes the necessity to develop good robotics systems a priority and a race within a race. How the fifth generation of AI tools turns out will affect our economy in many ways.

Most concepts of machine vision have to do with robots doing welding or some similar operation on a production line. Machine vision is beginning to be used for production other than heavy manufacturing. For example, machine vision is used in data processing. The Storage Technology Corporation has announced the production of their Model 4400 Automated Cartridge System. This device is a fully automated information storage system. It automatically mounts and dismounts IBM 3480 or compatible 18-track data storage cartridges. A robotics subsystem within the system "sees" the correct cartridge by means of a solid-state camera and two lights mounted on either side of the camera. The camera locates the cartridge and "reads" the volume serial number in both bar code and OCR type. The system can house up to 6000 cartridges. At 200 MB per cartridge, this provides storage for 1200 GB of data.

Years ago, on an IBM 360 computer, the University of Illinois used fiber optics attached to the hundreds of lights on the old operator's console to assist in decision making faster and more accurately than the operators could. Multiple optical fibers are not quite what we would consider machine vision but they were in fact a form of machine vision to collect information and act on it. The acquisition of the visual information was a key element in a closed-loop control system just as we use robot vision today.

Another application of machine vision, not as part of heavy machine tools, is security. Computer vision, either as a fixed installation or as part of a mobile robot system, can be used for detecting motion. If successive vision frames are subtracted from each other, the fixed (or nonmoving) images will cancel out. Only the images that were not the same in successive images will remain. By using this technique, not only can motion in a place where motion is not expected be detected but action can be taken. Very slow or very fast motion can be detected and identified as such. A security guard can be alerted, doors electrically locked, or other appropriate action can be initiated.

In addition to the hazardous or impossible locations for humans are outer space and the depths of the oceans. TV cameras have been used for some time in these applications. The techniques of signal processing to enhance images has been used and is being improved to provide more information. Image processing can be used to extract weak data signals from noise, i.e., where the signal-to-noise ratio is very low. Another kind of "noise" can be local to the object. If an object has weathered, been damaged, or corroded so that it cannot be immediately or absolutely identified, signal processing can be used to remove, to some extent, the "local noise" and to determine the features of the object.

12. References

Agin, G. J. "Vision Systems," Chap. 14 in *Handbook of Industrial Robotics*, ed. by S. Y. Nof, New York: John Wiley & Sons, 1985.

Baxes, G. *Digital Image Processing*, Englewood Cliffs: Prentice-Hall, 1983.

Dawson, B. M. "Introduction to Image Processing Algorithms," *Byte*, March 1987, pp. 169–186.

Dunbar, P. "Machine Vision," *Byte*, January 1986, pp. 161–176.

Engelberger, J. F. *Robotics in Practice: Management and Applications of Industrial Robots*, New York: AMA Com, 1980.

Feigenbaum, E. A., and P. R. Cohen. "Vision," Chap. XIII, Vol. III, in *The Handbook of Artificial Intelligence*, ed. by P. R. Cohen, Stanford: HeurisTech Press, 1982.

Frenzel, L. E., Jr. *Crash Course in Artificial Intelligence and Expert Systems*, Indianapolis: Howard W. Sams & Co., 1987, pp. 204–225.

Gleason, G. J., and G. J. Agin, "A Modular Vision System for Sensor-Controlled Manipulation and Inspection," *Ninth International Symposium on Industrial Robots*, SME, Washington D. C., March 1979, pp. 57–60.

Goodenough, F. "ADC Chips Leap Ahead – Both in Speed and Accuracy," *Electronic Design*, September 4, 1986, pp. 90–97.

Gonzalez, R. C., and R. Safabakhsh. "Robot Control: A Tutorial Overview," in *Tutorial on Robotics*, ed. by C. S. G. Lee, R. C. Gonzalez and R. S. Fu, Silver Spring, MD.: IEEE Computer Society Press, 1983.

Harris, L. R., and D. B. Davis. *Artificial Intelligence in the Marketplace*, Toronto: Bantam Books, 1986.

Holt, C. M., Stewart, A., Clint, M., and R. H. Perrott, "An Improved Parallel Thinning Algorithm," *Communications of the ACM,* Vol. 30, No. 2, February 1987, pp. 156–160.

Horn, B. K. P. *Robot Vision,* Cambridge: MIT Press, 1986, pp. 90–100, 308–310.

Marr, D. "Representing and Computer Visual Information," in *Artificial Intelligence: An MIT Perspective,* ed. by P. H. Winston and M. K. Brown, Cambridge: The MIT Press, 1979.

Redmond, R. W. "Machine Vision Broadens Its Horizons," *High Technology,* April 1987, p. 68.

Remhold, U., and C. Blume. "Interfacing a Vision System with a Robot," Chap. 15 in *Handbook of Industrial Robotics,* ed. by S. Y. Nof, New York: John Wiley & Sons, 1985.

Ritchie, D. *The Binary Brain: Artificial Intelligence in the Age of Electronics,* Boston: Little, Brown and Co., 1984.

Rosenfield, A. "Picture Processing: 1980," *Computer Graphics & Image Processing,* Vol. 16, No. 1, May 1981, pp. 52–59.

Sheldon, K. "Probing Space by Camera," *Byte,* March 1987, pp. 2–34.

Sweeney, D. "Two-Eyed Robots," *High Technology,* November 1986, pp. 64-65.

Toffler, A. *The Third Wave,* New York: William Morrow & Co., 1980.

Winston, P. H. *Artificial Intelligence,* Reading: Addison-Wesley Pub. Co., 1979.

Chapter 3

Analysis of Two-Dimensional Images

R. C. Gonzalez
Perceptics Corporation and University of Tennessee

D. Brzakovic
University of Tennessee

1. Abstract

The elements of machine vision were introduced in the preceding chapter. In the present and following chapters, attention is focused on dimensioned vision analysis, that is, the extraction of quantitative information from a sensed scene. This chapter deals with techniques for performing dimensioned analysis on two-dimensional images. Chapter 4 deals with three-dimensional vision techniques.

2. Introduction

For the most part, dimensioned analysis of two-dimensional images in industrial environments is performed on binary data. Binary images are generated from a sensed scene by application of segmentation algorithms, as discussed in Chap. 2. We consider three principal areas of work when dealing with this type of data: (1) representation, (2) description, and (3) matching.

Representation deals with expressing binary image data in a form suitable for computer processing. For example, we can represent a given object as a set of pixels comprising a region of an image, or we can represent it by its boundary. Description deals with extracting features of interest from a given representation. For example, an object represented as a region can be described (on a low-level basis) by the area of the region. Basically, descriptors form the basis for dimensioned analysis, and the choice of descriptors for a given application is strongly influenced by the type of dimensioning one wishes to perform. Finally, matching is a process that compares a set of descriptors used to describe a given object against a set of the same descriptors extracted from a similar object that is, by definition, dimensionally correct.

In the following discussion, attention is focused on the introduction and development of techniques suitable for the representation, description, and matching of binary structures. Since the results of these techniques are directly dependent on the quality of the images themselves, we first digress slightly for a brief discussion of the role played by illumination in the formation of images which, when segmented, yield binary images of suitable quality in terms of the processes discussed above. We also give a brief account of some basic relationships between pixels in an image.

3. The Role of Illumination

In this section, an image will be denoted by $f(x, y)$, where x and y are *spatial coordinates*, and the value of f at coordinate (x, y) is the *intensity* or *gray level* of the image at that point. When dealing with digital images, x, y, and the values of f are discrete quantities. In this case, points (x, y) and their corresponding intensity values are called *pixels*.

We may view the formation of an image $f(x, y)$ as the product of a reflectance component $r(x, y)$ and an illumination component $i(x, y)$; that is, $f(x, y) = i(x, y) r(x, y)$. As an introduction to the role played by illumination in image formation, consider the computer-generated reflectance function shown in Fig. 1A. The histogram of this function, shown in Fig. 1B, is clearly bimodal and could be easily segmented by placing a single threshold in the histogram valley to yield a "proper" binary image. Suppose, however, that we multiply the reflectance function in Fig. 1A by the illumination function shown in Fig. 1C to yield the image $f(x, y)$ shown in Fig. 1D. The histogram of this image is shown in Fig. 1E. It is noted that the original valley was virtually eliminated, making segmentation by a single threshold an impossible task. Of course, we never really have the reflectance function by itself to work with, but this simple example illustrates that the nature of objects and background could be such that they are easily separable, while the image resulting from poor (in this case nonuniform) illumination could be quite difficult to segment.

The reason why the histogram in Fig. 1E has been so corrupted can be explained by taking the natural logarithm of $f(x, y) = i(x, y) r(x, y)$ to yield the sum $z(x, y) = \ln f(x, y) = \ln i(x, y) + \ln r(x, y) = i'(x, y) + r'(x, y)$. We know from probability [Papoulis 1965] that if $i'(x, y)$ and $r'(x, y)$ are independent random variables, the histogram of $z(x, y)$ is given by the convolution of the histograms of $i'(x, y)$ and $r'(x, y)$. If $i(x, y)$ were constant, $i'(x, y)$ would be constant also and its histogram would be a

(A) Computer-generated reflectance function.

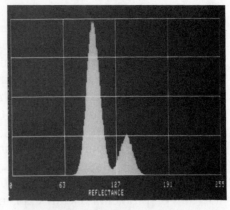

(B) Histogram of reflectance function.

(C) Computer-generated
illumination function.

(D) Image produced by the product of the
illumination and reflectance functions.

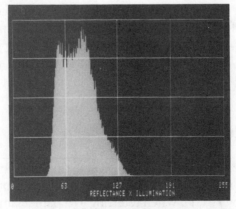

(E) Histogram of image.

Fig. 1. Illumination in image formation.

simple spike (like an impulse). The convolution of this impulselike function with the histogram of $r'(x, y)$ would leave the basic shape of this histogram virtually unchanged since convolution of a function with an impulse simply "copies" the function at the location of the impulse. On the other hand, if $i'(x, y)$ had a broader histogram (resulting from nonuniform illumination), the convolution process would smear the histogram of $r'(x, y)$ yielding a histogram for $z(x, y)$ whose shape could be quite different from the shape of the histogram of $r'(x, y)$. The degree of distortion depends on the broadness of the histogram of $i'(x, y)$, which in turn depends on the nonuniformity of the illumination function.

In the preceding discussion we have dealt with the logarithm of $f(x, y)$ instead of dealing with the image function directly, but the essence of the problem is clearly explained by using the logarithm to separate the illumination and reflectance components. This allows us to view histogram formation as a convolution process, thus explaining why a valley in the histogram of the reflectance function could be virtually eliminated by improper illumination.

When access to the illumination source is available, a solution frequently used in practice to compensate for nonuniformity is to project the illumination pattern onto a constant, white, reflective surface. This yields an image $g(x, y) = k i(x, y)$, where k is a constant that depends on the surface and $i(x, y)$ is the illumination pattern. Then, for any image $f(x, y) = i(x, y) r(x, y)$ obtained with the same illumination function, we simply divide $f(x, y)$ by $g(x, y)$, yielding a normalized function $h(x, y) = f(x, y) / g(x, y) = r(x, y)/k$. Thus, if $r(x, y)$ can be segmented by using a single threshold, T, then $h(x, y)$ can also be segmented by using a single threshold of value T/k. It is noted that this method works well only if the illumination pattern produced by $i(x, y)$ does not change from image to image.

The preceding discussion has dealt with segmentation by a single threshold. Although more sophisticated techniques, such as variable thresholding or edge detection (see Chap. 2), could certainly be used, the point remains that even these techniques are often incapable of yielding binary images of high quality in the presence of poorly controlled illumination.

4. Some Basic Relationships Between Pixels

In this section we consider several primitive, but important relationships between pixels in a digital image. As in the previous section, an image will be denoted by $f(x, y)$. When referring to a particular pixel, we will use lowercase letters, such as p and q. A subset of pixels of $f(x, y)$ will be denoted by S.

Neighbors of a Pixel

A pixel p at coordinates (x, y) has four *horizontal* and *vertical* neighbors whose coordinates are given by

$$(x + 1, y), (x - 1, y), (x, y + 1), (x, y - 1)$$

This set of pixels, called the *4-neighbors* of p, will be denoted by $N_4(p)$. It is noted that each of these pixels is a unit distance from (x, y) and also that some of the neighbors of p will be outside the digital image if (x, y) is on the border of the image.

The four *diagonal* neighbors of p have coordinates

$$(x + 1, y + 1), (x + 1, y - 1), (x - 1, y + 1), (x - 1, y - 1)$$

and will be denoted $N_D(p)$. These points, together with the 4-neighbors defined above, are called the *8-neighbors* of p, denoted $N_8(p)$. As before, some of the points in $N_D(p)$ and $N_8(p)$ will be outside the image if (x, y) is on the border of the image. The neighborhood arrangements just discussed are illustrated in Fig. 2.

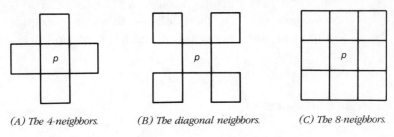

(A) The 4-neighbors.   (B) The diagonal neighbors.   (C) The 8-neighbors.

Fig. 2. Neighbors of pixel p.

Connectivity

Connectivity between pixels is an important concept used in establishing boundaries of objects and components of regions in an image. To establish whether two pixels are connected we must determine if they are adjacent in some sense (e.g., if they are 4-neighbors) and if their gray levels satisfy a specified criterion of similarity (e.g., if they are equal). For instance, in a binary image with values 0 and 1, two pixels may be 4-neighbors, but they are not said to be connected unless they both have the same value.

Let V be the set of gray-level values used to define connectivity; for example, if only connectivity of pixels with intensities of 59, 60, and 61 is important, then $V = \{59, 60, 61\}$. For binary images, V contains only two elements, generally denoted by $V = \{0, 1\}$. We consider two basic types of connectivity:

(a) *4-connectivity.* Two pixels p and q with values from V are 4-connected if q is in the set $N_4(p)$.

(b) *8-connectivity.* Two pixels p and q with values from V are 8-connected if q is in the set $N_8(p)$.

A pixel p is adjacent to a pixel q if they are connected. We may define 4-adjacency or 8-adjacency, depending on the type of connectivity specified. Two image subsets S_1 and S_2 are adjacent if some pixel in S_1 is adjacent to some pixel in S_2.

A *path* from pixel p with coordinates (x, y) to pixel q with coordinates (s, t) is a sequence of distinct pixels with coordinates

$$(x_0, y_0), (x_1, y_1), \ldots, (x_n, y_n)$$

where $(x_0, y_0) = (x, y)$ and $(x_n, y_n) = (s, t), (x_i, y_i)$ is adjacent to $(x_{i-1}, y_{i-1}), 1 \leq i \leq n, n$ is the *length* of the path. We may define 4-paths or 8-paths, depending on the type of adjacency used.

If p and q are pixels of an image subset S, then p is *connected* to q in S if there is a path from p to q consisting entirely of pixels in S. For any pixel p in S, the set of pixels in S that are connected to p is called a *connected component* of S. It then follows that any two pixels of a connected component are connected to each other, and that distinct connected components are disjoint.

Distance Measures

Given pixels p, q, and z, with coordinates (x, y), (s, t), and (u, v) respectively, we call D a *distance function* or *metric* if

(a) $D(p, q) \geq 0$ $[D(p, q) = 0$ iff $p = q]$

(b) $D(p, q) = D(q, p)$

(c) $D(p, z) \leq D(p, q) + D(q, z)$

The *Euclidean distance* between p and q

$$D_e(p, q) = [(x - s)^2 + (y - t)^2]^{1/2} \tag{1}$$

For this distance measure, the pixels having a distance less than or equal to some value, r, from (x, y) are the points contained in a disk of radius r centered at (x, y).

The D_4 *distance* (also called *city-block distance*) between p and q is defined as

$$D_4(p, q) = |x - s| + |y - t| \tag{2}$$

In this case the pixels having a D_4 distance from (x, y) less than or equal to some value, r, form a diamond centered at (x, y). For example, the pixels with distance $D_4 \leq 2$ from (x, y) (the center point) form the contours of constant distance shown in Fig. 3. The pixels with $D_4 = 1$ are the 4-neighbors of (x, y).

```
            2
          2 1 2
        2 1 0 1 2
          2 1 2
            2
```

Fig. 3. Pixels with distance $D_4 \leq 2$ from (x, y).

The D_8 *distance* (also called *chessboard distance*) between p and q is defined as

$$D_8(p, q) = \max(|x - s|, |y - t|) \qquad (3)$$

In this case the pixels with D_8 distance from (x, y) less than or equal to some value, r, form a square centered at (x, y). For example, the pixels with distance $D_8 \leq 2$ from (x, y) (the center point) form the contours of constant distance shown in Fig. 4. It is noted that the pixels with $D_8 = 1$ are the 8-neighbors of (x, y).

```
        2 2 2 2 2
        2 1 1 1 2
        2 1 0 1 2
        2 1 1 1 2
        2 2 2 2 2
```

Fig. 4. The pixels with $D_8 \leq 2$ from (x, y).

It is also of interest to note that the D_4 distance between two points p and q is equal to the length of the shortest 4-path between these two points. Similar comments apply to the D_8 distance. In fact, we can consider both the D_4 and D_8 distances between p and q regardless of whether or not a connected path exists between them since the definition of these distances involves only the coordinates of these points.

Relations and Transitive Closure

A *binary relation R* on a set *A* is a set of pairs of elements from *A*. If the pair (a, b) is in *R*, we often write this fact using the notation *aRb* and say that "*a* is related to *b*." Consider, for example, the set of points $A = \{p_1, p_2, p_3, p_4\}$ arranged in the order shown in Fig. 5, and define the relation "4-connected." In this case, *R* is the set of pairs of points which are 4-connected, that is, $R = \{(p_1, p_2), (p_2, p_1), (p_1, p_3), (p_3, p_1)\}$. Thus, p_1 is related to p_2 and p_1 is related to p_3, and vice versa, but p_4 is not related to any of the other three points under this definition.

$$p_1 \quad p_2$$
$$p_3$$
$$p_4$$

Fig. 5. Defining the relation "4-connected" on the set A.

A binary relation R over a set A is said to be

(a) *reflexive* if for each a in A, aRa;

(b) *symmetric* if for each a and b in A, aRb implies bRa; and

(c) *transitive* if for a, b, and c in A, aRb and bRc implies aRc.

A relation satisfying properties (a) through (c) is called an *equivalence relation*. An important property of equivalence relations is that if R is an equivalence relation on a set A, then we can divide A into k disjoint subsets, called *equivalence classes*, for some k between 1 and infinity, inclusive, such that aRb if and only if a and b are in the same subset.

In terms of our present discussion, the importance of relations is that they can be used to establish a systematic way for examining connectivity. Consider, for example, the problem of establishing adjacency of connected components in an image. (Recall from our previous discussion that, for any point p in a set S, the set of points in S that are connected to p is called a connected component of S.) This problem is basic in finding objects in a binary image. In order to see the application of relations to this problem, it is useful to express a relation in terms of a binary matrix. For example, let $R = \{(a, a), (a, b), (b, d), (d, b), (c, e)\}$. We then form the matrix

$$\mathbf{B} = \begin{array}{c} \\ a \\ b \\ c \\ d \\ e \end{array} \begin{array}{c} \begin{array}{ccccc} a & b & c & d & e \end{array} \\ \left[\begin{array}{ccccc} 1 & 1 & 0 & 0 & 0 \\ 0 & 0 & 0 & 1 & 0 \\ 0 & 0 & 0 & 0 & 1 \\ 0 & 1 & 0 & 0 & 0 \\ 0 & 0 & 0 & 0 & 0 \end{array} \right] \end{array}$$

by inserting a 1 in the locations corresponding to elements that are related and 0s elsewhere. It is noted that if the relation in question were reflexive all the main diagonal terms would be 1, and that if R were symmetric then $\mathbf{B}$ would be a symmetric matrix.

As indicated above, transitivity implies that if aRb and bRc, then aRc. In the example just given, a is related to b and b is related to d since (a, b) and (b, d) are in R. It is noted, however, that (a, d) is not in the set R. The set containing these "implied" relations is called the *transitive closure* of R and is denoted by R^+. In the present example, $R^+ = \{(a, a), (a, b), (a, d), (b, b), (b, d),$

$(d, b), (d, d), (c, e)\}$. The fact that the pairs (b, b) and (d, d) are included in the set follows from the definition of transitivity (i.e., *bRd* and *dRb*, so *bRb*; and *dRb* and *bRd*, so *dRd*). In matrix representation, we have

$$\mathbf{B}^+ = \begin{array}{c} \\ a \\ b \\ c \\ d \\ e \end{array} \begin{array}{ccccc} a & b & c & d & e \\ \left[\begin{array}{ccccc} 1 & 1 & 0 & 1 & 0 \\ 0 & 1 & 0 & 1 & 0 \\ 0 & 0 & 0 & 0 & 1 \\ 0 & 1 & 0 & 1 & 0 \\ 0 & 0 & 0 & 0 & 0 \end{array} \right] \end{array}$$

The importance of this concept is that, given pairwise adjacency of connected components expressed in terms of the matrix **B**, the output matrix $\mathbf{B}^+$ contains the information required to establish strings of adjacent components.

Finding Connected Components

The concepts just discussed form the basis for finding connected components in a binary image. In the present discussion, we are interested in connected components of 1s which we are assuming are objects of interest in the image. Suppose that we run the window that is shown in Fig. 6 through every pixel in an image, starting at the top left pixel and scanning the image row by row.

Fig. 6. Window to scan all the pixels.

We are interested in labeling pixel p based on its value and on the labels already assigned to its neighbors r, s, and t. If p is 0 we do nothing and move on since only connected components of 1s are of interest. If p is 1 and neither r, s, or t is labeled, we assign a new label to p and move on to the next location. If p is 1 and r has been labeled, we assign to p the same label and move to the next location. If p is 1 and either t or s is labeled, we again assign that label to p and move on. The same holds true if both t and s have the same label. If t and s are labeled with different labels, we pick one of the labels arbitrarily, but make note of the fact that t and s are connected through p (i.e., the two different labels are equivalent). A situation leading to two different labels being assigned to the same connected component is shown in Fig. 7.

This is a result of sequential scanning and can be fixed by means of a second pass. That is, after all the 1-valued pixels have been labeled, we form a matrix **B** (see above) with all the labels that were found to be related, and then find the transitive closure, **B**$^+$. From this, we can assign a unique label to each connected component (object) in a binary figure.

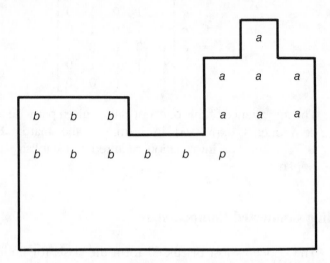

Fig. 7. A connected component assigned two different labels as a result of sequential scanning. Point *p* is arbitrarily assigned one of the two labels, and the equivalence between the labels is noted for subsequent processing.

Boundary Tracking

Once an object of interest has been identified in an image, its contour is frequently used as the basis for object description and measurement. Contour tracking in a binary environment is a particularly simple process and is based on the following basic steps: (1) Obtain an initial border element and call it x_0. (2) Scan the 8-neighbors of x_0 in any direction, say clockwise, until the next border element is found. Call it x_1. (3) Obtain the rest of the elements of the contour of the digital figure in the same manner in which x_1 was obtained. (4) Stop when the sequence $x_0 x_1$ appears again.

It can be shown that such algorithms work in finding the contour of a digital image in linear time. Furthermore, it can be shown that there exists a smallest positive integer m such that the sequence $\{x_0, x_1, \ldots, x_{m-1}\}$ contains every border element of a digital figure S at least once and at most twice, with the latter holding if and only if the element has just two nonconsecutive 4-neighbors not in S and $x_m = x_0$, and $x_{m+1} = x_1$. Since the scanning of the 8-neighbors of a point involves at most 8 points, the complexity of such contour-following algorithms is linear in n, where n is the number of boundary points in S.

5. Representation

A binary image is an array of two-valued quantities, generally 0s and 1s. We assume that 0s correspond to background pixels and 1s to object pixels. Thus, the extraction of objects from a binary image consists simply of finding connected components of 1s, as discussed in the previous section. Given these connected components, the representation problem deals with choosing a scheme for expressing this data in a form suitable for a given processing task. In some cases the "raw" data is sufficient. An example of this is in the computation of the area of an object. In more detailed dimensioned analysis, such as shape determination, other representations usually lead to more efficient processing. In this section, we discuss a number of representation techniques commonly used in practice.

Chain Codes

Chain codes are used to represent a boundary by a connected sequence of straight line segments of specified length and direction. Typically, this representation is based on the 4- or 8-connectivity of the segments, where the direction of each segment is coded using a numbering scheme such as the one shown in Fig. 8.

Since digital images are usually acquired and processed in a grid format with equal spacing in the x and y directions, one could generate a chain code by following a boundary in, say, a clockwise direction and assigning a direction to the segments connecting every pair of pixels. This is generally unacceptable for two principal reasons: First, the resulting chain of codes will usually be quite long; second, any small disturbances along the boundary due to noise or imperfect segmentation could cause changes in the code which may not necessarily be related to the shape of the boundary.

An approach frequently used to circumvent the problems just discussed is to "resample" the boundary by selecting a larger grid spacing, as illustrated in Fig. 9A. Then, as the boundary is traversed, we assign a boundary point to each node of the large grid, depending on the proximity of the original boundary to that node, as shown in Fig. 9B. The resampled boundary obtained in this way can then be represented by a 4- or 8-code, as shown in Figs. 9C and 9D, respectively, where the starting point is at the dot, and the boundary in Fig. 9C was obtained by following the shortest allowable external 4-path in the grid of Fig. 9B. The boundary representation in Fig. 9C is the chain code 0330...01, and in Fig. 9D it is the code 0660...12. As might be expected, the accuracy of the resulting code representation depends on the spacing of the sampling grid.

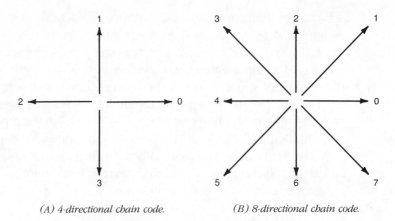

(A) 4-directional chain code.   *(B) 8-directional chain code.*

Fig. 8. Numbering schemes for chain codes.

It is important to note that the chain code of a given boundary depends on the starting point. It is possible, however, to normalize the code by a straightforward procedure: Given a chain code generated by starting in an arbitrary position, we treat it as a circular sequence of direction numbers and redefine the starting point so that the resulting sequence of numbers forms an integer of minimum magnitude. We can also normalize for rotation by using the first difference of the chain code, instead of the code itself. The difference is computed simply by counting (in a counterclockwise manner) the number of directions that separate two adjacent elements of the code. For instance, the first difference of the 4-direction chain code 10103322 is 3133030. If we treat the code as a circular sequence, then the first element of the difference is computed using the transition between the last and first components of the chain. In this example the result is 33133030.

Polygonal Approximations

A digital boundary can be approximated with arbitrary accuracy by a polygon. For a closed curve, the approximation is exact when the number of segments in the polygon is equal to the number of points in the boundary so that each pair of adjacent points defines a segment in the polygon. In practice, the goal of a polygonal approximation is to capture the "essence" of the boundary shape with the fewest possible polygonal segments. Although this problem is in general not trivial and can very quickly turn into a time-consuming iterative search, there are a number of polygonal approximation techniques whose modest complexity and processing requirements makes them well-suited for industrial vision applications.

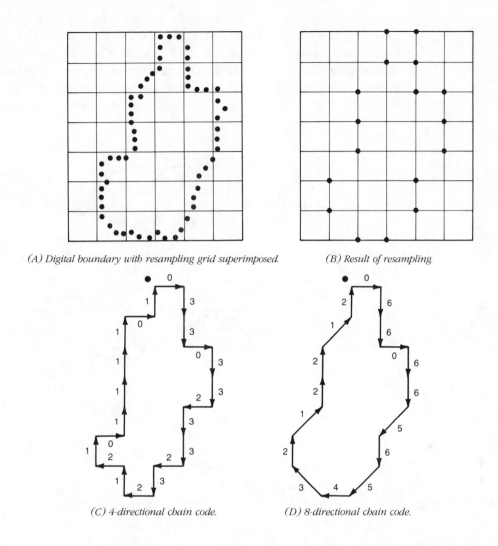

(A) Digital boundary with resampling grid superimposed.

(B) Result of resampling.

(C) 4-directional chain code.

(D) 8-directional chain code.

Fig. 9. Resample the boundary to generate an acceptable chain code.

The polygonal approximation problem may be illustrated by discussing a method proposed by Sklansky, Chazin, and Hansen [1972] for finding minimum perimeter polygons. The procedure is best explained by means of an example. With reference to Fig. 10, suppose that we enclose a given boundary by a set of concatenated cells, as shown in Fig. 10A. We can visualize this enclosure as consisting of two walls corresponding to the outside and inside boundaries of the strip of cells, and we can think of the object boundary as a rubber band contained within the walls. If we now allow the rubber band to shrink, it will take the shape shown in Fig. 10B, thus producing a polygon of minimum perimeter which fits in the geometry established by the cell strip. If the cells are chosen so that each cell encompasses only one point on the boundary, then the error in each cell between the original boundary and the rubber band approximation would be at most $\sqrt{2}\,d$, where d is the distance between pixels. This error can be reduced in half by forcing each cell to be centered on its corresponding pixel.

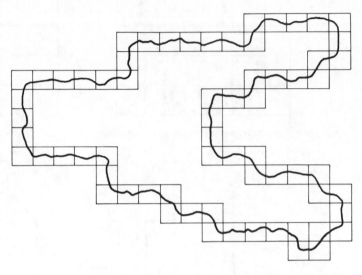

(A) Object boundary enclosed by cells.

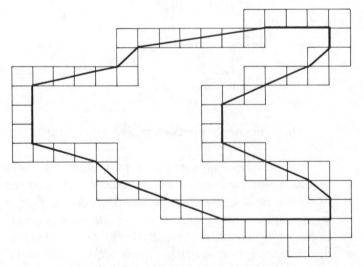

(B) Minimum-perimeter polygon.

Fig. 10. Procedure for finding minimum-perimeter polygons.

Signatures

A signature is a one-dimensional functional representation of a boundary. There are a number of ways to generate signatures. One of the simplest is to plot the distance from the centroid to the boundary as a function of angle, as illustrated in Fig. 11. Regardless of how a signature is generated, however, the basic idea is to reduce the boundary representation to a one-dimensional function which, presumably, is easier to describe than the original two-dimensional boundary.

Signatures generated by the approach just described are obviously dependent on size and starting point. Size normalization can be achieved simply by normalizing the $r(\theta)$ curve to, say, unit maximum value. The starting-point problem can be solved by first obtaining the chain code of the boundary and then using the approach discussed earlier.

Distance versus angle is, of course, not the only way to generate a signature. We could, for example, traverse the boundary and plot the angle between a line tangent to the boundary and a reference line as a function of position along the boundary [Ambler et al. 1975]. The resulting signature, although quite different from the $r(\theta)$ curve, would carry information about basic shape characteristics. For instance, horizontal segments in the curve would correspond to straight lines along the boundary since the tangent angle would be constant there. A variation of this approach is to use the so-called slope density function as a signature [Nahim 1974]. This function is simply a histogram of tangent angle values. Since a histogram is a measure of concentration of values, the slope density function would respond strongly to sections of the boundary with constant tangent angles (straight or nearly straight segments) and have deep valleys in sections producing rapidly varying angles (corners or other sharp inflections).

The Skeleton of a Region

Thus far, attention has been focused on boundary representations. In this and the next section we consider techniques suitable for representating regional properties directly.

An important approach for representing the structural shape of a plane region is to reduce it to a graph. This is often accomplished by obtaining the *skeleton* of the region via a thinning (also called *skeletonizing*) algorithm. Thinning procedures play a central role in a broad range of problems in image processing, ranging from automated inspection of printed-circuit boards to counting of asbestos fibers in air filters.

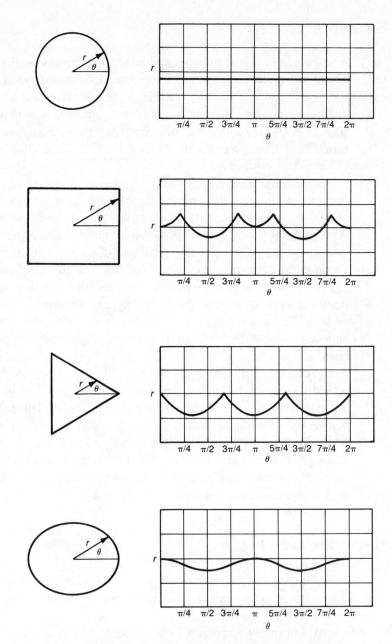

Fig. 11. Some simple boundary shapes and their corresponding distance versus angle signatures.

The skeleton of a region may be defined via the medial axis transformation (MAT) proposed by Blum [1967]. The MAT of a region R with border B is as follows. For each point p in R, we find its closest neighbor in B. If p has more than one such neighbor, then it is said to belong to the *medial axis* (skeleton) of R. It is important to note that the concept of "closest" depends on the definition of a distance and, therefore, the results of a MAT operation will be influenced by the choice of a given metric. Some examples using the Euclidean distance are shown in Fig. 12.

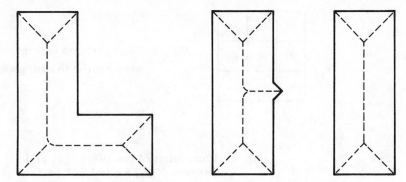

Fig. 12. Medial axes of three simple regions.

Although the MAT of a region yields an intuitively pleasing skeleton, a direct implementation of the above definition is typically prohibitive from a computational point of view because it potentially involves calculating the distance from every interior point to every point on the boundary of a region. A number of algorithms have been proposed for improving computational efficiency while, at the same time, attempting to produce a medial axis representation of a given region. Typically, these are thinning algorithms that iteratively delete edge points of a region subject to the constraints that the deletion of these points (1) does not remove end points, (2) does not break connectedness, and (3) does not cause excessive erosion of the region. Although some attempts have been made to use skeletons in gray-scale images [Dyer and Rosenfeld 1979, Salari and Siy 1984] this type of representation is usually associated with binary data.

This section presents an algorithm developed by Zhang and Suen [1984] for thinning binary regions. In the following discussion it is assumed that region points have value 1 and background points have value 0. The method consists of successive passes of two basic steps applied to the contour points of the given region, where a *contour point* is any pixel with value 1 and having at least one 8-neighbor valued 0. With reference to the 8-neighborhood definition shown in Fig. 13, the first step flags a contour point p for deletion if the following conditions are satisfied:

(a) $2 \leq N(p_1) \leq 6$

(b) $S(p_1) = 1$

(c) $p_2 \cdot p_4 \cdot p_6 = 0$ (3)

(d) $p_4 \cdot p_6 \cdot p_8 = 0$

where $N(p_1)$ is the number of nonzero neighbors of p_1; that is,

$$N(p_1) = p_2 + p_3 + \ldots + p_8 + p_9 \qquad (4)$$

and $S(p_1)$ is the number of 0–1 transitions in the ordered sequence of $p_2, p_3, \ldots, p_8, p_9$. For example, $N(p_1) = 4$ and $S(p_1) = 3$ in Fig. 14.

p_1	p_2	p_3
p_4	p_5	p_6
p_7	p_8	p_9

**Fig. 13. Neighborhood arrangement
used by the thinning algorithm.**

```
0   0   1
1   p₁  0
1   0   1
```

**Fig. 14. Illustration of conditions (*a*) and (*b*).
In this case $N(p_1) = 4$ and $S(p_1) = 3$.**

In the second step, conditions (*a*) and (*b*) remain the same, but conditions (*c*) and (*d*) are changed to

$$(c') \; p_2 \cdot p_4 \cdot p_8 = 0 \qquad (5)$$
$$(d') \; p_2 \cdot p_6 \cdot p_8 = 0$$

Step 1 is applied to every border pixel in the binary region under consideration. If one or more of the conditions (*a*) through (*d*) are violated, the value of the point in question is not changed. If all conditions are satisfied, the point is flagged for deletion. It is important to note, however, that the point is not deleted until all border points have been processed. This prevents changing the structure of the data during execution of the algorithm. After step 1 has been applied to all border points, those that were flagged are deleted (i.e., changed to 0). Then, step 2 is applied to the resulting data in exactly the same manner as step 1.

Based on the foregoing comments, it is noted that one iteration of the thinning algorithm consists of (1) applying step 1 to flag border points for deletion; (2) deleting the flagged points; (3) applying step 2 to flag the remaining border points for deletion; and (4) deleting the flagged points. This basic procedure is applied iteratively until no further points are deleted, at which time the algorithm terminates, yielding the skeleton of the region.

Condition (*a*) is violated when contour point p_1 has only one or seven 8-neighbors valued 1. Having only one such neighbor implies that p_1 is the end point of a skeleton stroke and obviously should not be deleted. If p_1 had seven such neighbors and it were deleted, this would cause erosion into the region. Condition (*b*) is violated when it is applied to points on a stroke one pixel thick. Thus, this condition prevents disconnecting segments of a skeleton during the thinning operation. Conditions (*c*) and (*d*) are satisified simultaneously by the following minimum set of values: $p_4 = 0$, or $p_6 = 0$, or ($p_2 = 0$ and $p_8 = 0$). Thus, with reference to the neighborhood arrangement in Fig. 13, a point that satisfies these conditions, as well as conditions (a) and (b), is an east or south boundary point, or a northwest corner point in the boundary. In either case, p_1 is not part of the skeleton and should be removed. Similarly, conditions (c') and (d') are satisfied simultaneously by the following minimum set of values: $p_2 = 0$, or $p_8 = 0$, or ($p_4 = 0$ and $p_6 = 0$). These correspond to north or west boundary points, or a southeast corner point. It is noted that northeast corner points have $p_2 = 0$ and $p_4 = 0$ and thus satisfy conditions (c) and (d), as well as (c') and (d'). This is also true for southwest corner points which have $p_6 = 0$ and $p_8 = 0$.

As an illustration of the method just described, Fig. 15A shows the result of applying step 1 of the thinning algorithm to the boundary of a simple region. The dots indicate the points flagged and subsequently removed at the end of step 1. Figure 15B shows the results obtained with step 2, and Fig. 15C is the skeleton obtained after several iterations through these two steps.

Convex Hull and Convex Deficiency

If we consider an object region as a planar set, a great deal can be said in general about the shape of the region by analyzing its convex hull and its convex deficiency.

A set C is *convex* if any two points in C can be joined by a straight line lying entirely in C. The *convex hull*, H, of an arbitrary set S is the smallest convex set containing S. The difference set $H - S$ is called the *convex deficiency*, D, of the set S. These concepts are illustrated in Fig. 16.

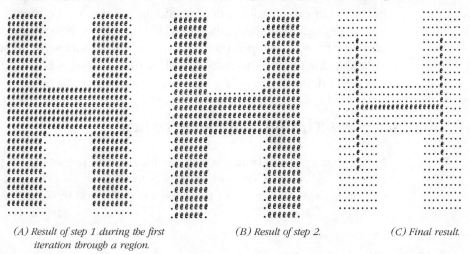

(A) Result of step 1 during the first   (B) Result of step 2.   (C) Final result.
     iteration through a region.

Fig. 15. The thinning algorithm. *(From Zhang and Suen [1984])*

Sometimes a region is represented by its boundary and we refer to the convex hull and convex deficiency of the boundary, with the understanding that the boundary encloses a solid region.

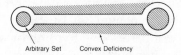

Arbitrary Set   Convex Deficiency

Fig. 16. An arbitrary set and its convex deficiency (shown shaded).

The convex hull and convex deficiency of a region or boundary have a number of important properties in machine vision. For example, the hull and deficiency are independent of rotation. They also carry a significant amount of shape information.

In practice, digital boundaries tend to be irregular as a result of digitization, noise, and variations in segmentation. These effects usually result in a convex deficiency which has small, meaningless components scattered randomly throughout the boundary. Rather than attempting to sort out these irregularities by postprocessing, it is common practice to smooth a boundary prior to partitioning. There are a number of ways to do this. One approach is to use lowpass filtering or neighborhood averaging [Gonzalez and Wintz 1987]. Another approach is to traverse the boundary and replace the coordinates of each pixel by the average coordinates of m of its neighbors along the boundary. This works for small irregularities, but it is time consuming and difficult to control in the sense that large values of m can result in excessive smoothing while small values of m might not be sufficient in some segments of the boundary. A more rugged technique is to use a polygonal approximation prior to finding the convex deficiency of a given region. Regardless of the method used for smoothing, most digital boundaries of interest are simple polygons (i.e., polygons without self-intersection). An algorithm for finding the convex hull of such polygons is given by Graham and Yao [1983].

6. Boundary Description and Measurement

In this section typical (and popular) techniques are presented for performing dimensioned analysis on regions represented by their boundaries. A more comprehensive discussion of this topic can be found in Gonzalez and Wintz [1987].

Some Simple Descriptors

The *length* of a contour is one of its simplest descriptors. A rough approximation of the length may be obtained simply by counting the number of pixels along the contour. For a chain-coded curve with unit spacing in both directions, the length is given exactly by the number of vertical and horizontal components plus $\sqrt{2}$ times the number of diagonal components.

The *diameter* of a boundary *B* is defined as

$$\text{Diam}(B) = \max_{i,j} [D(p_i, p_j)] \tag{6}$$

where *D* is a distance measure and p_i and p_j are points on the boundary. The value of the diameter and the orientation of a line connecting the two extreme points which comprise the diameter (this line is called the *major axis* of the boundary) are useful descriptors of a boundary. Algorithms for computing the diameter may be found in Shamos [1978], in Fischler [1980], and in Toussaint [1982].

Curvature is defined as the rate of change of slope. In general, it is difficult to obtain reliable measures of curvature at a point in a digital boundary because these boundaries tend to be locally "ragged." However, it is sometimes useful to use the difference between the slopes of adjacent boundary segments (which have been represented as straight lines) as a descriptor of curvature at the point of intersection of the segments. As the boundary is traversed in the clockwise direction, we say that a vertex point *p* is part of a *convex* segment if the change in the slope at *p* is nonnegative; otherwise, we say that *p* belongs to segment which is *concave*. One can further refine the description of curvature at a point by using ranges in the change of slope. For instance, we could say that *p* is part of a nearly straight segment if the change is less than 10° or that *p* is a *corner* point if the change exceeds 90°. It is noted, however, that these descriptors must be used with care because their interpretation is strongly dependent on the length of the individual segments relative to the overall length of the boundary.

Shape Numbers

A gross measure of the shape of a boundary may be obtained by computing its shape number [Bribiesca and Guzman 1980, Bribiesca 1981]. As discussed earlier, a chain-coded boundary has several first differences, depending on the starting point. The *shape number* of such a boundary, based on the 4-directional code of Fig. 8A is defined as the first difference of smallest magnitude. The *order*, *n*, of a shape number is defined as the number of digits in its representation. It is noted that *n* is even for a closed boundary, and that its value limits the number of possible different shapes. Figure 17 shows all the shapes of order 4, 6, and 8, along with their chain-code representations, first differences, and corresponding shape numbers. Note that the first differences were computed by treating the chain codes as a circular sequence in the manner discussed earlier.

Although the first difference of a chain code is independent of rotation, the coded boundary in general will depend on the orientation of the grid. One way to normalize the grid orientation is as follows. The *major axis* of a boundary is the straight line segment joining the two points farthest away from each other. The *minor axis* is perpendicular to the major axis and of length such that a box could be formed that just encloses the boundary. The ratio of the major to minor axis is called the *eccentricity* of the boundary, and the rectangle just described is called the *basic rectangle*. In most cases a unique shape number will be obtained by aligning the chain-code grid with the sides of the basic rectangle. Freeman and Shapira [1975] give a procedure for finding the basic rectangle directly from a closed, chain-coded curve.

In practice, given a desired order, we find the rectangle of order n whose eccentricity best approximates that of the basic rectangle, and use this new rectangle to establish the grid size. For example, if $n = 12$, all the rectangles of order 12 (i.e., those whose perimeter length is 12) are 2×4, 3×3, and 1×5. If the eccentricity of the 2×4 rectangle best matches the eccentricity of the basic rectangle for a given boundary, we establish a 2×4 grid centered on the basic rectangle and use the resampling procedure discussed earlier to obtain the chain code. The shape number follows from the first difference of this code, as indicated above. Although the order of the resulting shape number will usually be equal to n because of the way the grid spacing was selected, boundaries with depressions comparable to this spacing will sometimes yield shape numbers of order greater than n. In this case, we specify a rectangle of order lower than n and repeat the procedure until the resulting shape number is of order n.

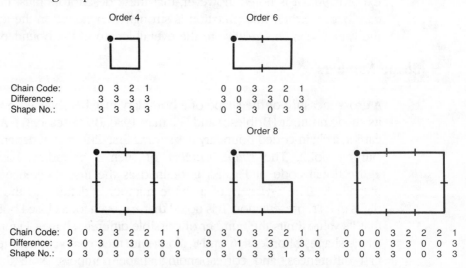

Fig. 17. All shapes of order 4, 6, and 8. The directions are from Fig. 8A, and the dot indicates the starting point.

Moments

The shape of boundary segments (and of signatures) can be described quantitatively by using moments. In order to see how this can be accomplished, consider Fig. 18A, which shows the segment of a boundary, and Fig. 18B, which shows the segment represented as a one-dimensional function $g(r)$ of an arbitrary variable r. Suppose that we treat the amplitude of g as a random variable v and form an amplitude histogram $p(v_i)$, $i = 1, 2, \ldots, K$, where K is the number of discrete amplitude increments. Then, the nth moment of v about its mean is

$$\mu_n(v) = \sum_{i=1}^{K} (v_i - m)^n p(v_i) \qquad (7)$$

where

$$m = \sum_{i=1}^{K} v_i p(v_i) \qquad (8)$$

The quantity m is recognized as the mean or average value of v and μ_2 as its variance. Only the first few moments are generally required to differentiate between signatures of clearly distinct shapes. Higher-order moments refine the tolerance of a measurement.

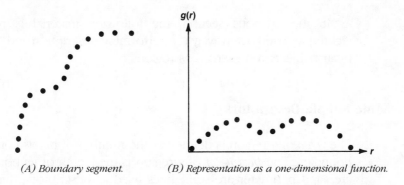

(A) Boundary segment.   *(B) Representation as a one-dimensional function.*

Fig. 18. Description of boundary segments using moments.

An alternative approach is to normalize $g(r)$ to unit area and treat it as a histogram. In this case, r becomes the random variable and the moments are given by

$$\mu_n(r) = \sum_{i=1}^{L} (r_i - m)^n g(r_i) \qquad (9)$$

where

$$m = \sum_{i=1}^{L} r_i g(r_i) \qquad (10)$$

In this notation, L is the number of points on the boundary, and $\mu_n(r)$ is directly related to the shape of $g(r)$. For example, the second moment $\mu_2(r)$ would measure the spread of the curve about the mean value of r and the third moment $\mu_3(r)$ would measure its symmetry with reference to the mean. Naturally, it is possible to use both moment representations simultaneously to describe a given boundary segment or signature.

Before leaving this section we should observe that, basically, what has been accomplished here is to reduce the description task to that of describing and measuring one-dimensional functions. Although moments are by far the most popular method, they are not the only descriptors that could be used for this purpose. For instance, we could also compute the one-dimensional discrete Fourier transform, obtain its spectrum, and use the first k components of the spectrum to describe $g(r)$. The advantage of moments over other techniques one could use is that they are straightforward to implement and also carry a "physical" interpretation of boundary shape. The insensitivity of this approach to rotation is clear from Fig. 18. Size normalization, if desired, can be achieved by scaling the range of r.

7. Region Description and Measurement

As in the previous section, the following material is representative of techniques used extensively for performing description and measurements of binary objects represented as regions.

Some Simple Descriptors

The *area* of a region is defined as the number of pixels contained within its boundary. The *perimeter* of a region is the length of its boundary. Although area and perimeter are sometimes used as descriptors, they are applicable primarily in situations in which the size of objects of interest is invariant. A more frequent use of these two descriptors is in establishing a measure of *compactness* of a region, defined as (perimeter)^2/area. It is of interest to note that compactness is a dimensionless quantity (and thus is insensitive to scale changes) and that it is minimum for a disk-shaped region. With the exception of errors introduced by rotation of a digital region, compactness is also insensitive to orientation.

The *principal axes* of a region are the eigenvectors of the covariance matrix obtained by using the pixels within the region as random variables. The two eigenvectors of the covariance matrix point in the directions of maximum region spread, subject to the constraint that they be orthogonal. A measure of the degree of spread is given by the corresponding eigenvalues. Thus, the principal spread and direction of a region can be described by the largest eigenvalue and its corresponding eigenvector. This type of description is insensitive to rotation, but does depend on scale changes if one uses eigenvalues as a measure of spread. One approach used frequently to compensate for this difficulty is to use the *ratio* of the large to the small eigenvalue as a descriptor.

Other simple measures used as region descriptors include the mean and median of the gray levels, the minimum and maximum gray values, and the number of pixels with values above and below the mean.

Topological Descriptors

As in the case of shape numbers for boundaries, topological properties are useful for gross descriptions of regions in the image plane. Simply defined, topology is the study of properties of a figure which are unaffected by any deformation, as long as there is no tearing or joining of the figure (these are sometimes called *rubber-sheet* distortions). Consider, for example, Fig. 19. If we define as a topological descriptor the number of holes in the region, it is evident that this property will not be affected by a stretching or rotation transformation. The number of holes, however, will in general change if we tear or fold the region. It is noted that, since stretching affects distance, topological properties do not depend on any notion of distance or any properties which are implicitly based on the concept of a distance measure.

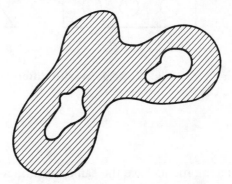

Fig. 19. A region with two holes.

Another topological property useful for region description is the number of connected components. A *connected component* of a set is a subset of maximal size such that any two of its points can be joined by a connected curve lying entirely within the subset. Figure 20 shows a region with three connected components.

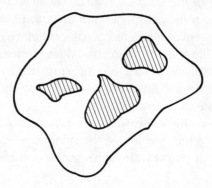

Fig. 20. A region with three connected components.

The number of holes (H) and connected components (C) in a figure can be used to define the *Euler number E* as follows:

$$E = C - H \qquad (11)$$

The Euler number is also a topological property. The regions which are shown in Fig. 21, for example, have Euler numbers equal to -5 and -2, respectively.

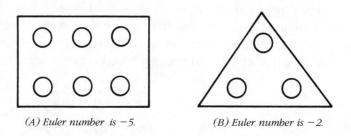

(A) Euler number is −5.   *(B) Euler number is −2.*

Fig. 21. Regions with different Euler numbers.

Moments

Regional moments have the same function as the one-dimensional moments defined in Eqs. 7 through 10. Given a two-dimensional continuous function $f(x, y)$ we define the moment of order $(p + q)$ by the relation

$$m_{pq} = \int_{-\infty}^{\infty} \int_{-\infty}^{\infty} x^p y^q f(x, y) \, dx \, dy \qquad (12)$$

for $p, q = 0, 1, 2, \ldots$.

A uniqueness theorem [Papoulis 1965] states that if $f(x,y)$ is piecewise continuous and has nonzero values only in a finite part of the xy plane, then moments of all orders exist and the moment sequence (m_{pq}) uniquely determines $f(x,y)$.

The *central moments* can be expressed as

$$\mu_{pq} = \int_{-\infty}^{\infty}\int_{-\infty}^{\infty} (x-\bar{x})^p (y-\bar{y})^q f(x,y)\ dx\ dy \qquad (13)$$

where

$$\bar{x} = \frac{m_{10}}{m_{00}}, \qquad \bar{y} = \frac{m_{01}}{m_{00}}$$

For a digital image, Eq. 13 becomes

$$\mu_{pq} = \sum_x \sum_y (x-\bar{x})^p (y-\bar{y})^q f(x,y) \qquad (14)$$

In the binary case we have that $f(x,y) = 0$ or 1, which simplifies the computation of the moments significantly.

The *normalized moments*, denoted by η_{pq}, are defined as

$$\eta_{pq} = \frac{\mu_{pq}}{\mu_{00}^{\gamma}} \qquad (15)$$

where

$$\gamma = \frac{p+q}{2} + 1 \qquad (16)$$

for $p + q = 2, 3, \dots$.

From the second and third moments, a set of seven *invariant moments* can be derived. This set of moments has been shown to be invariant to translation, rotation, and scale change [Hu 1962].

8. Matching

After an object has been represented and described by its boundary or region, we are still faced with the problem of determining how closely the dimensions and shape of the object match an acceptable prototype.

The complexity of the matching process depends on how exact we wish the dimensional analysis to be. For example, a gross measurement might consist of comparing the dimensions of the basic rectangle enclosing an object to the dimensions of a basic rectangle deemed to be acceptable. A more detailed analysis might consist of comparing the relative location of the vertices of a polygonal approximation against the location of the vertices of a prototype.

In this section matching is illustrated by a discussion of techniques representative of two basic approaches to the problem. The first approach is a *quantitative* approach; the second a *structural* approach. Quantitative measurements are based on descriptors such as length, area, and moments. Structural measurements rely on interrelationships between descriptors, such as *sequences* of boundary segments of the same length (as in a square object).

Matching Quantitative Descriptors

Suppose that we arrange a set of n quantitative descriptors for a boundary or region in the form of a column vector $\mathbf{x} = (x_1, x_2, \ldots, x_n)^T$, where x_k is the kth descriptor. Suppose also that an object known to have acceptable properties is described by the same type of descriptors, whose values $z_1, z_2, \ldots, z_n$ are also represented in the form of an n-dimensional column vector, $\mathbf{z} = (z_1, z_2, \ldots, z_n)^T$. We can compare $\mathbf{x}$ and $\mathbf{z}$ by computing the Euclidean distance between them:

$$D(\mathbf{x}, \mathbf{z}) = \|\mathbf{x} - \mathbf{z}\|$$
$$= [(\mathbf{x} - \mathbf{z})^T(\mathbf{x} - \mathbf{z})]^{1/2} \tag{17}$$

Then, we say that $\mathbf{x}$ is *acceptably similar* to $\mathbf{z}$ if

$$D(\mathbf{x}, \mathbf{z}) \leq T \tag{18}$$

where T is a nonnegative threshold.

Another popular matching technique is to compute a measure of correlation. Given a digital image $f(x, y)$ of size $M \times N$, suppose that we wish to determine if it contains a region which is similar to some region $w(x, y)$ of size $J \times K$, where $J < M$ and $K < N$. One of the methods most often used for the solution of this problem is to perform a correlation between $w(x, y)$ and $f(x, y)$.

In its simplest form, the correlation between these two real functions is given by

$$R(m, n) = \sum_x \sum_y f(x, y) w(x - m, y - n) \tag{19}$$

where $m = 0, 1, 2, \ldots, M - 1$, $n = 0, 1, 2, \ldots, N - 1$, and the summation is taken over the image region where $w(x, y)$ is defined. The procedure is illustrated in Fig. 22; for a value of (m, n) inside $f(x, y)$ we apply Eq. 19 to obtain one value of R. As m and n are varied, $w(x, y)$ moves around the image area and we obtain the function $R(m, n)$. The maximum value of $R(m, n)$ then indicates the position where $w(x, y)$ best matched $f(x, y)$. It is noted that accuracy will be lost for values of m and n near the edges of $f(x, y)$, with the amount of error being proportional to the size of $w(x, y)$. If the region in $f(x, y)$ containing an object of interest is known, then usually a few values of displacement in m and n are sufficient to bring $w(x, y)$ in registration with that region.

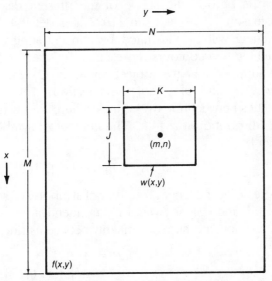

Fig. 22. Arrangement for obtaining the correlation of $f(x, y)$ and $w(x, y)$ at a given point (m, n).

A method frequently used to obtain a normalized result is to perform matching via the *correlation coefficient*, defined as

$$r(m, n) = \frac{\sum_x \sum_y F(x, y) W(x, y)}{\left[\sum_x \sum_y F^2(x, y) \sum_x \sum_y w^2(x, y) \right]^{1/2}} \qquad (20)$$

where

$$F(x, y) = f(x, y) - \bar{f}(x, y)$$
$$W(x, y) = w(x - m, y - n) - \overline{w}$$

where $m = 0, 1, 2, \ldots, M - 1$, $n = 0, 1, 2, \ldots, N - 1$, $\overline{w}$ is the average intensity of $w(x, y)$ (this value is computed only once), $\bar{f}(x, y)$ is the average value of

$f(x, y)$ in the region coincident with $w(x, y)$, and the summations are taken over the coordinates common to both f and w. It is not difficult to show that $r(m, n)$ is scaled to the range from -1 to 1, with 1 corresponding to a maximum match. We also note that, for binary images, all values of f and w are either 0 or 1.

Matching Structural Descriptors

In its most general formulation, the problem of matching structural descriptors falls in the domain of syntactic pattern recognition. A discussion of this topic is beyond the scope of the present discussion (see Gonzalez and Thomason [1978] and Fu [1982] for details). The concepts of structural matching will be illustrated by concentrating on the problem of directly matching two contours represented by structural strings.

Suppose that two object contours C_1 and C_2 are coded into strings $a_1 a_2 \ldots a_n$ and $b_1 b_2 \ldots b_m$, respectively. Let A represent the number of matches between the two strings, where we say that a match has occurred in the jth position if $a_j = b_j$. The number of symbols that do not match up is given by

$$B = \max(|C_1|, |C_2|) - A \qquad (21)$$

where $|C|$ is the length (number of symbols) of string C. It can be shown that $B = 0$ if and only if C_1 and C_2 are identical.

A simple measure of similarity between strings C_1 and C_2 is defined as the ratio

$$
\begin{aligned}
R &= A/B \\
&= A/[\max(|C_1|, |C_2|) - A] \qquad (22)
\end{aligned}
$$

Based on the above comment regarding B, R is infinite for a perfect match and zero when none of the symbols in C_1 and C_2 match (i.e., $A = 0$ in this case). Since the matching is done on a symbol-by-symbol basis, the starting point on each boundary when creating the string representation is important. Alternatively, we can start at arbitrary points on each boundary, shift one string (with wraparound), and compute Eq. 22 for each shift. The number of shifts required to perform all necessary comparisons is $\max(|C_1|, |C_2|)$.

As an example, Figs. 23A and 23B show a sample boundary from each of two classes of objects. The boundaries were approximated by a polygonal fit (Figs. 23C and 23D) and then strings were formed by computing the interior angle between the polygon segments as the polygon was traversed in a clockwise direction. Angles were coded into one of eight possible symbols corresponding to 45° increments, $s_1: 0° < \theta \leq 45°, s_2: 45° < \theta \leq 90°, \ldots,$ $s_8: 315° < \theta \leq 0°$.

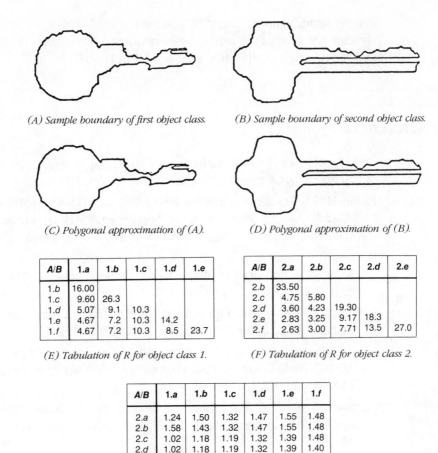

(A) Sample boundary of first object class.   (B) Sample boundary of second object class.

(C) Polygonal approximation of (A).   (D) Polygonal approximation of (B).

A/B	1.a	1.b	1.c	1.d	1.e
1.b	16.00				
1.c	9.60	26.3			
1.d	5.07	9.1	10.3		
1.e	4.67	7.2	10.3	14.2	
1.f	4.67	7.2	10.3	8.5	23.7

(E) Tabulation of R for object class 1.

A/B	2.a	2.b	2.c	2.d	2.e
2.b	33.50				
2.c	4.75	5.80			
2.d	3.60	4.23	19.30		
2.e	2.83	3.25	9.17	18.3	
2.f	2.63	3.00	7.71	13.5	27.0

(F) Tabulation of R for object class 2.

A/B	1.a	1.b	1.c	1.d	1.e	1.f
2.a	1.24	1.50	1.32	1.47	1.55	1.48
2.b	1.58	1.43	1.32	1.47	1.55	1.48
2.c	1.02	1.18	1.19	1.32	1.39	1.48
2.d	1.02	1.18	1.19	1.32	1.39	1.40
2.e	0.93	1.07	1.08	1.19	1.24	1.25
2.f	0.89	1.02	1.02	1.14	1.11	1.18

(G) Tabulation of R by comparing strings.

Fig. 23. Tabulations of $R = A/B$. (*Adapted from Sze and Yang [1981]*).

The results of computing the measure R for five samples of object 1 against themselves are shown in Fig. 23E, where the entries correspond to values of $R = A/B$ and, for example, the notation 1.c refers to the third string for object class 1. Figure 23F shows the results for the strings of the second object class. Finally, Fig. 23G is a tabulation of R values obtained by comparing strings of one class against the other. The important thing to note is that all values of R in this last table are considerably smaller than any entry in the preceding two tables, indicating that the R measure achieved a high degree of discrimination between the two classes of objects. For instance, if string 1.a had been an unknown, the smallest value in comparing it with the other strings of class 1 would have been 4.67. By contrast, the largest value in a comparison against class 2 would have been 1.24. Thus, classification of this string into class 1 based on the maximum value of R would have been a simple, unambiguous matter. By placing thresholds on the computation of *R*, we can get as close a match as is necessary for an acceptable degree of closeness, much in the same way we did in Eq. 18.

9. References

Ambler, A. P., et al. "A Versatile System for Computer Controlled Assembly," *Artificial Intelligence*, Vol. 6, No. 2, 1975, pp. 129–156.

Blum, H. "A Transformation for Extracting New Descriptors of Shape," in *Models for the Perception of Speech and Visual Form*, ed. by W. Wathen-Dunn, Cambridge, Mass.: The MIT Press, 1967.

Bribiesca, E., and A. Guzman. "How to Describe Pure Form and How to Measure Differences in Shape Using Shape Numbers," *Pattern Recognition*, Vol. 12, No. 2, 1980, pp. 101–112.

Bribiesca, E. "Arithmetic Operations Among Shapes Using Shape Numbers," *Pattern Recognition*, Vol. 13, No. 2, 1981, pp. 123–138.

Dyer, C. R., and A. Rosenfeld. "Thinning Algorithms for Grayscale Pictures," *IEEE Transactions on Pattern Analysis and Machine Intelligence*, Vol. PAMI-1, No. 1, 1979, pp. 88–89.

Fischler, M. A. "Fast Algorithms for Two Maximal Distance Problems With Applications to Image Analysis," *Pattern Recognition*, Vol. 12, 1980, pp. 35–40.

Freeman, H., and R. Shapira. "Determining the Minimum Area Encasing Rectangle for an Arbitrary Closed Curve," *Communications of the ACM*, Vol. 18, No. 7, 1975, pp. 409–413.

Fu, K. S. *Syntactic Pattern Recognition and Applications*, Englewood Cliffs: Prentice-Hall, 1982.

Gennery, D. B. "Object Detection and Measurement Using Stereo Vision," *Proceedings of Image Understanding Workshop*, College Park, Md., 1980, pp. 161–167.

Gonzalez, R. C., and P. Wintz. *Digital Image Processing*, 2nd ed., Reading, Mass.: Addison-Wesley, 1987.

Gonzalez, R. C., and M. G. Thomason. *Syntactic Pattern Recognition: An Introduction*, Reading, Pa.: Addison-Wesley, 1978.

Graham, R. L., and F. F. Yao. "Finding the Convex Hull of a Simple Polygon," *Journal of Algorithms*, Vol. 4, 1983, pp. 324–331.

Hu, M. K. "Visual Pattern Recognition by Moment Invariants," *IEEE Transactions on Information Theory*, Vol. 8, 1962, pp. 179–187.

Nahim, P. J. "The Theory of Measurement of a Silhouette Description for Image Processing and Recognition," *Pattern Recognition*, Vol. 6, No. 2, 1974, pp. 85–95.

Papoulis, A. *Probability, Random Variables, and Stochastic Processes*, New York: McGraw-Hill, 1965.

Salari, E., and P. Siy. "The Ridge-Seeking Method for Obtaining the Skeleton of Digital Images," *IEEE Transactions on Systems, Manual Cybernetics*, Vol. SMC-14, No. 3, 1984, pp. 524–528.

Shamos, M. I. "Computational Geometry," Ph.D. thesis, New Haven, Conn.: Yale University, 1978.

Sklansky, J., Chazin, R. L., and B. J. Hansen. "Minimum Perimeter Polygons of Digitized Silhouettes," *IEEE Transactions on Computers*, Vol. C-21, No. 3, 1972, pp. 260–268.

Sze, T. W., and Y. H. Yang. "A Simple Contour Matching Algorithm," *IEEE Transactions on Pattern Analysis and Machine Intelligence*, Vol. PAMI-3, No. 6, 1981, pp. 676–678.

Toussaint, G. T. "Computational Geometric Problems in Pattern Recognition," in *Pattern Recognition Theory and Applications*, ed. by J. Kittler, K. S. Fu, and L. F. Pau, New York: D. Reidel Publishing Co., 1982, pp. 73–91.

Zhang, T. Y., and C. Y. Suen. "A Fast Parallel Algorithm for Thinning Digital Patterns," *Communications of the ACM*, Vol. 27, No. 3, 1984, pp. 236–239.

Chapter 4

Three-Dimensional Machine Vision

R. C. Gonzalez
Perceptics Corporation and University of Tennessee

D. Brzakovic
University of Tennessee

1. Abstract

Although the objective of most 3-D vision systems is to imitate human vision, their sensory inputs are not limited to the visible part of the electromagnetic spectrum. Based on the type of sensory input, 3-D vision systems can be classified in two basic groups: (1) camera-based systems, and (2) structured light systems. The following discussion gives a detailed description of camera-based systems, as well as a synopsis of structured light systems, emphasizing ability of these systems to measure depth.

2. Introduction

Automation of remote sensing, surveillance, and industrial processes requires the ability to deal with inherently three-dimensional (3-D) environments. Understanding the structure of a 3-D environment requires carrying out tasks such as measurement of scene depth, assessment of relative positioning of objects, and 3-D object recognition. In robot guidance, for example, these tasks enable obstacle avoidance and acquisition of parts from unknown locations. Depth measurement is also essential to inspection of surface finish and detection of missing or incorrectly placed parts. Recently, 3-D scene understanding has found application in data acquisition for CAD/CAM and automatic 3-D copying and scaling of parts. In principle, using 3-D vision systems in industrial processes leads to production cost savings, increased quality control, consistent performance, 100% inspection, and provides for automation of dangerous tasks in hazardous environments.

All 3-D vision systems share the problem of coping with many-to-one mappings between scenes and images. Usually, a scene is interpreted by combining image processing and artificial-intelligence techniques. In particu-lar, knowledge about objects likely to be encountered in a scene greatly enhances the performance of a vision system. For example, vision systems that perform *a priori* known tasks in controlled environments, e.g., a robot that services production systems, function very accurately and at high speed. On the contrary, when the characteristics of environments are incompletely known, e.g., robot guidance in an unknown environment, the performance and speed of 3-D vision systems are frequently inadequate.

3. Camera-Based 3-D Vision Systems

Camera-based 3-D vision systems infer information about the depth of a scene by analyzing images (of a scene) acquired in a particular region of the electromagnetic spectrum. Usually, cameras acquire images in the visible or infrared spectrum. Just like images acquired by the human eye, the images acquired by cameras are inherently two-dimensional; this indicates that a fruitful research direction is to study functional similarities between camera-based and human vision systems. Indeed, research in the psychology of visual perception has provided invaluable insight for developing computer vision systems for image interpretation. In particular, Gibson's [1960] studies have stimulated the development of computer-based theories of 3-D scene perception. Gibson noted about 23 distinct cues that play important roles in determining the structure of a visual scene. Although the usefulness of some of these cues is still controversial, the research in the psychology of visual perception has nevertheless established that binocular vision, shading, and texture are among the most important cues. Consequently, research in 3-D computer vision has focused on development of methods that utilize these cues. It is important to note that methods of binocular vision give the actual 3-D coordinates of individual points, while the methods of shading and texture only give information on the *relative depth*, i.e., positions of points relative to each other.

The first step in applying any of these methods is to model the image formation process; this involves projecting a 3-D scene onto a 2-D image. Most frequently, the image formation processes are modeled by planar geometric projections wherein the projection of a point P (in a 3-D scene) is defined by the intersection of a projection plane, called an *image plane*, with a projecting ray emanating from the center of projection and passing through P. Planar geometric projections are called *perspective projections* or *ortho-graphic projections* depending on whether the distance between the projec-tion plane and the center of projection is finite or infinite. Perspective projection is a realistic model for all image formation processes while orthographic projection is limited to modeling image formation processes, such as aerial photography, where the size of objects in the 3-D scene is small compared with the distance between the objects and the image plane. Projection models are comprehensively discussed by Carlbom and Paciorek [1978].

A perspective projection model of particular importance in applications is the one defined in the *image-based coordinate system* (see Fig. 1). In this system, the coordinate axes are chosen such that the image plane, I, coincides with the $z = 0$ plane and the origin of the coordinate system coincides with the center of I; therefore, a point $P(X, Y, Z)$ in a 3-D scene projects onto I as $p(p_x, p_y, 0)$, where

$$p_x = \frac{\lambda X}{\lambda - Z} \tag{1}$$

and

$$p_y = \frac{\lambda Y}{\lambda - Z} \tag{2}$$

and $(0, 0, \lambda)$ is the position of the center of projection. Note that throughout the remainder of this discussion, the projection of $P(X, Y, Z)$ onto the image plane I is the pixel denoted as $p(p_x, p_y, 0)$, and $i(p_x, p_y)$ denotes the intensity of the pixel p.

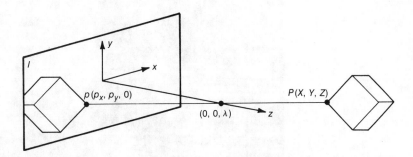

Fig. 1. Image-based coordinate system.

Camera-based methods usually rely on knowing the set of parameters that specify the relationships between points in a 3-D space and their projections. The most frequently required parameter is the position of the center of projection, i.e., the *focal length*. Additional parameters that may be needed are the camera offsets and angles of pan and tilt. The procedure for determining such parameters is referred to as *camera calibration*. Camera calibration procedures generally obtain the calibration parameters by using projections of points whose 3-D coordinates are known and solving the resulting projection equations that model the image formation process. When the calibration parameters need to be known accurately, the differences between the projection models and the corresponding physical camera systems can be taken into account by performing distortion calibration procedures (see Moravec [1979] for details). The mathematical aspects of calibration procedures are described by Fu, Gonzalez, and Lee [1987], and many practical aspects are discussed by Yakimovsky and Cunningham [1978].

The remainder of this section describes the three most commonly used camera-based 3-D vision methods: shading, texture, and binocular vision. The possibilities of incorporating the cues corresponding to these methods are discussed at the end of this section. It is important to note that shading and texture methods lead to depth measurements based on a monocular view of a scene. By contrast, binocular vision methods lead to depth measurements based on multiple views of a scene.

Measurements of Depth From Shading

The importance of shading visible surfaces to create realistic images is well understood in art and computer graphics. Shading reveals the three-dimensionality of objects that would otherwise take on ambiguous shapes. The importance of shading to image understanding is illustrated by the example shown in Fig. 2.

Fig. 2. Effects of shading on understanding object shape.

Shading is determined by the laws of reflectance in physics; it is a function of illumination and the reflecting characteristics of the surface curvature and material, and is described by the reflectance function, φ. This function depends on the incident angle, α, the emergent angle, β, and the phase angle, γ (see Fig. 3). The reflectance function of a perfectly diffusing surface, known as a *Lambertian surface*, is modeled as

$$\varphi_L(\alpha,\beta,\gamma) \;=\; \rho \cos \alpha \tag{3}$$

where ρ is the reflectance factor and accounts for the reflectance properties of the surface's material. Presence of specular reflection is accounted for by incorporating the emergent angle into the reflectance function, which becomes

$$\varphi_s(\alpha,\beta,\gamma) \;=\; \frac{\rho \cos \alpha}{\cos \beta} \tag{4}$$

In most cases, the reflectance function incorporates both φ_L and φ_s; Bui-Tuong [1975] describes more complete models of surface reflectance. See also the book by Horn [1986].

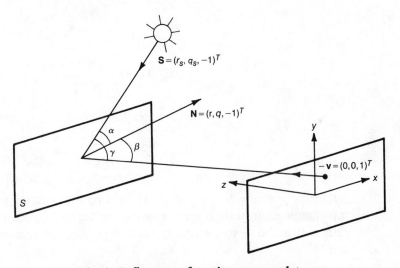

Fig. 3. Reflectance function nomenclature.

In computer vision, the reflectance laws of physics are fundamental to the development of *shape from shading methods*. These laws are used to deduce the normal of any surface in the scene (and, implicitly, to deduce the scene's relative depth) from image intensities. The basic assumption underlying these methods is that the imaging device produces an image in which the intensities $i(x,y)$ are directly proportional to the reflectance function, φ. Usually, the problem is simplified by considering scenes in which objects are small compared with the viewing distance. This simplification arises from using an orthographic projection to model the image formation process. In this orthographic projection, the viewing direction is constant, so the phase angle γ is also constant for all surface elements.

The coordinates of the normal, $\mathbf{N}$, of surface $z = f(x, y)$ are most frequently given in the *gradient space* described by

$$r = \frac{\partial f(x, y)}{\partial x} \tag{5}$$

and

$$q = \frac{\partial f(x, y)}{\partial y} \tag{6}$$

so that $\mathbf{N} = (r, q, -1)^T$ (see Fig. 4). In this gradient space, the quantities $\cos \alpha$, $\cos \beta$ and $\cos \gamma$ are given by the following normalized dot products:

$$\cos \alpha = \frac{\mathbf{N} \cdot \mathbf{S}}{\|\mathbf{N}\| \|\mathbf{S}\|} \tag{7}$$

$$\cos \beta = \frac{\mathbf{N} \cdot \mathbf{v}}{\|\mathbf{N}\| \|\mathbf{v}\|} \tag{8}$$

$$\cos \gamma = \frac{\mathbf{S} \cdot \mathbf{v}}{\|\mathbf{S}\| \|\mathbf{v}\|} \tag{9}$$

respectively, where $\mathbf{S} = (r_s, q_s, -1)^T$ is a vector pointing in the direction of the illumination source, and $\mathbf{v} = (0, 0, -1)^T$ is a vector pointing in the direction of the viewer. Consequently, Eqs. 3 and 4 become

$$\varphi_L(\alpha, \beta, \gamma) = \frac{p(1 + rr_s + qq_s)}{\sqrt{1 + r^2 + q^2} \sqrt{1 + r_s^2 + q_s^2}} \tag{10}$$

and

$$\varphi_s(\alpha, \beta, \gamma) = \frac{p(1 + rr_s + qq_s)}{\sqrt{1 + r_s^2 + q_s^2}} \tag{11}$$

respectively. The right sides of Eqs. 10 and 11 are called *reflectance maps* and are usually denoted by $R(r, q)$. A reflectance map can be represented graphically in the gradient space by contours of constant intensity. The contours can be obtained either experimentally—by directly measuring the reflectance of the object under consideration—or theoretically—if the surface reflectance is known as the function of angles a, β, and γ (for details see Horn [1986]). An equation in which φ is replaced by image intensities, i.e., an equation of the form

$$i(x,y) = R(r,q) \qquad (12)$$

is called the *image irradiance equation.*

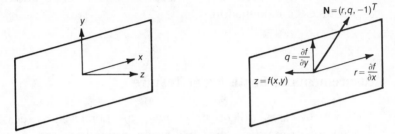

Fig. 4. The gradient space notation.

In general, in shape from shading problems the surface normal cannot be determined from the intensities of the surface's image because one needs to solve a nonlinear first-order partial differential equation with two unknowns, of the type shown in Eqs. 10 and 11. The additional equation needed to make this problem well-posed is usually obtained by imposing a constraint on the geometrical properties of the surface. Horn [1975] has imposed a surface smoothness constraint to solve the shape from shading problem by the modified characteristic strip-expansion method, wherein the surface smoothness equation and the partial differential equation of the type given by Eq. 10 or 11 are replaced by five ordinary differential equations. (The class of image irradiance equations for which Horn's method is applicable has been investigated by Bruss [1981].) Ikeuchi and Horn [1981] have reformulated the original problem addressed by the shape from shading method as a problem of finding a surface orientation that minimizes the integral of the intensity error

$$\int \int [i(x,y) - R(r(x,y), q(x,y))]^2 dx \, dy \qquad (13)$$

This new formulation led to algorithms that employ calculus of variations to obtain the normal of a surface from its image intensities [Ikeuchi and Horn 1981, Horn and Brooks 1986].

Shape from shading methods require precise knowledge about sources of illumination and are constrained to a controlled environment. Nevertheless, these methods are still applicable to cases when this knowledge is not available although significant errors may occur in such cases; for example, Ikeuchi and Horn [1981] report that an error of 7.5° in estimating the illumination source direction may lead to a 20% error in the measurement of surface orientation.

The shape from shading methods underlie the emergence of a method that utilizes multiple views obtained by varying the direction of illumination between the successive views of the scene. As will be shown in the section Cooperative Methods, this method measures the normal of a surface directly from its intensities and requires only knowledge about positions of the sources of illumination.

Measurements of Depth From Texture

In many cases, objects in an image are perceived as regions having distinct texture properties rather than clearly defined regions of contrasting intensity. The term *texture* usually refers to a large number of alike patterns, called *texels* (*tex*ture *el*ements), densely and evenly arranged over a field of view. Mathematically, the modeling of texture relies on the theory of regular figures (e.g., [Zucker 1976]), statistics (e.g., [Haralick et al. 1973]) and structural pattern recognition (e.g., [Lu and Fu 1978]). Texture features serve as a basis for classifying parts of an image and are essential in many image processing tasks. Consequently, understanding texture features has attracted considerable attention in recent years (see Rosenfeld [1985] and Gonzalez and Wintz [1987] for the most recent list of references).

The hypothesis that texture is the primary cue of visual space perception by humans [Gibson 1960] has led to several computational theories relating texture to the description of a scene. The common idea underlying these studies, collectively known as *shape from texture methods*, is that surface orientation (and, implicitly, relative depth) may be obtained by measuring changes in shape, size, and spacing of texels. Shape from texture methods are important for surface analysis and, in particular, for determining relative distances for autonomous vehicle guidance in unknown environments.

Shape from texture methods describe a scene in terms of planar surfaces and their orientations relative to the image plane. Curved surfaces are approximated locally by planes. An example of a 3-D scene description from texture is shown in Fig. 5. The orientation of a planar surface, S, relative to the image plane, I, is expressed in terms of the normal $\mathbf{N}$ of S. In turn, the surface normal is most commonly described by the surface slant, σ, and the surface tilt, τ. In the image-based coordinate system, σ is the angle between S and I, and τ is the angle between the projection of the surface normal onto I and the x axis in I (see Fig. 6). Note that σ and τ are related to the parameters of the gradient space described in the previous section, via the formulas

$$\sigma = \tan^{-1}(r^2 + q^2)^{1/2} \tag{14}$$

and

$$\tau = \tan^{-1}(q/r) \tag{15}$$

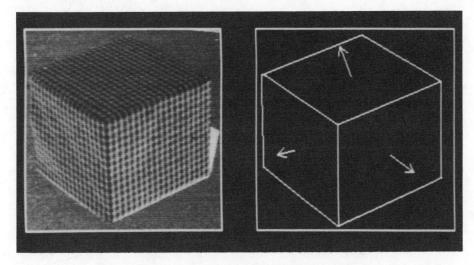

Fig. 5. Scene description obtained from texture.

The descriptors that relate the orientation of S to observable changes in the texture of I are *scaling* and *foreshortening*. Scaling describes the fact that texels in I appear smaller as S recedes from the image plane, i.e., the viewer. Foreshortening describes the compression of texture elements in I in the direction of τ; for this reason, this direction is usually called the *direction of texture gradient*.

The choice of the model of image formation process determines whether measurements of scaling or foreshortening (or both) are necessary to determine the parameters σ and τ. Models using orthographic projection rely on foreshortening. Witkin [1981] designed a maximum likelihood estimator that deduces surface orientation by assuming that changes in the orientation of texel edges arise from foreshortening, and measuring these changes.

Models using perspective projection obtain a 3-D scene description by using either knowledge-based or model-free methods. Kender [1980] presents a knowledge-based method that uses the Normalized Texture Property Map (NTPM); this map encodes the observed effects of the surface orientation on a particular texture property. The choice of texture measurements depends on the texture property used to generate the NTPM. The strategy underlying Kender's method is similar to that underlying the methods described in the previous section.

Information available in a single image, without *a priori* knowledge about the scene, is not sufficient to measure accurately both τ and σ. Therefore, model-free methods typically measure τ and only roughly estimate σ. Measuring τ and estimating σ invariably requires measurements of both

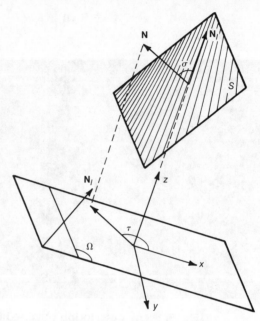

Fig. 6. Description of a surface normal in terms of the surface slant and the surface tilt.

scaling and foreshortening [Stevens 1980, Brzakovic 1984]. Model-free methods capitalize on the fact that texture regularity remains preserved (in an image) along the lines parallel to the surface *S*. These lines are called the *characteristic lines.* Note that the characteristic lines are orthogonal to the direction of texture gradient. The angle that a characteristic line in an image plane forms with the *x* axis, measured counterclockwise, is the *characteristic angle,* Ω (see Fig. 7 for an illustration of these terms). Geometrically, the relations between τ, σ, and Ω are

$$\tau = \Omega \pm \pi/2 \qquad (16)$$

and

$$\sigma \cong \tan^{-1}(\lambda\zeta/v) \qquad (17)$$

where λ is the focal length, and ζ denotes the measured gradient of scaling between the characteristic lines at a distance v (see Fig. 7).

Measuring τ based on Eq. 16 requires determining Ω or, equivalently, determining the direction in which texture regularly is preserved. The direction of Ω can be measured by performing a Fourier power spectrum analysis of the textured region under consideration. Details of this method are described in Brzakovic and White [1986]. Once Ω is determined, the quantity v can be measured by methods that analyze texture coarseness (e.g., Haralick et al. [1973]).

Usually, shape from texture methods can yield fairly accurate measurements of the surface tilt (by statistically averaging several measurements), but less accurate measurements of surface slant (see Kender [1980], Witkin [1981]). When two views of a scene are available, it is possible to measure accurately both surface tilt and slant, as will be described in the section titled Cooperative Methods.

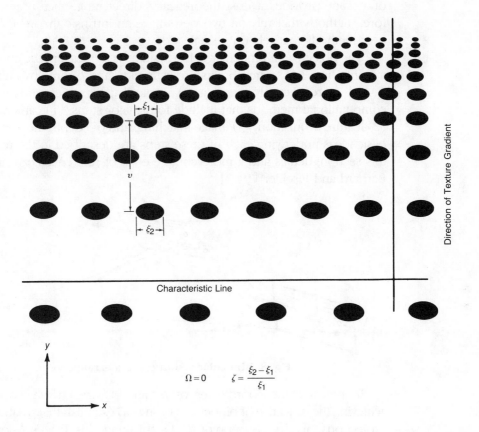

$$\Omega = 0 \qquad \zeta = \frac{\xi_2 - \xi_1}{\xi_1}$$

Fig. 7. Texture geometry nomenclature.

Measurements of Depth From Binocular Views

Binocular vision improves the resolution of spatial perception. Studies on the psychology of binocular vision, such as that of Julesz [1970], have motivated research in computer vision toward the development of methods for image understanding by using two views of a scene. Such methods belong to the area known as *stereo vision*. Note, though, that the origin of the word stereo means "solid" in Greek; thus, the term stereo may not necessarily be limited to two images, but may generally imply 3-D vision. This distinction has been made by authors such as Haddow et al. [1985], who refer to two views of a scene as stereoscopic binocular vision rather than just stereo vision.

In contrast to techniques described in the section Structured Light Systems, binocular vision is applicable to many types of environments, and has been used extensively for interpretation of aerial images (see Case [1981], Konecny and Pape [1981]), autonomous vehicle guidance (Moravec [1981], Hannah [1980]), and robotics (Baylou et al. [1984]). Furthermore, two views of a scene provide, at least theoretically, direct range measurements; therefore, methods that rely on two views have an intrinsic theoretical advantage over methods that rely on a single view.

The objective of binocular vision systems is to measure the coordinates of a point P in a 3-D scene from its projections p_1 and p_2 onto two image planes I_1 and I_2, respectively (see Fig. 8). Typically, this objective is achieved by computational methods that include four major steps: (1) camera modeling, (2) feature acquisition, (3) image matching, and (4) depth measurement. The basic ideas underlying each of these steps are described in the remainder of this section; details and a more complete list of references can be found in Barnard and Fischler [1982].

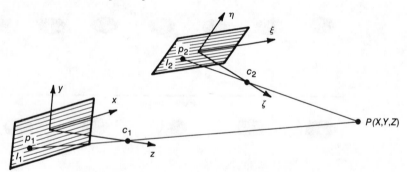

Fig. 8. Binocular vision camera arrangement.

In practice, the coordinates of p_1 and p_2 are known, so the key to achieving the objective of binocular vision is to establish that p_1 and p_2 are the projections of *the same* point P. Establishing this fact is known as the *correspondence problem* or *image matching*. The difference between the positions of the two points p_1 and p_2, both originating from the point P, is known as *parallax* or *disparity*.

Parallax is a function not only of the location of P but also of the characteristics of the two cameras that generate I_1 and I_2. Cameras are generally modeled as pinhole lenses. Thus, the image formation process is modeled using the methods of perspective projection. More refined camera models usually account for various distortions by using compensation methods (see Moravec [1979]).

The coordinates of P are expressed in terms of its projections p_1 and p_2 by introducing two image-based coordinate systems (see Fig. 8) related by

$$(\xi, \eta, \zeta)^T = \mathbf{R}(x, y, z)^T + (x_t, y_t, z_t)^T \tag{18}$$

where

$$\mathbf{R} = \begin{bmatrix} a_{11} & a_{12} & a_{13} \\ a_{21} & a_{22} & a_{23} \\ a_{31} & a_{32} & a_{33} \end{bmatrix} \tag{19}$$

is the rotation matrix, whose elements are the direction cosines of the ξ, η, and ξ axes relative to the x, y, and z axes, respectively; the subscript t appearing in Eq. 18 denotes translation parameters. The coordinates of P may be expressed either in an image-based coordinate system or in a global coordinate system whose position relative to (x, y, z) and (ξ, η, ζ) is known.

Suppose that each image I_1 and I_2 consists of an $M \times N$ array of pixels. For a known point p_1, the point p_2 may lie anywhere in I_2 when the camera arrangement is arbitrary, so that there are MN candidate pixels to match p_1. This maximum number of candidate pixels can be reduced by choosing a particular geometry of camera arrangements. When the two image planes are parallel, the matrix $\mathbf{R}$ becomes a unitary matrix, i.e.,

$$\mathbf{R} = \begin{bmatrix} 1 & 0 & 0 \\ 0 & 1 & 0 \\ 0 & 0 & 1 \end{bmatrix} \tag{20}$$

Furthermore, if $y_t = 0$ and $z_t = 0$, a point $p_1(p_x, p_y, 0)$ in I_1 has its correspondent $p_2(p_\xi, p_\eta, 0)$ on the line $p_y = p_\eta$ in I_2, since the relations between the coordinates of the point $P(X, Y, Z)$ and its projections (expressed in the xyz coordinate system) become

$$p_x = \frac{\lambda X}{\lambda - Z} \tag{21}$$

$$p_y = \frac{\lambda Y}{\lambda - Z} \tag{22}$$

and

$$p_\xi = \frac{\lambda(X + x_t)}{\lambda - Z} - x_t \tag{23}$$

$$p_\eta = \frac{\lambda Y}{\lambda - Z} \tag{24}$$

repectively, where λ denotes the focal length. Thus, as Eqs. 22 and 24 show, to establish the correspondence between I_1 and I_2, it is necessary to consider only N rather than MN candidate pixels. Such a camera arrangement has been the subject of studies conducted by Marr and Poggio [1979], Grimson [1980], and Goshtasby [1984].

An alternative arrangement of cameras may be obtained by choosing $(x_t, y, z_t) = (0, 0, z_t)$ (see Fig. 9). In this case, the candidate pixels corresponding to $p_1(p_x, p_y, 0)$, with polar coordinates (ρ, θ), form in I_2 a line segment of length $v \le \rho$ passing through the origin of the coordinate system (ξ, η, ζ) at an angle θ with ξ (see Fig. 9). This camera arrangement can be realized by a single camera moving along the z axis, and is suitable for robotics applications (see Itoh et al. [1984]). Note that significant differences in reflectance and shadows between the two images I_1 and I_2 are unlikely to occur in this case.

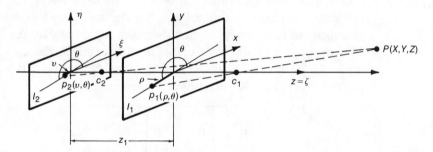

Fig. 9. Camera arrangement wherein cameras are displaced in depth.

Although particular camera arrangements can simplify the correspondence problem, this problem is difficult to resolve in general. In particular, occlusions, optical illusions and shadows pose difficulties [Goshtasby 1984] and may cause the correspondence problem to be ill-posed. Even for the scene consisting of the simple objects shown in Fig. 10, the two images I_1 and I_2 of the scene do not contain the same object surfaces and the same number of object edges. Therefore, as this example shows, not all points in I_1 necessarily have correspondents in I_2, and vice versa.

As previously mentioned, the second computational step towards achieving the objective of binocular vision is feature acquisition. The function of this step is to increase the likelihood of successful matches by considering only points with special properties. Usually, these special points are nontexture pixels with high neighborhood variances (see Barnard and Fischler [1982]). This selection process is accomplished by operators specially designed to identify pixels that have high variance (Moravec [1981], Hannah [1980]) or by edge detectors (Marr and Poggio [1979], Grimson [1980]) which assign to these special points a direction and a magnitude of intensity change.

The objective of the image matching computational step is to establish the correspondence between a selected point p_1 in I_1 and a point in a particular region (as determined by camera arrangement) in I_2 having characteristics similar to p_1. Two general methodologies, correlative and combinatorial, are employed in image matching. The correlative methodologies (see the discussion at the end of Chap. 3) use area correlation to establish the conditions under which two points p_1 and p_2 originate from the same point P; area correlation is suitable for texture images in which the disparity between I_1 and I_2 is very small (see Lucas and Kanade [1981], Moravec [1979]). By contrast, combinational methodologies use distinct properties of selected points to find the correspondence between I_1 and I_2. The most commonly used such properties are: sign and magnitude of intensity change [Marr and Poggio 1979, Grimson 1980], edges [Baker 1980, Baker and Binford 1981], and chain envelopes about edge contours [Bellugi et al. 1985]. A particular group of combinatorial methods capitalizes on *a priori* knowledge about the scene, e.g., knowledge about the object shape [Baylou et al. 1984], or probability distribution of particular features [Gennery 1981].

Fig. 10. An example of two views of a scene obtained by camera arrangement wherein the two image planes are parallel and $(x_t, y_t, z_t) = (x_t, 0, 0)$.

Depth measurement is straightforward once the correspondence between points p_1 and p_2 is established, since the camera parameters are known (Yakimovsky and Cunningham [1978] give details on camera calibration). As an example, it follows from Eqs. 21 through 24 that the coordinates of $P(X, Y, Z)$ are

$$X = \frac{x_t p_x}{p_\xi + x_t - p_x} \tag{25}$$

$$Y = \frac{p_y X}{p_x} \tag{26}$$

and

$$Z = \lambda(1 - X/p_x) \qquad (27)$$

When cameras are mounted on a dynamic system and their positions are not exactly known, initial control points (see Hannah [1980]) are used to calculate simultaneously the coordinates of P, the camera parameters, λ, and the matrix **R**.

It is important to discuss the factors that contribute to the error in measuring the coordinates of P. As Eqs. 25 through 27 indicate, this measurement error is directly proportional to the error committed in establishing the correspondence between p_1 and p_2. This correspondence is usually established only to within a pixel (calibration procedures convert an error of a pixel into distance measurements for a particular camera). The number of erroneous matches can be reduced by adding a third camera [Bellugi et al. 1985, Ito and Ishii 1986] or by excluding shadows and occluding points from the matching procedure [Goshtasby 1984]. The accuracy in establishing the correspondence between p_1 and p_2 can be increased by considering multiple views and statistically averaging matches between different pairs of images [Moravec 1979].

Cooperative Methods

The early attempts to obtain a 3-D scene description from images were confined to rigidly constrained environments and could not accommodate information about more than one cue, e.g., texture, shading, at a time. More recent research focuses on incorporating multiple sources of information regarding the scene layout. In general, the availability of two or more cues simplifies the problem of scene understanding and increases the accuracy of the respective results. It is important to note that these recent methods, called cooperative methods, incorporate information that is not available to biological vision systems. This section briefly describes two such cooperative methods. Mitiche [1984] and O'Brien and Jain [1984], for example, describe different types of cooperative methods—obtained by using cues other than texture and shading.

The first cooperative method to be discussed in the following is the *photometric stereo* method [Woodham 1981, Colleman and Jain 1982]. This method uses information from two or more images generated by varying the incident illumination and preserving the same viewpoint. By preserving the same imaging geometry, this method overcomes the difficulties associated with the correspondence problem in that, in the image-based coordinate system, the pixel $p_i(p_x, p_y, 0)$ in image plane I_i and the pixel $p_j(p_x, p_y, 0)$ in the image plane I_j are unambiguously known to correspond to the same point $P(X, Y, Z)$ in the scene under consideration. Thus, the objective of the photometric stereo method is to measure the unit surface normal $\mathbf{N} = (N_x, N_y, N_z)^T$ using image intensities $i_j(p_x, p_y)$, $j = 1, 2, \ldots$. Note that all three components of $\mathbf{N}$ must be determined since the component N_z may take on any value that preserves the unitarity of $\mathbf{N}$. At least three images, generated by varying the incident illumination, are required to determine the three unknown components of $\mathbf{N}$. Examples of three such images are shown in Fig. 11.

Given three known sources of illumination $\mathbf{S}_1$, $\mathbf{S}_2$, and $\mathbf{S}_3$ and the corresponding intensity values $i_j(x, y)$, $j = 1, 2, 3$, the three unknown components of the unit surface normal $\mathbf{N}$ are determined by using the image irradiance equations

$$i_j(x,y) = \rho \cos(\mathbf{N}, \mathbf{S}_j), \qquad j = 1, 2, 3 \qquad (28)$$

where the parameter ρ is the reflectance factor as described in the section Measurements of Depth From Shading. These equations can be written in matrix form as

$$\rho \mathbf{N} = \mathbf{M}^{-1}\mathbf{I} \qquad (29)$$

where $\mathbf{M}$ denotes the illumination source matrix, whose rows contain the components of $\mathbf{S}_1$, $\mathbf{S}_2$, and $\mathbf{S}_3$, and $\mathbf{I} = (i_1(x,y), i_2(x,y), i_3(x,y))^T$. Since $\mathbf{N}$ is the unit vector, it follows that $\rho = \mathbf{M}^{-1}\mathbf{I}$ and

$$\mathbf{N} = \frac{1}{\rho}\mathbf{M}^{-1}\mathbf{I} \qquad (30)$$

Equation 30 shows that using the photometric stereo method the surface normal can be measured directly from the image intensities. Note that, by contrast to the shape from shading methods, photometric stereo does not require camera calibration and is therefore best suited for determining the position and orientation of known objects in a controlled environment.

The second cooperative method discussed in this section is the *texture stereo* method. This method obtains accurate measurements of the orientation of various texture surfaces in a scene by taking two views of the scene; these views are obtained by rotating the camera between the two exposures. Consequently, the two image-based coordinate systems are related by the rotational matrix $\mathbf{R}$ introduced in the section Measurement of Depth From Binocular Views. The various surface orientations are then inferred solely from the geometry of the perspective projection underlying the model of image formation process. Just like the photometric stereo method, the texture stereo method avoids the need for the complicated and computationally expensive matching procedures required to solve the correspondence problem (for details, see Brzakovic and White [1986]). An example of two views of a scene obtained by rotating the camera between exposures is shown in Fig. 12.

Fig. 11. Three photometric stereo images.

The texture stereo method capitalizes on the fact that the characteristic lines in both images are parallel to the surface S (see the section Measurement of Depth From Texture). Therefore, the two families of the characteristic lines uniquely determine the components (N_x, N_y, N_z) of the surface normal $\mathbf{N}$, giving

$$N_x = \sin \Omega_1 (a_{13} \cos \Omega_2 + a_{23} \sin \Omega_2) \quad (31)$$

$$N_y = -\cos \Omega_1 (a_{13} \cos \Omega_2 + a_{23} \sin \Omega_2) \quad (32)$$

and

$$N_z = \cos \Omega_1 (a_{21} \cos \Omega_2 + a_{22} \sin \Omega_2)$$
$$-\sin \Omega_1 (a_{11} \cos \Omega_2 + a_{21} \sin \Omega_2) \quad (33)$$

where Ω_1 and Ω_2 are the characteristic angles in I_1 and I_2, respectively, and a_{ij} are the direction cosines that relate the two image-based coordinate systems.

Fig. 12. Two views of a scene obtained by rotating camera between the two exposures.

From Eqs. 31 through 33, it follows that the components of the surface normal can be determined by measuring the characteristic angles in specific textured regions of the two images. In turn, the characteristic angles can be measured by intercomparing the distribution of energy in the Fourier power spectrum of the textured regions of interest (Brzakovic and White [1986]).

4. Structured Light Methods

Structured light methods measure the coordinates of points in a scene by measuring the coordinates of their projections onto the image plane and by using the geometrical information about the scene illumination. These methods operate only on those points in the scene that are illuminated by a stripe of light (Fig. 13). This stripe may result from a laser or from the projection of light through a slit. The applicability of using the projection of a slit is more restrictive than using a laser since the image of a respective stripe must be obtained in a darkened room.

Structured light methods use a known equation of the light plane, L, to determine the coordinates of a point $P(X, Y, Z)$ on the illuminated segment, ℓ_s. In the image-based coordinate system (see Fig. 13) the equation describing L is

$$Ax + By + Cz + 1 = 0 \qquad (34)$$

The point P projects onto the image plane as $p(p_x, p_y, 0)$. The equation of the projecting ray [determined by p and the center of projection $c(0,0,\lambda)$] is

Fig. 13. An example of projecting a light stripe onto a scene.

$$\frac{x - p_x}{-p_x} = \frac{y - p_y}{-p_y} = \frac{z}{\lambda} \qquad (35)$$

From Eqs. 34 and 35, it follows that the coordinates of P are

$$X = \frac{-p_x - C\lambda}{Ap_x + Bp_y - C\lambda} \qquad (36)$$

$$Y = \frac{-p_y - C\lambda}{Ap_x + Bp_y - C\lambda} \qquad (37)$$

and

$$Z = \frac{\lambda(Ap_x + Bp_y + 1)}{Ap_x + Bp_y - C\lambda} \qquad (38)$$

As Eqs. 36 though 38 show, structured light methods require knowledge of the parameters A, B, and C to determine the coordinates of P. Therefore, the camera and the illumination source must be calibrated to obtain these parameters.

Some structured light methods simplify the problem of measuring the coordinates of P by using the position of the light stripe in the image plane and comparing this position with a reference distance. For example, the camera, C, and the light source, S, can be placed on the same height at the known distance D (see Fig. 14) so that S generates the light plane, L. The calibration procedure for this method consists of arranging the plane π (formed by the points S and C and orthogonal to the L plane) so that any line segment ℓ_s in L projects parallel to the y axis onto the image plane, I. Then, the normal distance between ℓ_s and S is given by

$$D = \Delta \tan(\lambda / d_p) \qquad (39)$$

where d_p denotes the normal distance between the y axis and the projection of ℓ_s onto I. Upon accomplishing this calibration procedure, any point in the image plane I can be associated with a particular distance D by using Eq. 39. By storing in a tabular form the image coordinates of the points P together with the respective corresponding distances D, the scene can be analyzed efficiently by tabular lookup. Details of this calibration procedure and, in particular, derivation of Eq. 39 are described by Fu, Gonzalez, and Lee [1987].

In some structured light systems, the point coordinates are measured by using projections of multiple stripes or projecting particular patterns onto the scene (e.g., Tomita and Kanade [1984]). Note that these images can also be treated by methods that analyze scenes whose surfaces are characterized by known texture patterns. Therefore, methods (such as described in the section Measurement of Depth From Texture) that utilize textural information to deduce scene layout can be applied to the images obtained by projecting particular patterns. Furthermore, these images are easy to segment since the discontinuities in the image pattern correspond to changes in surface orientation or abrupt distance changes between the objects in the scene and the image plane. In many cases, segmentation of these images leads directly to object recognition (see Tomita and Kanade [1984]).

5. Concluding Remarks

Computer vision research dealing with understanding 3-D scene structure is the key to evolving from today's fixed automation to the flexible automation of the future. At present 3-D vision research is still in its infancy, although some notable developments have been achieved in recent years. In particular, over the past decade there has been considerable growth in the theory underlying 3-D vision systems. Some of the important findings of this theory, pertaining to the camera-based and structured light systems, are described in the preceding discussion.

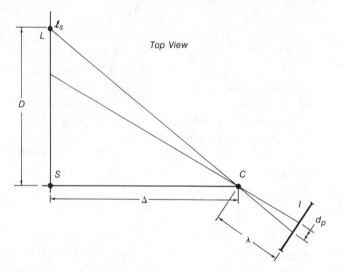

Figure 14. Geometry of a structured light system.

As already described, camera-based systems infer scene layout from images obtained by using natural unstructured lighting. Most of the early developments in camera-based systems were motivated by the findings in the psychology of visual perception. Consequently, research has focused on cues, such as shading, texture and binocular vision, which play important roles in human perception of space.

Shading and texture methods lead to relative depth measurements using a monocular view of a scene. The problem of obtaining scene depth from a single image is intrinsically difficult and becomes well posed only when additional constraints on the properties of surfaces appearing in a scene are imposed. The complexity of outdoor scenes and the intricacy arising from secondary illumination of indoor scenes preclude wider usage of shading methods in practice. In contrast, texture methods are appropriate for analysis of complex outdoor scenes; however, these methods lead frequently to inaccurate measurements of relative scene depth.

Binocular vision methods are a viable approach to obtaining structure of various scenes. These methods lead to measurement of the actual 3-D coordinates of points in a scene and therefore have a theoretical advantage over methods that rely on a single view. Practically, binocular vision methods require establishment of correspondence between the two images which is very difficult to attain in general.

More recent research has shifted from studying restrictions of a single cue to incorporating multiple sources of information regarding the scene layout. The resulting methods are generally simple and computationally efficient. Most importantly, the accuracy of the obtained measurements is considerably increased.

The second types of systems reviewed in this discussion are structured light systems. The corresponding methods, known as *active methods*, measure accurately the coordinates of points in a scene by capitalizing on the geometrical information on the scene's illumination. The active nature of structured light systems constrains their applicability to controlled environment.

6. References

Baker, H. H. "Edge Based Stereo Correlation," *Proceedings of Image Understanding Workshop*, College Park, Md., 1980, pp. 168–175.

Baker, H. H., and T. O. Binford. "Depth from Edge and Intensity Based Stereo," *Proceedings of the Seventh International Joint Conference on Artificial Intelligence*, Vancouver, Canada, 1981, pp. 631–636.

Barnard, S. T., and M. A. Fishler. "Computational Stereo," *ACM Computing Surveys*, Vol. 14, No. 4, 1982, pp. 553–572.

Baylou, P., El Hadj, A. B., Monsion, M., Bouvet, C., and G. Bousseau. "Detection and Three-Dimensional Localization by Stereoscopic Visual Sensor and Its Application to a Robot for Picking Asparagus," *Pattern Recognition*, Vol. 17, No. 4, 1984, pp. 377–384.

Bellugi, D., Dammagio, G., and A. Schiavoni. "RAMAN: A 3-D Stereoscopic Vision System," *Proceedings of the Fourth Scandinavian Conference on Image Processing*, Trondheim, Norway, 1985, pp. 445–453.

Bruss, A. R. "The Image Irradiance Equation: Its Solution and Application," Ph.D. dissertation, 1981, Massachusetts Institute of Technology.

Brzakovic, D. "Computer Based Description of 3-D Scenes From Texture," Ph.D. dissertation, 1984, University of Florida.

Brzakovic, D., and B. White. "Surface Orientation Using Texture Gradient Derived From Two Views of a Scene," *Proceedings of the Eighth International Conference on Pattern Recognition*, Paris, France, 1986, pp. 1045–1047.

Bui-Tuong, P. "Illumination for Computer-Generated Pictures," *Communications of the ACM*, Vol. 18, No. 6, 1975, pp. 311–317.

Carlbom, I., and J. Paiorek. "Geometric Projections and Viewing Transformations," *Computing Surveys*, Vol. 1, No. 4, 1978, pp. 465–502.

Case, J. G. "Automation in Photogrammetry," *Photogrametric Engineering and Remote Sensing*, Vol. 47, No. 3, 1981, pp. 335–341.

Colleman, E. N., and R. Jain. "Obtaining 3-Dimensional Shape of Textured and Specular Surfaces Using Four-Source Photometry," *Computer Graphics and Image Processing*, Vol. 18, 1982, pp. 309–328.

Fu, K. S., Gonzalez, R. C., and C. S. G. Lee. *Robotics: Control, Sensing, Vision, and Intelligence*, New York: McGraw-Hill, 1987.

Gennery, D. B. "Object Detection and Measurement Using Stereo Vision," *Proceedings of Image Understanding Workshop*, College Park, Md., 1980, pp. 161–167.

———. "A Feature-Based Scene Matcher," *Proceedings of the Seventh International Joint Conference on Artificial Intelligence*, Vancouver, Canada, 1981, pp. 667–673.

Gibson, J. J. *Visual World*, Cambridge, Mass.: The Riverside, 1960.

Gonzalez, R. C., and P. Wintz. *Digital Image Processing*, 2nd ed., Reading, Mass.: Addison-Wesley, 1987.

Goshtasby, A. "A Refined Technique for Stereo Depth Perception," *Proceedings of the IEEE Workshop on Computer Vision*, Annapolis, Md., 1984, pp. 3–7.

Grimson, W. E. L. "Aspects of a Computational Theory of Human Stereo Vision," *Proceedings of Image Understanding Workshop*, College Park, Md., 1980, pp. 128–149.

Haddow, E. R., Boyce, J. F., and S. A. Lloyd. "A New Binocular Stereo Algorithm," *Proceedings of the Fourth Scandinavian Conference on Image Processing*, Trondheim, Norway, 1985, pp. 175–182.

Hannah, M. T. "Bootstrap Stereo," *Proceedings of Image Understanding Workshop*, College Park, Md., 1980, pp. 201–208.

Haralick, R. M., Shanummgam, K., and I. Dinstein. "Textural Features for Image Classification," *IEEE Transactions on Systems, Man and Cybernetics*, Vol. SMC-3, No. 6, 1973, pp. 610–621.

Horn, B. K. P. *Robot Vision*, Cambridge, Mass.: MIT Press, 1986.

———. "Obtaining Shape From Shading Information," in *Psychology of Computer Vision*, ed. by P. H. Winston, New York: McGraw-Hill, 1975.

Horn, B. K. P., and M. Brooks. "The Variational Approach to Shape from Shading," *Computer Vision, Graphics and Image Processing*, Vol. 33, 1986, pp. 174–208.

Ikeuchi, K., and B. K. P. Horn. "Numerical Shape from Shading and Occluding Boundaries," *Artificial Intelligence*, Vol. 17, 1981, pp. 141–184.

Ito, M., and A. Ishii. "Three-View Stereo Analysis," *IEEE Transactions on Pattern Analysis and Machine Intelligence*, Vol. PAMI-8, No. 6, 1986, pp. 524–532.

Itoh, H., Miyauchi, A., and A. Ozawa. "Distance Measuring Method Using Only Simple Vision Constructed for Moving Robots," *Proceedings of the Seventh International Conference on Pattern Recognition*, Montreal, Canada, 1984, pp. 192–195.

Julesz, B. *The Cyclopean Eye*, New York: Academic Press, 1970.

Kender, J. R. "Shape from Texture," Ph.D. dissertation, Carnegie-Mellon, 1980.

Konecny, C., and D. Pape. "Correlation Techniques and Devices," *Photogrammetric Engineering Remote Sensing*, Vol. 47, No. 3, 1981, pp. 323–333.

Lu, S. Y., and K. S. Fu. "A Syntactic Approach to Texture Analysis," *Computer Graphics and Image Processing*, Vol. 7, 1978, pp. 303–330.

Lucas, B. D., and T. Kanade. "An Iterative Image Registration Technique With an Application to Stereo Vision," *Proceedings of the Seventh International Joint Conference on Artificial Intelligence*, Vancouver, Canada, 1981, pp. 674–679.

Marr, D., and T. Poggio. "A Computational Theory of Human Stereo Vision," *Proceedings of Royal Society of London*, Vol. B-204, 1979, pp. 301–328.

Mitiche, A. "On Combining Stereopsis and Kineopsis for Space Perception," *The First Conference on Artificial Intelligence Applications*, Denver, Colo., 1984, pp. 156–160.

Moravec, H. P. "Rover Visual Obstacle Avoidance," *Proceedings of the Seventh International Joint Conference on Artificial Intelligence*, Vancouver, Canada, 1981, pp. 785–790.

———. "Visual Mapping by a Robot Rover," *Proceedings of the Sixth International Joint Conference on Artificial Intelligence*, Tokyo, Japan, 1979, pp. 598–600.

O'Brien, N., and R. Jain. "Axial Motion Stereo," *Proceedings of the IEEE Workshop on Computer Vision*, Annapolis, Md., 1984, pp. 88–92.

Rosenfeld, A. "Image Processing: 1984," *Computer Vision, Graphics, and Image Processing*, Vol. 30, 1985, pp. 189–242.

Stevens, K. A. "Surface Perception by Local Analysis of Texture and Contour," AI-512, Artificial Intelligence Lab, MIT, Cambridge, Mass., 1980.

Sze, T. W., and Y. H. Yang. "A Simple Contour Matching Algorithm," *IEEE Transactions on Pattern Analysis Machine Intelligence*, Vol. PAMI-3, No. 6, 1981, pp. 676–678.

Tomita, F., and T. Kanade. "A 3-D Vision System: Generating and Matching a Shape Descriptions in Range Images," *Proceedings of the First Conference on Artificial Intelligence Applications*, Denver, Colo., 1984, pp. 156–160.

Witkin, A. P. "Recovery of Surface Shape and Orientation from Texture," *Artificial Intelligence*, Vol. 17, 1981, pp. 17–47.

Woodham, R. J. "Analyzing Images of Curved Surfaces," *Artificial Intelligence*, Vol. 17, Nos. 1–3, 1981, pp. 117–140.

Yakimovsky, Y., and R. Cunningham. "A System for Extracting Three-Dimensional Measurements from a Stereo Pair of TV Cameras," *Computer Graphics and Image Processing*, Vol. 7, 1978, pp. 195–210.

Zucker, S. "Toward a Model of Texture," *Computer Graphics and Image Processing*, Vol. 5, No. 2, 1976, pp. 190–202.

Chapter 5

Sensors: A Key to Successful Robot-Based Assembly

S. Ahmad
Purdue University

1. Abstract

The appropriate utilization of sensor technology is the key to the successful application of robots in a flexible manufacturing system, or FMS. This chapter discusses the role of sensor technology and its impact on industrial robotics. Most importantly, it contains an in-depth analysis of a practical application of a sensor-based robot assembly system. An experimental robot assembly system is described in this chapter. This system is able to perform a complex assembly task, independent of the exact location and orientation of the parts.

2. Introduction

Computer-controlled robots offer a number of significant advantages in manufacturing and assembly tasks. These advantages include consistent product reliability and the ability to work in harsh environments. The programmable nature of robotics automation allows the possibility of applying robots to a number of tasks. In particular, significant savings can be expected in batch production, if robots can be applied to produce numbers of products successfully without plant retooling. Unfortunately, despite considerable progress made in robot programming [Lozano-Perez 1983, Paul 1981, Ahmad 1984, Gruver et al. 1984, Bonner and Shin 1982], in sensing [Gonzalez and Safabakhsh 1982, Fu 1982, Hall et al. 1982, Goto et al. 1980, Hirzinger and Dietrich 1986, Harmon 1984], and in kinematics and control strategies [Whitney 1985, Luh 1983, Lee 1982], a number of problems still must be solved before en-mass applications can take place. In fact, in current applications, the specialized tooling for manufacturing a particular product may make up as much as 80% of the production line cost. In such a production line the robot is often used only as a programmable parts-transfer device.

Improving the robots' ability to sense and adapt to different products or environments so as to handle a larger variety of products without retooling is essential. It is just as important to be able to program them easily and quickly, without requiring the user to have a detailed understanding of complex robot programming languages and control schemes such as RCCL [Hayward and Paul 1984], VAL-II [Shimano et al. 1984], AML [Taylor et al. 1983], SRIL-90 [Ahmad 1984] or AL [Mujtaba and Goldman 1979]. Currently there are a number of computer-aided design (CAD) packages available which simplify the robot programming problem. Such packages allow the automation system designer to simulate the assembly workcell, which may consist of various machines and robots. The designer can then pick the motion sequences the robot has to execute in order to achieve the desired assembly task. This is done by viewing the motions on a graphics screen from different viewing angles to check for collisions and to ensure the relative positioning is correct, much the same way as it is done in on-line teach playback methods (see Fig. 1). Off-line robot programming on CAD stations does not always lead to successful results due to two reasons:

(*a*) The robot mechanism is inherently inaccurate due to incorrect kinematic models programmed in their control system [Wu 1983, Hayati 1983, Ahmad 1987, Whitney et al. 1984].

(*b*) The assembly workcell model represented in the controller is not accurate. As a result, parts and tools are not exactly located and their exact position may vary. This causes a predefined kinematic motion sequence program to fail, as it cannot deal with positional uncertainties.

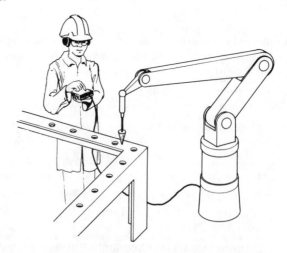

Fig. 1. On-line teach playback methods.

Sensors to detect real-time errors in the part and tool positions are obviously required with tailored sensor-based motion strategies to ensure assembly accomplishment. In this chapter we deal with how sensors are used to successfully ensure the accomplishment of assembly tasks. The use of various sensors is illustrated by going through an actual assembly of an oil pump. Additionally we will examine a number of motion strategies which have been developed to deal with assembly errors. In Sec. 3 we will discuss a number of sensors found in typical robotics assembly systems. Section 4 illustrates how and when sensors are to be used during an assembly operation. Issues relating to sensing and robust assembly systems are discussed very briefly in Sec. 5. The next section details a sensor-based robot assembly to illustrate practical applications. Section 7 summarizes the preceding material.

3. Types of Sensors Utilized in Robotics Applications

There are fundamentally two types of sensors. There are those that rely on mechanical contact via the robot structure to the sensors, that is they contact their environment directly, such as force and touch sensors. Other sensors do not require contact with the environment. Such noncontacting sensors include vision, optical and ultrasonic ranging sensors. Thermal sensors may also be of noncontacting type. The mode of operation of these sensors is also different. For example, force or tactile sensors do not reveal useful information about an object until a contact is made. Similarly, ranging or visual feature identification cannot be carried out if the view is obscured or is out of the ranging distance. These issues are further discussed in Sec. 4. The following is a brief description of some commonly found sensors and the physics of their operations.

Contacting Sensors

Contacting sensors may include a force-sensing structure, a mechanical limit switch, a linear potentiometer, a linear voltage differential transformer (LVDT), a tactile sensor, and so on. We, however, limit our discussion to a force-sensing structure, an optical-touch sensor array, and a linear potentiometer. Figure 2 illustrates a force-sensing structure which was developed by DFVLR of West Germany [Hirzinger and Dietrich 1986].

When a force is applied at a point on the sensing structure, the elemental members of this structure will deform much like a spring, except the structure

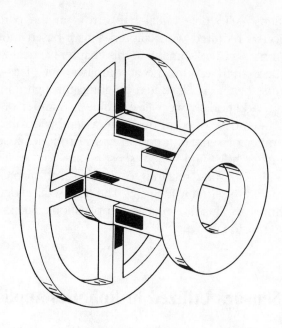

Fig. 2. DFLVR force torque sensor.

is designed to behave like a six-dimensional spring. The deformation is small but can be measured by optical or electromechanical techniques, such as with strain gauges. The sensor may employ n strain-gauge elements with $R^{n \times 1}$ output column vector

$$\boldsymbol{\varepsilon} = (\varepsilon_1, \ldots, \varepsilon_n)^T \tag{1}$$

where R denotes the real numbers.

A force sensor which is deformed by a vector $\mathbf{x} \in R^{6 \times 1}$ would output a force $\mathbf{f} \in R^{6 \times 1}$. If $\mathbf{K}$ is an $R^{6 \times 6}$ matrix representing the structural stiffness in the elastic region of operation, then

$$\mathbf{f} = \mathbf{Kx} \tag{2}$$

If $\mathbf{C}$ is an $R^{6 \times n}$ matrix which transforms n strain-gauge sensor readings to deformation $\mathbf{x}$, then

$$\mathbf{f} = \mathbf{KC}\boldsymbol{\varepsilon} \tag{3}$$

assuming a linear relationship exists between the strain-gauge deformation and the applied force. Most commercially available force-sensing structures will process the signals from the strain-gauge element reading to a force signal in a user-defined coordinate frame. Force sensors employing capacitive measurement techniques have also been developed [Sinden and Boie 1986].

A linear potentiometer may be used to measure displacement or a force (if combined with a compliant structure). A possible use is shown in Fig. 3. The linear displacement $\mathbf{x}$ between the contact point and the path of the robot end effector is used to obtain the shape of the surface.

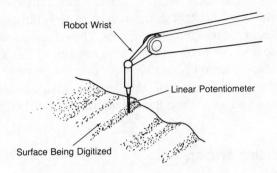

Fig. 3. A linear potentiometer used to obtain surface shape.
The method is simple and lengthy, but effective.

An optical touch sensor is shown in the Fig. 4. It was reported by Bege [1984].

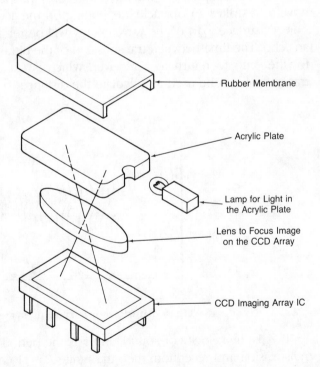

Fig. 4. An optical tactile sensor.

A number of other tactile array sensors have been constructed based on various technologies [Raibert and Tanner 1982, Hillis 1982]. The underlying physics on which this device functions are as follows: When there are no objects placed on the elastic membrane, total internal refraction is experienced by the light waves in the acrylic plate, hence the image formed by the lens on the CCD array is black. Once an object is placed on the elastic membrane, the light in the acrylic plate is diffracted by the higher refractive index of the touching membrane. The diffracted rays travel through the acrylic plate and are focused by a lens onto the CCD array. The advantage of this sensing scheme is that the actual contact between the sensor surface and the environment is minimal. Also, existing image processing techniques may now be utilized to analyze the image formed on the CCD array.

Noncontacting Sensors

Noncontacting sensors include optical, acoustic ranging, vision and magnetic sensors. Vision sensing is explained in greater detail in other chapters of this text. In this section we briefly discuss acoustic ranging.

An ultrasonic ranging system relies on the fact that sound at a constant temperature and pressure will travel at a constant speed. Also, if an ultrasonic wavefront strikes an obstacle, depending on the acoustic impedance of the object's surface, part of the wave energy will be retransmitted in the form of an echo. The time between transmission of the ultrasonic pulse and the time for the echo to return to a receiver, which is usually located close to the transmitter, can be used to calculate the distance to the object (see Fig. 5).

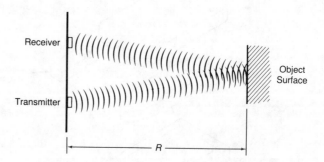

Fig. 5. An ultrasonic ranging system.

If v_s is the velocity of sound, and τ is the period of time between pulse transmission and reception, then the range R is given as

$$R = \tfrac{1}{2} v_s \tau$$

A practical ultrasonic ranging system would have to employ various pulsing frequencies to deal with noise and temperature or pressure variations. For more detailed description on an ultrasonic system refer to [Polaroid 1982]. Methods of determining surface information specifically from ultrasonic data are discussed in Brown [1985, 1986].

4. How and When to Use Sensors in Robot Assembly Programs

As mentioned in the introduction, kinematically programmed robot programs can fail if parts become slightly displaced from their preprogrammed paths, or if other uncertainties arise.

Consider an assembly, such as the oil pump shown in Fig. 6, which consists of two gears enclosed in the oil pump casing. The robot's task consists of manipulating the gears from their initial position and inserting them into their respective bearing housings. In order for this assembly to be successful, it is necessary that the trajectory of the gear shaft follow a predefined path relative to the bearing housing. This is not necessarily a unique sequence. If there is a deviation from the set of possible paths the assembly sequence may fail. It is therefore necessary to utilize sensing to indirectly and directly verify the relative motion sequence. Indirect operations would include obtaining the correct position and orientation of the gear shaft and the oil pump casing prior to grasping the parts, and obtaining the position of the pump casing before the gear insertion. Direct measurements would include measuring the relative orientation of the gear shaft with respect to the bearing housing (located on the pump casing) during the insertion process. In these instances the sensing operation is being used to verify and calibrate the manipulation.

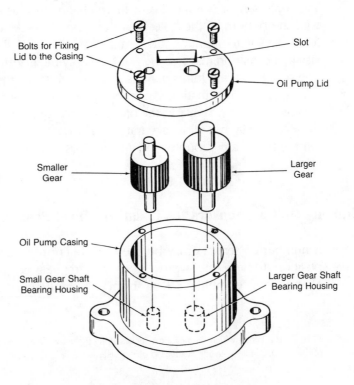

Fig. 6. Oil pump components.

Only in certain instances, however, will the sensor give useful information. An example of this is that vision will only provide useful information if the view is not obscured and the measurable features are in range. Similarly, the force sensors can only give useful information if the robot tools are in contact with the environment. Likewise, the tactile sensor will provide usable data only when the part is in contact with the touch sensor. The sensing instance has to be in a correct geometric context in order for the sensing operation to be useful. This implies the viewpoint has to be appropriately selected, as well as the sensing operation has to be as close as possible in time to the related motion sequence.

Which Sensor to Use

In a predefined robot assembly system the question of which sensor to use is relatively easy to answer. A robot motion sequence can be broken down into transfer operations and contact operations, such as grasping, insertions, and other mating operations.

The type of sensor to utilize for an assembly sequence verification can be approximately determined from the type of manipulation operation. An example of this occurs during the termination phase of an insertion process. The force sensor will monitor a sharp change in f_z as the peg makes contact with the bottom of the hole.* It would therefore be appropriate to utilize a force sensor to monitor the termination phase of the insertion. However, visual information may also be used to verify the insertion if the peg is visible. The position of the joints may also be used to verify the insertion. The rate at which visual information must be processed may not be economically feasible, however. Similarly, the backlash and compliance present in the robot drive train may not allow accurate measurement of the peg's position if the joint sensors are mounted on the motors instead of on the actual robot joints.

Utilizing Multiple Sensors for Updating Object Position Information

A number of sensors may be used to obtain information about an object's position (where the word "position" implies position and orientation). Methods of combining data from different sensors is currently under

---

*The force f_z is that which the peg experiences along the z direction, the direction along which the axes of the peg and hole coincide at the end of the insertion process.

investigation [Henderson and Shilcrat 1984, Durrant-Whyte 1986, Stevenson 1986]. Figure 7 illustrates this concept.

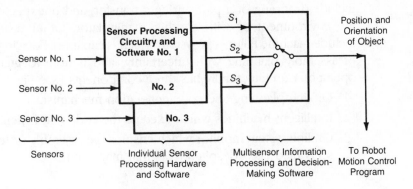

Fig. 7. Multiple sensor utilization method.

In such a system a number of questions must be answered by the mechanism which combines the sensory data. These include the following:

1. The correctness of the geometric context:

   (*a*) Viewpoint: Is the data originating from the sensor viewing the desired object surface, edge, or other usable features?

   (*b*) Sensing instance: Will the data from this sensing process be useful for immediate manipulation sequence?

2. Statistics of the sensors being used: How error-prone is the extracted data from a particular sensor?

A number of researchers approach these problems from a statistical [Durrant-Whyte 1986] or a numerical standpoint [Stevenson 1986]. A hierarchical conceptual servo has also been discussed as a method of interfacing sensors to a manipulation sequence [Kent and Albus 1984]. Such a system must address the above fundamental questions directly or indirectly in its sensor-fusion process. Grimson [1986] developed an algorithm to recognize and locate an object utilizing a minimal set of sensory data. He also considers the determination of the optimal viewpoint, i.e., viewpoints which require the minimum number of sensed points to uniquely identify the object's position and orientation.

5. Robust Sensor-Based Assembly Systems

The objective of research in the area of robust sensor-based robot assembly systems is to develop a formal theory for programming and planning of sensor-based robot assembly systems. These systems must be able to guarantee robustness even though assembly parts position, sensing actions, and robot operation may have uncertainty associated with them. Additionally, events which disturb the preplanned program can be expected. Such events include dropping of a part during a transfer, and unexpected collision with the environment or with another manipulator. Other disturbances would include machine failures. A system which is capable of dealing with all aspects of assembly planning with uncertainty, and is able to guarantee real-time operations, architecturally has three components (see Fig. 8).

1. Off-line planning and code generation mechanism.
2. Intelligent machines which execute the code that is generated.
3. On-line system monitor which ensures the assembly system performs the scheduled tasks despite errors that may occur.

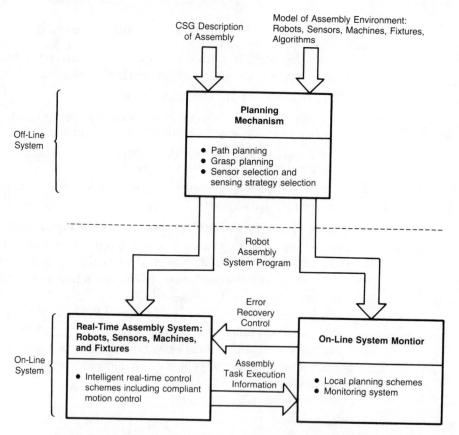

Fig. 8. Assembly planning, execution, and monitoring system.

The *planning mechanism* deals with the path planning of the manipulator and that of the machines in the assembly environment, given the solid-geometric description of the object it is to assemble. It also selects the sensing operations which are essential to add robustness to the assembly operations. Motion strategies which deal with uncertainty are also selected by the planner. The set of grasping positions for the assembly components must also be calculated by the grasp planner.

The *assembly system*, which consists of various sensors, robots and other machines, must be able to respond and synchronize to the primitive actions specified by the planner.

The *on-line system monitor* receives information on the assembly from the planning mechanism, and it receives the execution information from the assembly system components. From the two sets of information, it can decide whether an assembly system error has occurred. If so, it can take over and provide error recovery.

There has been considerable research effort in robot path planning, grasping, error recovery, and assembly planning. We will only briefly discuss previous efforts in assembly planning systems.

Past Research in Assembly Planning

Lozano-Pérez, Taylor, and Brooks have considered assembly planning systems. Lozano-Pérez [1976] considers an assembly planning process to be a three-stage effort. In the first stage, a general plan is developed in terms of the class of operations to be performed. For example, object *A* is to be placed on object *B*. In the second stage, the grasp planning and robot path planning is carried out. In the third stage sensing is incorporated to deal with uncertainty.

Taylor [1976] considered each operation to possess a certain set of preconditions and to achieve a certain set of postconditions. The task of the planner is then to satisfy these conditions subject to the constraints imposed by the geometry of the task.

Brooks [1982] developed a symbolic error-analysis package. This package is able to propagate errors through a motion sequence and is used to check generated plans. These plans are checked in terms of whether they satisfy the required error constraints. If the constraints are not satisfied, the plans can be altered by introducing new operations so as to guarantee satisfaction.

6. A Practical Implementation of a Sensor-Based Robot Assembly System

In order to gain an understanding of the task involved in the design of a practical sensor-based robot assembly program utilizing currently available industrial equipment, an experiment performed in the Purdue robot laboratory class will be documented. This experiment is performed by first-year graduate students and seniors in the School of Electrical Engineering atPurdue University. It is a part of a laboratory class titled Real-Time Robot Control Laboratory. The sensor-based robot assembly experiment is used as a base to educate research students in the area of automated sensor-based robot assembly systems. It involves the assembly of an oil pump in which the assembly sequence is manually generated and programmed. It is interesting to note that the oil pump assembly is not difficult to perform manually. It is, however, not possible to perform this assembly reliably (every time) with kinematic programming techniques that are quite commonly used in pick and place industrial operations. The reasons for this have been stated earlier and are reiterated here. They are as follows:

1. The parts have manufacturing tolerance [Requicha & Chan 1986].
2. The parts are not exactly located due to inaccuracy in the assembly setup or inaccurate calibration of the assembly environments.
3. The robots are not accurate in absolute programmed mode [Ahmad 1987, Whitney et al. 1984]; they introduce errors into the assembly operations.

In order to make assembly systems robust, sensing must be used before and after an assembly action to verify its completion. At this point, a general theory to plan assembly operations which guarantees robustness does not exist. The patterns of information which are received at each stage of assembly must be manually generated, verified, and programmed, even though these information patterns are derived from geometric properties of the assembly components.

In order to cope with various assembly errors, a number of practical calibration techniques and sensor-based motion strategies have been developed [Inoue 1974, Wills and Grossman 1974, Goto et al. 1980, Mason and Salisbury 1985, Brady et al. 1982]. Some of these practical strategies are demonstrated in the following oil pump assembly experiment. This experiment is described in three subsections. The first subsection describes the equipment and experimental setup. The second subsection details the sensing and sensor-based motion strategies employed to make the assembly robust. The third subsection pictorially depicts the assembly sequence.

Equipment and Assembly Description

The main purpose of this experiment was to examine the practical use of different sensors in a complex assembly task and to expose various problems involved in a real-time robot assembly. The task is to assemble an oil pump independently of exact location and orientation of parts by using a sensor-guided manipulator. The apparatus which was available for the implementation was an IBM RS-1 robot and GE Optomation vision system.

Description of Experimental Apparatus

We may study the experimental apparatus as comprising the following subsystems.

Robot and Imbedded Sensors—The RS-1 robot is a 6–degree-of-freedom Cartesian robot. This robot has three linear joints, a three-rotary-joint wrist, and a gripper (see Fig. 9). The robot has a six strain-gauge force sensor built into the gripper which detects forces at the tips, sides, and perpendicular to the gripper surfaces. It is also equipped with a part detector which consists of an infrared light-emitting diode (LED) and a phototransistor located in the gripper. Once the part is in the grasp position between the two fingers of the gripper, the LED infrared beam is broken, indicating the presence of a part. These sensors are shown in Fig. 10. The RS-1 robot is programmed via AML (A Manufacturing Language) to control the manipulator [Taylor et al. 1983].

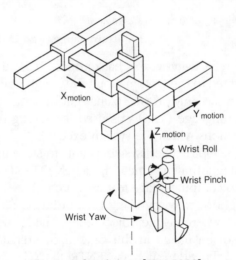

Fig. 9. Robot joints [IBM 1983].

Binary Image Processing System—A GE Optomation binary image processor [General Electric Company] is also used in this assembly. The binary image processor can provide information only about the silhouette of an object. A binary image is defined as a binary function which takes a value of 0 or 1 over the entire image plane. The image of an object in the field of view is converted to digital video data. This binary representation occurs before feature-based recognition is carried out. Up to four solid-state CCD cameras can be simultaneously processed by the Optomation system. The CCD cameras which are used have a 256 × 256 matrix of photosensitive pixels. The camera used in this experiment is mounted on the robot and it moves with the arm in a horizontal plane to monitor the assembly workspace.

The Optomation system has a relatively fast processing time, but it is incapable of distinguishing overlaps, shadows, and images with nearly the

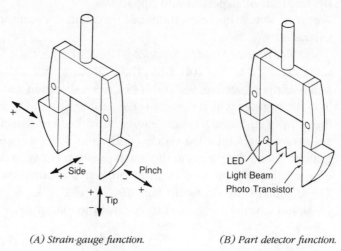

(A) Strain-gauge function.   *(B) Part detector function.*

Fig. 10. Strain gauges and LED part detector.

same reflectivity as the background. It is necessary that images which are presented to the Optomation have a high object-to-background contrast. The system can only provide planar information about an object. Visual Programming Language (VPL) was used for setting up the image processing macro instructions which the system executes.

The Optomation system is able to store up to 100 objects in its data base by using a built-in function, namely QTY.ITEMS. The Optomation system is able to compute image features, such as the area and perimeter of an item in the field of view, by using built-in functions such as AREA(i) and PERIME-TER(i), where i is the object index. The X and Y coordinates of the center of mass of an image in the camera coordinates can also be determined by built-in functions such as CENTROID.X(i), CENTROID.Y(i).

Integration of the Automation Devices—The vision system is set up to communicate with the RS-1 controller through a parallel port. This allows the RS-1 controller to obtain data processed by the vision system about the objects in the workspace, and then to generate the manipulator movement accordingly. The Optomation is also connected to a VAX 11/780 UNIX machine through a serial port; this connection is only used to back up software. The overall hardware configuration is summarized in Fig. 11.

Assembly Components—Figure 6 shows the eight components of the oil pump assembly. The pump casing has two bearing housings which have to be mated with the gear shafts. The pump casing lid is assembled such that the gear shafts are inserted into the bearings located on the lid. Four bolts are used to fix the lid to the casing; these bolts and bolt holes are symmetrically located around the oil pump casing.

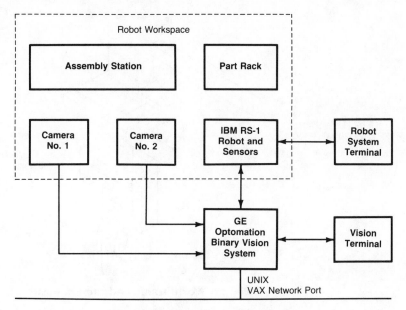

Fig. 11. Workstation configuration.

Layout of the Assembly Workstation—The pump casing is securely located by a fixture, but the pump casings lid, the gears, and the bolts are randomly located on a light box. Since the image processor is binary, the lighting is an important factor in accurately locating the part features. Back lighting created by the light box provides clear images and eliminates possible shadows. This lighting strategy improves the accuracy of visual sensing and subsequently enhances the manipulator's precision.

Coordinate Frames: The height (Z coordinate) of the table and hence the Z-axis locations of all the assembly components are known. To locate a feature point such as the centroids of the parts or holes, the processor finds the X and Y coordinates of the feature points in the camera's coordinate frame. These positions are sent to the robot controller where they are converted into the world coordinates. The world coordinate frame, which is also called *box frame*, is parallel to the robot wrist coordinates when the wrist roll, pitch and yaw rotational angles have values of zero as shown in Fig. 12.

The camera is mounted on the robot (see Fig. 12), and its coordinate frame is always at a fixed offset in the X and Y direction from the robot's X and Y Cartesian joints. Therefore, if the position of the X and Y joints of the robot is known in the world frame, the relative position of the camera in the world frame can be determined by one physical measurement. Once this relationship is found, the conversion of coordinates from the camera frame to the box frame is easily carried out by a scaling and a transformation matrix.

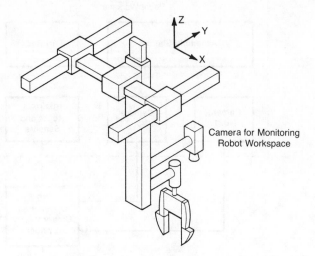

Fig. 12. World frame and camera location.

Assembly Sequence

The assembly sequence can be outlined in three general stages. First, the gears are located and then placed into the gear housing. The lid is then mated with the two gear shafts already in their respective bearing housings. Finally, the four bolts are located and placed into the four holes around the pump casing. This sequence is summarized in Table 1.

Table 1. Assembly Sequence

Sequence	Step 1	Step 2	Step 3
Stage 1	Determine gear locations, grasp	Gross transfer motion	Insert gears into pump housing
Stage 2	Determine lid location and orientation, grasp	Gross transfer motion	Place lid on pump housing
Stage 3	Determine bolt location, grasp	Gross transfer motion	Insert bolts into pump housing

Practical Sensor-Based Motion Strategies

In this section we discuss a number of practical sensor-based motion strategies which were employed in the oil pump assembly.

Move ( ) Until Condition ( )

This motion strategy relies on an event to occur in order to terminate a motion. The first parenthesis will usually contain a position goal which may be predefined, the second parenthesis may contain a sensor or other conditional events. This strategy has often been called a *guarded move* [Will and Grossman 1975, Brady et al. 1982]. An example use of this strategy is during placement when there is uncertainty about the height of the platform.

If an object's position is not exactly known and it must be grasped, this conditional movement can be used to center the gripper accurately. Assume that the maximum width of the object is smaller than the maximum opening of the gripper. Assume also that an LED beam sensor is available on the gripper and the height of the object and the table on which the object is placed are known. A conditional move in the X direction, with the gripper wide open until the LED sensor beam is broken, allows the determination of a face of the box that bounds the object. A second conditional move in the Y direction allows the determination of the second face of the bounding box. Knowing the faces of the bounding box, and if the orientation of the part can be determined from this information, an accurate centered grasp can be found.

Servo ( ) While Condition ( )

This is a servo process. The first parenthesis will contain an expression which will be updated to represent a position or a force goal, while the second will represent a logical or a sensor-directed condition. Examples of this strategy include force, position servoing, compliant motions, visual servoing, and other sensor-directed servoprocesses. Suppose that an object is to be visually tracked, and the gripper frame is to be aligned with the object frame which is obtained from the vision processor. This can be implemented by the above sensor-based motion construct.

Insertions and Spiral Searching

A number of strategies are required to correctly perform an insertion.

Approach From a Fixed Direction—This ensures that the direction in which the gear shaft (the peg) is to be moved is always the same [Goto et al. 1980, Inoue 1974].

Compliant Motion—In order to complete the insertion, the peg is required to be placed over the hole, planar XY motions are required to locate it, and a force along the Z direction is required to maintain contact with the XY plane. Once the peg is located over the hole, forces in the XY directions must be minimized to prevent jamming of the peg. In this motion sequence, the force servoing is specified in the directions orthogonal to those in which position servoing is desired [Mason 1981].

Spiral Searching—During an insertion, if the hole is not located at the approach phase, a spiral search is initiated to locate it. This search may be decomposed into incremental movements in the X and Y directions. Each of these increments must be smaller than the diameter of the hole.

Conditions for Detecting the Hole and the Termination of the Insertion Phase—If the hole is detected, there will be a momentary change in the force along the Z direction. This condition must be monitored and used to initiate the insertion phase. At the completion of the insertion phase, the force f_z will again return to the prespecified value and the position of the peg should be at the bottom of the hole. Once this occurs, the insertion phase is complete [Goto et al. 1980].

Visual Search Strategy—This strategy is used to locate the objects in the workspace. This routine is an example of "Move (   ) until condition (   )" movement which is executed while the vision system is constantly trying to locate the objects. Once a desired object is found in the field of vision, the motion is terminated.

The visual search algorithm can be translated to VPL language as follows:

```
ITEMS = 0
DO WHILE ITEMS = 0
   ...
   ITEMS = QTY.ITEMS
END WHILE
```

When a part is detected, the variable QTY.ITEMS becomes nonzero at that stage the while loop is exited. A message is then sent to the robot indicating that the part is found. Upon the robot's receiving that message, the search motion is terminated by the robot controller once the signal from the vision system is received.

Part Recognition—A challenging problem in robot vision tasks is to identify each component with the minimum number of features in a short period. Fortunately in this assembly with adequate lighting, simple binary features can be used to distinguish between objects. Features of each component, such as area, perimeters, and number of holes, are used to identify the presence of an object in the workspace. For example, the screws have smaller areas and circumferences than do the gears, and the lid has several holes which distinguish it from all others.

The recognition algorithm is implemented in vision software by adding conditional statements inside the while loop in the search routine discussed above; for example, the following modification may be used to distinguish the bolts from the gears based on the area of the parts:

```
ITEMS = 0
DO WHILE ITEMS = 0
...
TAKE.PIX(1)
IF QTY.ITEMS<>0 THEN
   FOR I=1 TO QTY.ITEMS DO
     IF AREA(I)>(SCREW_AREA_MIN)AND
     AREA(I)<(SCREW_AREA_MAX)
     THEN ITEMS=QTY.ITEMS
   NEXT I
END IF
END WHILE
```

The first if statement checks the presence of parts, the second if statement uses the feature of the part, namely the area, to identify the screw. The "for" loop is used to index through all the items in the field of view.

Calculating the Orientation of an Oil Pump Lid From a 2-D Binary Image

In order to grasp a geometrically known object correctly, the position and the orientation of the object has to be precisely determined. Symmetric 2-D objects, such as the gears and bolts, can be grasped once the binary image centroid is computed. The oil pump lid is circular and has four bolt holes symmetrically located about its circumference. Furthermore, it has two holes to locate the gearshaft and a slot is also located on the lid (see Fig. 13).

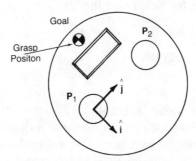

Fig. 13. Oil pump lid features.

In order to determine the exact orientation of the lid, the following procedure is used.

1. The position of the two holes to locate gear shafts are determined as $\mathbf{P}_1$ and $\mathbf{P}_2$.
2. A coordinate frame is located at $\mathbf{P}_1$, such that the unit vector $\hat{\mathbf{j}}$ is given as

$$\hat{\mathbf{j}} = (\mathbf{P}_2 - \mathbf{P}_1)/|\mathbf{P}_2 - \mathbf{P}_1|$$

3. The unit vector $\hat{\mathbf{i}}$ is determined as

$$\hat{\mathbf{i}} = \hat{\mathbf{j}} \times \hat{\mathbf{k}}, \quad \hat{\mathbf{k}} = (0,,0,1)^T$$

If the position of the slot in the established coordinate is in the first quadrant, then the grasp position GOAL in this frame is given as

$$\text{GOAL} = (x_g, y_g)^T$$

Otherwise,

$$\text{GOAL} = (-x_g, y_g)^T$$

This is shown in Fig. 14.

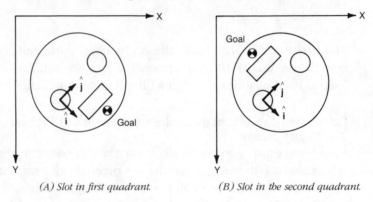

(A) Slot in first quadrant.   (B) Slot in the second quadrant.

Fig. 14. Two orientations of the oil pump lid.

This information is needed to position and orientate the gripper accurately prior to picking up the lid.

The Assembly Program

First Stage: Gear Assembly

Figure 15 illustrates the sequence of motions the robot must execute in order to assemble the gearbox. The robot initiates the assembly by sending a message to the Optomation to locate the gears. The approximate position of the light table on which the gears are placed is known. A visual search is performed to locate a gear exactly. The vision system constantly takes pictures and, based on the visual search strategies discussed above, it stops when a gear is found. The robot is then signaled to grasp the gear, which it approaches to a known height with a guarded move. The LED and force sensors are used to trigger this conditional move. When the LED, or the force sensor is tripped, the robot will grasp the gear shaft and commence the departure from the grasp position.

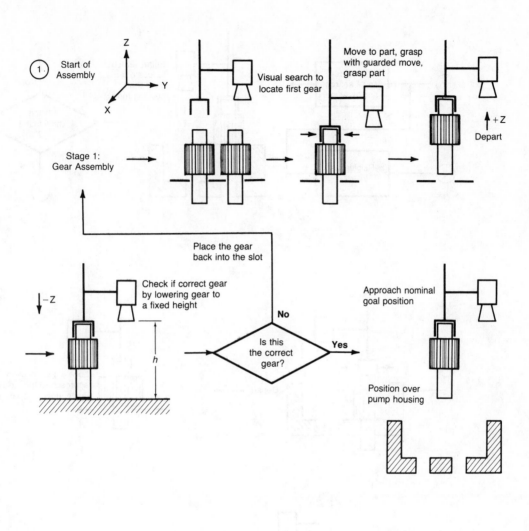

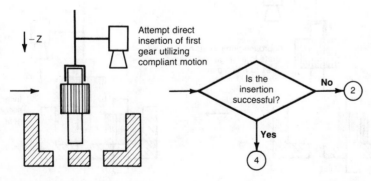

Fig. 15. Gear assembly.

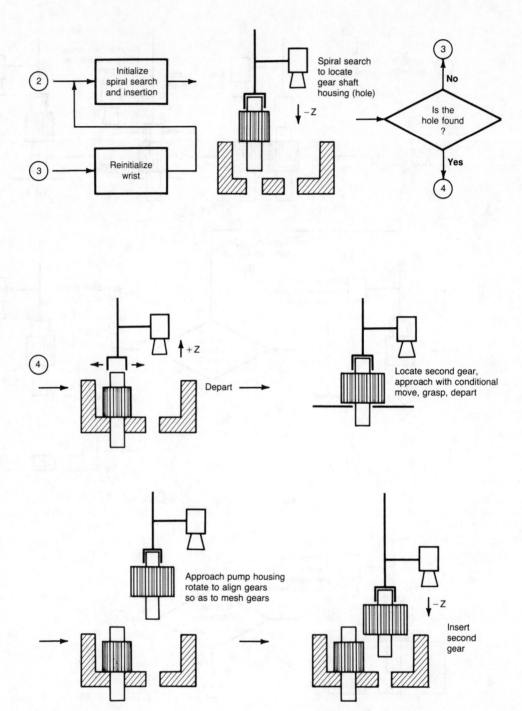

Fig. 15. Gear assembly.

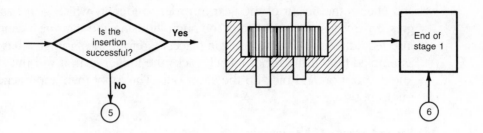

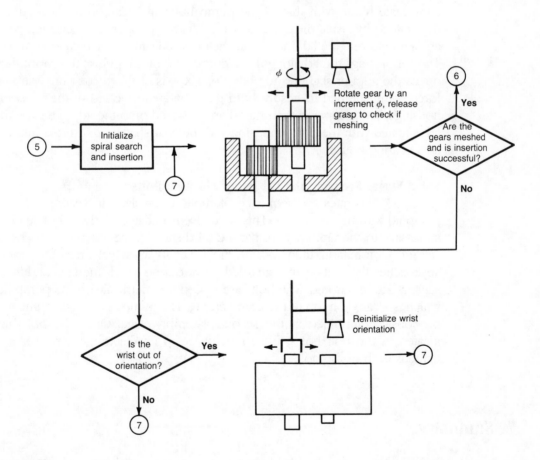

Fig. 15. Gear assembly.

The robot then moves the gear above a solid surface of a known height and checks the height of the gear in order to identify which gear has been grasped. Because of the depth of the pump housing, the short gear cannot be inserted if the long one is already in place; therefore, the short gear has to be assembled first. If the robot initially picks the longer gear, it will put it in a known position and pick up the short one. The robot then approaches the pump housing.

Second Stage: Lid Assembly

Figure 16 depicts the motion sequence for the lid assembly. The sequence is initiated by sending a message to Optomation indicating that the lid is to be located. Once the lid is located, the robot tries to grasp it. If it is unsuccessful, a spiral search is executed to locate the grasp position accurately.

The robot then approaches the pump housing, and aligns the lid's coordinate frame with that of the pump housing (this coordinate frame is determined by visual measurements). It tilts the gripper to a specified pitch angle and lowers the lid until contact is made utilizing a force guarded move. The robot drags the lid along the Y coordinate of the pump, the robot then opens the gripper slightly and pulls along X axis of the gripper until desired force is thresholded to ensure both gear shafts are located in their bearing housings. The gripper is then raised and lowered onto the lid, to ensure the lid is mated with the pump housing and the gear shafts are inserted into the lid's bearing housings.

Third Stage: Securing the Oil Pump Lid With Bolts

Figure 17 illustrates the sequence of motions involved in securing the oil pump lid with the four bolts. This sequence is initiated by the robot sending a message to the Optomation that the third stage in the assembly process is started. Optomation then locates the bolts in its visual area. The robot approaches the bolts with a guarded move during which the LED and force sensors are monitored. The bolts are placed symmetrically on the pump lid, which is located on top of the pump casing. The pump coordinate frame was previously determined in the second assembly stage. Once the bolts are located in the bolt holes, the robot picks up an electric screwdriver and tightens each of the bolts.

7. Summary

In this chapter we briefly discussed the major problems encountered in robot-based assembly systems. It is evident from current applications that ease of programming and the ability of the robot systems to deal with

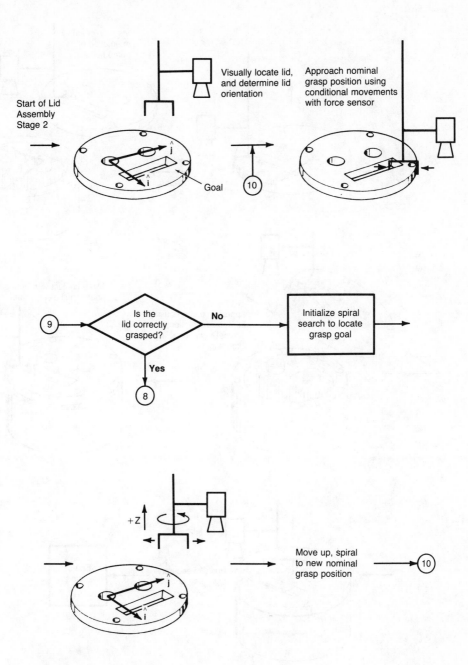

Fig. 16. Lid assembly.

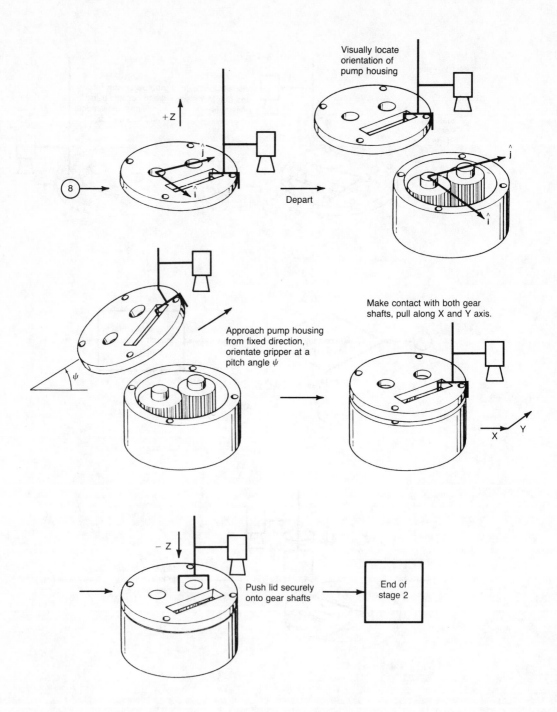

Fig. 16. Lid assembly.

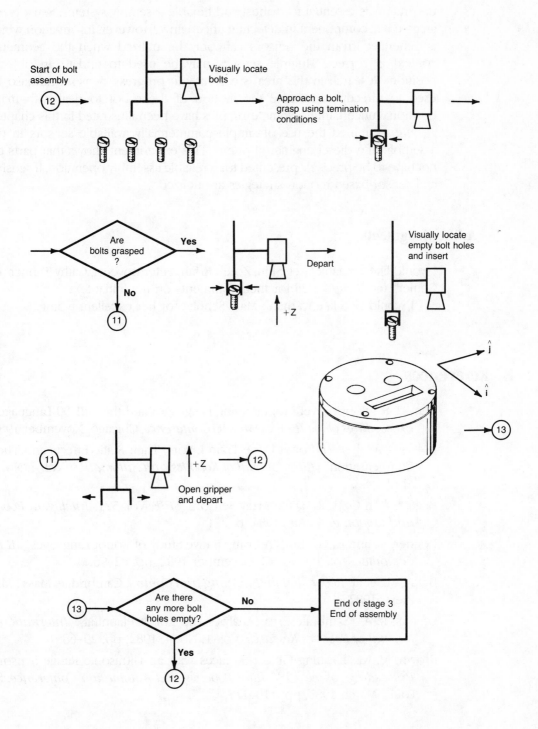

Fig. 17. Bolt assembly.

uncertainty is essential for robust and flexible assembly systems. Sensors are an essential component in detecting uncertainty. However, information which is generated from the sensors can only be utilized when the geometric context is correct. Multiple sensors may be used to update an object's position. Research in this area is currently in progress. Sensors can also be used to directly coordinate the motion of the robot to deal with many positional uncertainties. Some examples have been illustrated in this chapter.

We examined the use of simple commercially available sensors in the assembly of a diesel engine oil pump. This experiment shows that parts do not have to be precisely presented for a reliable assembly operation, if sensing and sensor-based motion strategies are utilized.

Acknowledgments

I would like to thank Greg Shiu, Zoreh Erfan, Peter Bovenzi, Cathy Tanner, Jill Comer, and Rick Guptill for their comments on the initial text.

I would also like to thank Mary Schultz for her excellent typing.

8. References

Ahmad, S. "Robot Level Programming Languages and the SRIL-90 Language," *Proceedings of the IEEE COMPSAC Conference*, Chicago, November 1984.

———. "Analysis of Robot Drive Train Errors, Their Static Effects and Their Compensation," *IEEE Journal of Robotics and Automation*, Vol. 4, No. 2, April 1988.

Bege, S. "An Optical Tactile Array Sensor," *SPIE*, Vol. 521, *Intelligent Robots and Computer Vision*, 1984, p. 271.

Bonner, S., and K. G. Shin. "A Comparative Study of Robot Languages," *IEEE Computer*, Vol. 15, No. 12, December 1982, pp. 82–96.

Brady, M., et al. *Robot Motion: Planning and Control*, Cambridge, Mass.: MIT Press, 1982.

Brooks, R. A. "Symbolic Error Analysis and Robot Planning," *International Journal of Robotics Research*, Vol. 1, No. 4, 1982, pp. 29–68.

Brown, M. K. "Locating Object Surfaces with an Ultrasonic Range Sensor," *Proceedings of the 1985 IEEE Robotics and Automation Conference*, St. Louis, March 1985, pp. 110–115.

————. "On Ultrasonic Detection of Surface Features," *Proceedings of the 1985 IEEE Robotics and Automation Conference*, San Francisco, April 1986, pp. 1785–1790.

Durrant-Whyte, H. F. "Consistent Integration and Propagation of Disparate Sensors Observations," Grasp Laboratory Report, University of Pennsylvania, April 1986.

Fu, K. S. "Pattern Recognition for Automatic Visual Inspection," *IEEE Computer*, Vol. 15, No. 12, December 1982, pp. 34–40.

General Electric Company. "PN-2304 Optomation II VPL Reference Manual," New York: General Electric Company.

Gonzalez, R. C., and R. Safabakhsh. "Computer Vision Techniques for Industrial Applications and Robot Control," *IEEE Computer*, Vol. 15, No. 12, December 1982, pp. 17–32.

Goto, I., Takaeyasu, K., and T. Inoyama. "Control Algorithm for Precision Insert Operation Robots," *IEEE Transactions on Systems, Man, and Cybernetics*, Vol. SMC-10, No. 1, 1980, pp. 19–25.

Grimson, W. E. L. "Disambiguating Sensory Interpretations Using Minimal Sets of Sensory Data," *Proceedings of the 1986 IEEE Conference on Robotics and Automation*, San Francisco, March 1986, pp. 286–292.

Gruver, W. A., Soroka, B. I., Craig, J. J., and T. L. Turner. "Industrial Robot Programming Languages: A Comparative Evaluation," *IEEE Transactions on Systems, Man, and Cybernetics*, Vol. SMC-14, No. 4, July 1984, pp. 565–571.

Hall, E., Tio, J. B. K., McPherson, C. A., and F. A. Sadjadi. "Measuring Curved Surfaces for Robot Vision," *IEEE Computer*, Vol. 15., No. 12, December 1982, pp. 42–54.

Harmon, L. D. "Automated Touch Sensing," *International Journal of Robotics Research*, Vol. 1, No. 2, 1982, pp. 3–32.

Hayati, S. "Robot Arm Geometric Link Parameter Estimation," *Proceedings of the 22nd IEEE Conference on Decision and Control*, December 1983, pp. 1477–1483.

Hayward, V., and R. P. Paul. "Introduction to RCCL: A Robot Control "C" Library," *Proceedings of the IEEE Robotics and Automation Conference*, Atlanta, March 1984, pp. 293–297.

Henderson, T., and E. Shilcrat. "Logical Sensor Systems," *Journal of Robotic Systems*, Vol. 1, No. 2, 1984, pp. 169–193.

Hillis, W. D. "A High-Resolution Image Touch Sensor," *International Journal of Robotics Research*, Vol. 1, No. 2, 1982, pp. 33–44.

Hirzinger, G., and J. Dietrich. "Multisensory Robots and Sensor Based Path Generation," *Proceedings of the 1985 IEEE Robotics and Automation Conference*, San Francisco, April 1986.

IBM. "A Manufacturing Language Concepts and User's Guide," International Business Machines, 1983.

Inoue, H. "Force Feedback in Precise Assembly Laboratory," AIM-308, Massachusetts Institute of Technology, August 1974.

Kent, E. W., and J. S. Albus. "Servoed World Models as Interfaces Between Robot Control Systems and Sensory Data," *Robotics*, Vol. 2, 1984, pp. 17–25.

Lee, C. S. G. "Robot Arm Kinematics, Dynamics and Control," *IEEE Computer*, Vol. 15, No. 12, December 1982, pp. 63–80.

Lozano-Pérez, T. "The Design of a Mechanical Assembly System," AI-TR-397, Artificial Intelligence Laboratory, Massachusetts Institute of Technology, 1976.

———. "Robot Programming," *Proceedings of the IEEE*, Vol. 71, No. 7, July 1983, pp. 821–841.

Luh, J. Y. S. "An Anatomy of Industrial Robots and Their Controls," *IEEE Transaction on Automatic Control*, Vol. AC-28, February 1983, pp. 133–153.

Mason, M. T., and J. K. Salisbury Jr. *Robot Hands and the Mechanics of Manipulation*, Cambridge, Mass.: MIT Press, 1985.

Mason, M. T. "Compliance and Force Control for Computer Controlled Manipulators," *IEEE Transactions on Systems, Man, and Cybernetics*, Vol. SMC-11, No. 6, 1981, pp. 418–432.

Mujtaba, S. M., and R. Goldman. "The AL Users Manual," STAN-CS-79-718, Stanford University, January 1979.

Paul, R. P. *Robot Manipulators: Mathematics, Programming and Control*, Cambridge, Mass.: MIT Press, 1982.

Polaroid Corporation. *Ultrasonic Ranging System Handbook*, Polaroid Corporation, Cambridge, Mass.: 1982.

Raibert, M. H., and J. E. Tanner. "Design and Implementation of a VLSI Tactile Sensing Computer," *International Journal of Robotics Research*, Vol. 1, No. 3, 1982, pp. 33–44.

Requicha, A., and S. C. Chan. "Representation of Geometric Features, Tolerances, and Attributed in Solid Modelers Based on Constructive Geometry," *IEEE Journal of Robotics and Automation*, Vol. RA-2, No. 3, 1986, pp. 156–167.

Shimano, B. E., Clifford, C. G., and C. H. Spalding III. "VAL-II: A New Robot Control System for Automatic Manufacturing," *Proceedings of the IEEE Robotics and Automation Conference*, Atlanta, March 1985, pp. 278–291.

Sinden, F. W., and R. A. Boie. "A Planar Capacitive Force Sensor With Six Degrees of Freedom," *Proceedings of the 1985 IEEE Robotics and Automation Conference*, San Francisco, April 1986, pp. 1806–1814.

Stevenson, C. "Offline Programming for Model Based Sensor Controlled Robots," Ph.D. thesis, School of Electrical Engineering, Purdue University, West Lafayette, Indiana, 1986.

Taylor, R. H. "The Synthesis of Manipulator Control Programs from Task-Level Specifications," AIM-282, Artificial Intelligence Laboratory, Stanford University, July 1976.

Taylor, R. H., Summers, P. D., and J. M. Meyer. "AML: A Manufacturing Language," *The International Journal of Robotics Research*, Vol. 1, No. 3, 1982, pp. 19–41.

Whitney, D. E., Lozinski, C. A., and J. M. Rourf. "Industrial Robot Calibration Method and Results," *Proceedings of ASME Computers in Engineering Conference*, Las Vegas, August 1984, pp. 92–100.

Whitney, D. E. "Historical Perspective and State of the Art in Robot Force Control," *Proceedings of the 1985 IEEE Conference on Robotics and Automation*, St. Louis, March 1985, pp. 262–269.

Will, P. M., and D. D. Grossman. "An Experimental System for Computer Controlled Mechanical Assembly," *IEEE Transactions on Computers*, Vol. C-24, No. 9, 1975, pp. 879–888.

Wu, C. H. "The Kinematic Error Model for the Design of Robot Manipulators," *Proceedings of the 1983 American Controls Conference*, San Francisco, June 1983.

Chapter 6

Artificial Intelligence— The Basics

T. M. Hancock, III
Private Consultant

1. Abstract

This chapter focuses on an overview of artificial intelligence, or AI. After an introduction and brief history of AI, it reviews topics such as heuristics, natural-language comprehension, memory organization, deduction, learning, search, and general problem solver, AI languages, and current and future AI applications.

2. Introduction

There is probably no other area of computer science that is more glamorous, well-known, and misunderstood than artificial intelligence. The average reader therefore will probably come to this chapter with a general idea of what artificial intelligence is and hopes to accomplish.

Artificial intelligence is becoming the area of computer science that is drawing more interest and relative funding than any other. More and more each day articles on AI appear in lay and professional magazines—even newspapers are covering the subject in greater detail. Movies and television shows feature the concepts of AI as integral parts of their themes. The common portrayals of AI today help alert all sections of society to the eventual benefits that will be reaped. A view of AI applications is being made available to everyone.

Granted, this view can range from high-technology toasters to a human-like system that enjoys chess and remarks that it has every confidence in the mission. But it is important to stress the real goal of AI research—that being to produce a machine that can think. More precisely put: "Artificial intelligence involves the study of mental processes through the use of computer models."

Models

One of the most commonly asked questions is: why use models to study or emulate intelligence? The answer is basic: Through the use of modeling techniques researchers can begin to understand the processes that are needed in an AI system. Thinking and reasoning capabilities are not as easy to understand as they may appear. They seem to be simple because everyone uses these abilities every day. Modeling permits a study of one part or the whole of an item or system in question. When NASA designed the space shuttle, they modeled the aerodynamic factors, software, flight performance, etc., separately. By modeling each area separately, they were able to produce a complete vehicle. The shuttle is too complex, and involves too many components, to be modeled in the required detail as a whole. The same is true of AI. In addition, thinking processes are not understood in sufficient detail to permit the straight coding of software. Modeling will permit researchers to gain insights into human intelligence and move forward toward elucidating a true machine intelligence.

Models are necessary to help us understand and map thinking processes. Artificial intelligence, despite a common belief, is NOT a science in itself; rather it is a merging of psychology and computer science. To investigate the basics of AI we must first study an area that is traditionally removed from computer science: the working of the human mind. By this is meant the function of the thinking process.

Automation and Expert Systems

As we have seen examples of what AI is, it is important to discuss what AI is not or what areas are similar to AI but not a part of it. The two most common associated and confused topics in AI are automation and expert systems. A clear definition of each follows:

Automation   A system that allows the repeated completion of tasks without human intervention.

Expert systems   A system or methodology that will control, adjust, or assist in a set task.

Examples of automation can be found in Japanese automobile factories, and examples of expert systems can be found in medical diagnosis programs and spacecraft systems. One common misunderstanding is confusing auto-mation with AI. The general public and some professionals not associated with AI will assume that because a robot (automated) system replaces a human worker, the application is therefore intelligent (i.e., the human worker is an intelligent creature, so the machine that replaces him or her is also intelligent). This is obviously a false conclusion. The human worker is usually not functioning in a capacity that is using 100% of available mental ability; unless intelligence is measured by the task level only and no other capability, it can be stated that a pseudointelligent application has been achieved, but not AI.

The Areas of AI

With the preceding definitions at hand, we are now ready to discuss the basics of AI. In this chapter we will investigate the following:

1. Problem-solving "heuristics."
2. Natural-language comprehension.
3. Memory organization.
4. Deduction.
5. Learning.
6. Search.
7. General problem solver.
8. Languages of AI.
9. Current AI applications.
10. Future AI applications.

There are several other areas involved in AI research (e.g., vision, automatic programming, robotics), but the ten listed above are some of the most important and represent the topics that will be addressed in this chapter.

The Current State of AI

It is important to note that despite all the attention and work being devoted to AI, it is still in a somewhat primitive state. To understand this, let us consider an example familiar to almost everyone, something taken for granted every day—talking—the ability to communicate ideas and concepts verbally. Then we will extrapolate a meaning of the data transmitted through mental processes. This simple action, diagrammed in Fig. 1, is not very well understood, that is, the particular functions and subfunctions of the process are not completely understood. Without this information the general structure of code begins to break down, and bridging is necessary to span the areas in code where data is missing. Therefore, it may be concluded that one cannot create code for a function unless the characteristics of the function are fairly well understood.

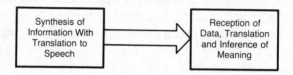

Fig. 1. The basic flow of oral communication.

In general, a problem such as this may be solved in the following steps.

1. Develop an understanding of the problem.
2. Determine the levels of knowledge lacking to produce a formula for the solution.
3. Investigate and produce an understanding of the required information.
4. Produce a model of the function.
5. Integrate data from the model into the overall problem.
6. Develop a new model of the problem-emulating task.
7. Utilize data from the model to develop a system for resolution of the problem.

If the example above of talking was broken down into relative AI applications, we could state it as follows: (*a*) information breakdown, (*b*) transmission, (*c*) natural-language filter or machine-readable translator, (*d*) input and utilization.

Today there have been several programs developed that produce acceptable models of some AI functions (e.g., heuristics, deduction). But even these models are handicapped by the current knowledge state. Information necessary to produce the model (i.e., refine its ability to work at a level that begins to emulate human intelligence) is yet to be achieved. This is a case of the data simply not being available to allow an adequate model to be produced. Even the best inference engine (if-then reasoning) is valid only 70% of the time.

It is important to note that while the topics in this chapter highlight particular functions, each function is interdependent to some degree, just as we are dependent on most mental functions when solving problems. Refer to Fig. 2.

The subject of artificial intelligence, because of its popularity, is a topic of considerable publication in the professional and popular press. Unfortunately because of this popularity, there is a large number of books and papers which contain massive errors, "popular folklore," and general misconceptions. The

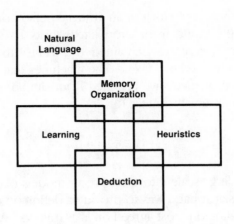

Fig. 2. The overlapping boxes demonstrate the interdependence of AI topics.

writer brings this to the reader's attention because it is his hope that the readers will become familiar enough with the true aspects of AI that they will be able to distinguish between data and drivel.

3. The History and Future of AI

Artificial-intelligence research for all practical purposes has been active for the last 30 years, with work and funding continuously escalating. See Fig. 3. At present almost every major university, business, and research laboratory is funding in-depth AI programs in some form.

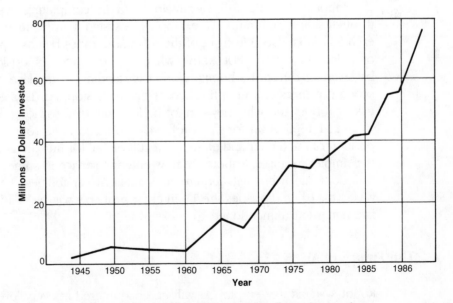

Fig. 3. Research funding of AI has been increasing.

Although the idea of an artificial person or entity is quite old, practical AI concepts range from dronelike robots to semi-intelligent machines. The long-term goal has remained the same—the production of an artificially intelligent machine. (*Note:* The machines that were designed to be endowed with intelligence have changed from simple robots to reasoning computers. The goal remains intact.)

Defining AI

When large-scale efforts to create models of intelligence began, one of the first tasks at hand was to provide a definition of what artificial intelligence is. The definition most agreed on is as follows: "Artificial intelligence is the study of human mental processes utilizing computer models for the understanding of mental functions and future application in computer science."

After the creation of and agreement on a definition, the next task was to develop a method for emulating intelligence. The method selected, as previously mentioned, was modeling.

AI and Robotics

Artificial intelligence is a subject that is simple to embrace but complicated to investigate and fully understand. Most people understand AI at the level of general applications (i.e., a popular view). One such popular view of AI is in conjunction with robotics. While this may be a natural meld of two different areas, the two fields are not interdependent but complementary.

Robotics to date is basically involved in completing repetitive tasks through simple programs. An example is a system that paints car fenders. As each fender is placed in front of the robot, the robot begins a preset pattern of painting. It does not know whether the fender is upside down or backwards or even if a human worker is standing in its place. It will simply proceed with its task until finished or manually stopped. This is an inherent risk of robots and why they cannot be left untended for long periods.

An AI application for this problem would allow the robot to check the position of the fender and either correct it or call for human assistance. Here is a simpler example. Robots are now entering service in some homes, but a true domestic robot will require substantial AI capabilities. The robot that waxes the cat and washes the TV in error probably will be heading toward a fate better left unmentioned.

The Future of AI

Robot systems that employ AI will be encountered at every level. Intelligent robot systems will fight in our wars and run parts of our industry. The applications of robotics in medicine for surgery and space exploration are incredible. There are plans in space exploration to produce systems that will analyze information on board and transmit to Earth this information in the form of data and conclusions.

In the first 20 years of the next century, any nation that wishes to compete within foreign markets will be forced to automate factories and equip these facilities with AI governing systems. Robot systems utilizing AI may not require total AI capabilities but may plug in one or more capabilities to complete their task. Some robot systems may not need a natural language or heuristic capabilities or machine vision. The ability to plug AI capabilities into generic robots, whether developed for space or production work in factories, will bring about a revolution in society similar to that created by the mass-production assembly lines of 80 years ago.

AI at Present

To date there have been several milestone programs—tools and techniques developed—such as LISP, memory and data base tools, and data deduction framework. Each of these has helped pave the way to a functioning AI system. While there have been many milestone systems to date, there has yet to be produced anything similar to what the public perceives as a true AI system. To date, computers do not have virtual reasoning capabilities and cannot learn as well as a very young child, but that day may not be too far away (10 to 20 years).

4. Heuristics

Simply put, heuristics is problem solving (i.e., problem resolution through the use of rules and definitions). Heuristics has also been called rules of thumb and trial-and-error methods. When involved in multiple decision making or working through to the best possible solution of a problem, this method is referred to as a heuristic search function. Heuristics is probably the closest that researchers have yet come to modeling human thinking processes; like us, a heuristic does not always get the answer right.

A Saturn V Moonshot Example

To illustrate this let us consider a statement and a problem: "The United States yesterday launched a Saturn V toward the moon." When the mind reads the above sentence, it first breaks it down into its basic structure utilizing known references held in memory to extrapolate an understanding. Let us now break this sentence down and assume that there is one area that is not understood.

New Data	Related Data
United States	Home/nation
Yesterday	Past
Launched	Sent
Saturn V	?
Moon	Satellite of earth

As one can see from the list, there is one area where we have no corresponding data: that being a Saturn V. Therefore, a problem has been identified for the heuristic system to solve. In the heuristic problem it will be necessary for the system to attempt to identify what a Saturn V is. To do this the system would access a second or external list of things that are launched toward the moon.

List of Things Launched to the Moon
Rockets   Satellites   Spacecraft   Humans

From this list the heuristic system may infer that a Saturn V is a human but it would also accept the possibility that a Saturn V could be one of the first three items listed. To solve this problem, the heuristic system would then need to check the definition of each item on its list. This is also referred to as a heuristic search function. Suppose the first three items were defined as follows.

1. Rockets—Machines used to transport items from the surface of the Earth.
2. Spacecraft—Systems which may or may not contain humans and which are sent into space by rockets.
3. Satellites—Craft which do not contain humans and which are sent to orbit a planetary body.

From these simple definitions the logical selection would be the first one from the list of definitions. But what if there had not been a logical choice available from the two levels the system utilized in this problem? Then the heuristic system would then begin to utilize a topic that will be addressed later on—deduction. An additional example of a heuristic problem is that of a Mars rover (MR-1).

A Mars Rover Example

Suppose that the United States has sent a rover to the surface of Mars. After landing, the rover runs through a simple program that gets it off its descent stage and reports to Earth that all is well. It starts to roam around the surface of Mars, investigating items of interest based on a predetermined list. After investigating a failed Soviet spacecraft, the rover finds itself within a meter of the edge of a very deep canyon. The scene could look like the one in Fig. 4.

Fig. 4. An artist's concept of two future Mars rovers scouting the surface. *(Courtesy NASA)*

With the time between communications between Earth and Mars possibly taking as long as one hour, it would not be very wise for the billion-dollar rover to sit on the unstable edge of a cliff, waiting for instructions from home. Therefore, here is a practical application for a heuristic system. On recognizing the problem and identifying the conditions involved, the rover would then begin a heuristic search.

Problem
The rover is positioned dangerously close to the edge of a cliff.

Possible Solutions
The following four options are available:
  1. Turn left

Turn right
Turn around
Back up

Therefore, as the rover is located within one meter of the edge, it is necessary to consult the definition of each option.

1. Turn left: when rover is at least $2N$ meters from hazard.
2. Turn right: when rover is at least $2N$ meters from hazard.
3. Turn around: when a sufficient arc of $5N$ meters from hazard is available.
4. Back up: back up in reverse of last direction traveled until hazard is cleared by $5N$ meters, then proceed to next assignment.

From these four simple definitions, the logical choice is obviously option 4. For if the rover turns left or right, it will then be parallel to the edge and have only increased the hazard. It if attempts to turn around, it will not clear the edge and will fall into the canyon. Only option 4 permits the rover to clear the hazard and then proceed with its mission.

Three Basic Areas of Heuristics

Heuristics can be divided into three basic areas: (1) heuristic search functions, (2) heuristic methods, and (3) heuristic evaluation functions.

Heuristic methods basically are the general embodiment of problem solving—"the rule of thumb." What method or path should be followed to solve a problem? *Heuristic search functions,* such as are diagrammed in Fig. 5, deal with methodology used for searching preset data (i.e., a data base for appropriate information to deal with a problem). *Heuristic evaluation functions* are a bit more ambiguous. These evaluation functions are typically based on heuristics. In them, a basic problem structure known as solution logic is used as a guide, but this type of an aid cannot be exact; therefore, as stated in the beginning of this section, heuristics, like humans, will not always obtain the right answer. Both of these functions occur in the examples previously given of a heuristics system.

5. Natural-Language Comprehension

Natural-language comprehension is one of the most interesting parts of AI research as the natural language front will permit the use of common English in computer science applications. The basic definition of natural-language comprehension (NLC) is "the translation of natural language into a data-base

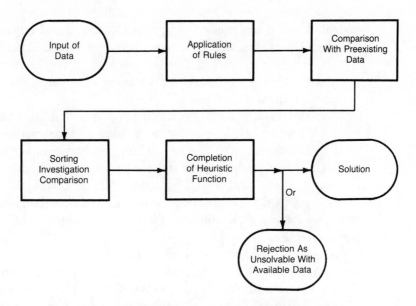

**Fig. 5. Heuristic search function ([Charniak and
McDermott 1985], pp. 456–457).**

query language." More simply put, it is running common language through a
filter that equates relative meaning. See Fig. 6.

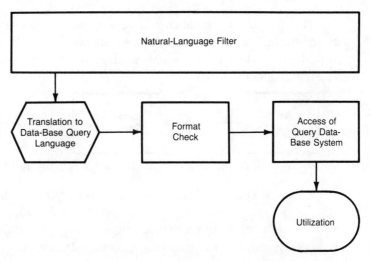

Fig. 6. Natural-language/AI translation.

This is no simple task as a common language like English is continuously
evolving and has many illogical meanings. (Remember when saying that
someone was "bad" meant that he or she is good? Coding that along with the
word's traditional meaning is very difficult.) There have been several bench-

mark programs created to date, for example, the Lunar data-base query system, medical diagnostics programs (Mindus), and engineering aids. An NLC data-base query system analyzes language and, as stated, interprets it to a machine-readable format. The critical parts of NLC systems are (*a*) NLC front ends (filters), (*b*) data dictionaries, (*c*) search functions, and (*d*) comparison queues.

Natural-language comprehension programs that are utilized in concert with heuristic and deduction functions have a more user-friendly front end than those which aren't so utilized. There are, however, as with the rest of AI research, several problems that still need to be resolved, such as the use of the connectives "and" and "or." What types of things do they join together? How are the problems of improper usage to be solved? These are but two examples of the problems still faced in the research of natural-language comprehension.

A natural-language front end permits the use of common English in a structured format for the interpretation of information. A structured format does not mean a structure similar to BASIC, but rather a more structured form of speech—one that removes unnecessary parts. For example:

Natural Language		Machine-Interpreted Language
How many chips does it	:	Number chips produce domestic
take to construct a	:	robot.
household robot?	:	

The format shown above is very basic and illustrates only a simple restructuring and deletion of data. A data-base query language filter (Fig. 7) would break down the natural-language statement similar to the method illustrated above.

Fig. 7. Action of data-base query language filter.

A natural language front end can be referred to as the protocol for the system, both input and output. Information leaving or questions asked would be formatted in a natural language. Fig. 8 shows an example of the structured flow of data from query data base language through the filter and out to the user in a natural-language format.

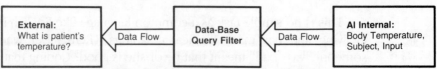

Fig. 8. The flow of data from query data-base to user.

Natural-language comprehension is in a primitive state at this point. There are examples that emulate NLC functions, but this is done through hard code methodology. Most of the programs available to date operate in a clumsy fashion and are structured like a BASIC programming language. A very good example of this is the automatic translation programs used to produce an English-readable version of Soviet and other foreign documents. The documents produced are 50% to 60% readable in a natural flowing form. But a large amount of information is scrambled. In some instances words cannot be translated and are spelled out phonetically. (Reading an automatically translated Soviet technical paper on high-energy lasers would be mind-bending to someone who did not know a little Russian.) Although this represents an example of hard coding to emulate an NLC-like capability, there is no doubt that soon (in 5 to 15 years) NLC capabilities will be developed to the point that it will be difficult to distinguish machine-produced material from a human's. Further details are given in Charniak and McDermott [1985], p. 2.

6. Memory Organization

Memory organization is one of the most important regions in artificial intelligence. The most agreed-on definition of memory organization is "the structure of information based on a set data-base methodology." Basically, memory organization is the structure of information based on facts. There are several techniques developed that permit sequential rule based memory organization. One method of organization divides data into active and inactive lists. With this method the active list holds most of the pertinent data, while the inactive list acts as an archive.

Other techniques involve indexing, sequencing, discrimination nets, scripts, sequence matching and associated networks. *Indexing* refers to the logical arrangement of data, *sequencing* refers to a preset group of instructions that will assist in the completion of tasks, and *discrimination nets* refers to small deduction methods used in a packaged format and set at required places in the code.

The basic premise in memory organization is that some type of data structure be available and that newly acquired information be broken down, analyzed, and sorted to the appropriate files. When scripts are used, events basically are broken down into a preset order. A script is just as it appears: a list of actions that are carried out in a sequence to produce a result. For example, the action of starting a car can be broken down as follows:

1. Insert key into starter.
2. Turn key.
3. After starting engine, select gear.

4. Apply gas to produce motion.

5*a*. Car moves—positive result.

5*b*. Car does not move—negative result.

This is a very basic example of a script, but it illustrates the organizational flow found in scripts. In this example the script has two variables, 5*a* and 5*b*. These script variables are what permits the utilization and organization of data, this data being one of the predetermined script variables.

Sequence matching is also a simple memory technique. In the use of sequence matching, data is broken down by section. Then a search is made of memory to identify any similar patterns or sequences. Patterns that can be matched or associated are stored together. New patterns are entered as new data and will be new memory.

Memory organization requires definitions and rules. These rules depend on the particular memory organization method that is used. The rules required can also be defined as parameters. For example, when a sequence-matching methodology is used, rules or definitions must be used for each sequence in comparison. This is called setting the parameters of each sequence. For example, find a corresponding sequence if possible for "w, e, t, y, g."

New Data: w, e, t, y, g.

Current sequences stored in memory:

1. w, s, d, f, g, t
2. e, r, t, y, u
3. p, l, o, k, i
4. w, e, t, y, f
5. w, r, t, y, g

Of these five sequences, two sequences contain a large number of the corresponding letters, but neither one is a complete match. However, between 4. w, e, t, y, f and 5. w, r, t, y, g it is clear that number 4 continues the sequence farther unbroken than number 5 even though each is off by one letter. Therefore, a rule is needed to distinguish whether a match occurs when four out of five letters appear or when the sequence is unbroken for the maximum number of letters.

To summarize, memory organization is the structure of data and this organization depends on the rules and methodology in force. For further discussion of these matters see Charniak and McDermott [1985], pp. 393, 630, and 634.

7. Deduction

Deduction has been called one of the most "fun" areas of AI research. Deduction by definition is the inference of facts from associated sources of information. See Fig. 9.

To better illustrate this, let us consider the following. A man goes to a toy store and purchases $100 in model kits, $25 in games, and $50 in stuffed animals. There are several logical deductions that can be made. The first is that the toys the man prefers most are model kits. This deduction is based on the amount purchased. There are several other conclusions that can be reached, however, each depending on the rules in effect at that time.

An example of how inference is used is deduction. Sam came home from college today. He came by plane. From this statement it can be deduced that Sam flew home. Because airplanes fly and because Sam came home by plane, one can deduce that Sam flew home. Deduction depends on beliefs. This process of deduction has been referred to as an *inference engine*.

The inference engine obtains its data or beliefs from its data base. By this it is meant an AI system involved in deduction like a human can only infer information (data) based on past experiences or stored information. In the last example it was not said that Sam flew. But it could be deduced or inferred that Sam did fly because when aircraft are used in transportation they are flown.

There are two types of inference: object and assertion. Object inference relies on *facts* (e.g., I know it's a ball, balls are round). Assertion is based on *supposition* (e.g., I believe this to be true because the evidence indicates such). An inference engine makes a distinction between the two. In the example given of Sam coming home from school, the inference engine would not need an assertion, but would use an object inference. The object inference is correct because it is known that planes fly and Sam came home by plane. An inference engine would be found between the program and the data base.

Before one can make a deduction, the definition of the data must be qualified. If, for example, people are asked to define a computer, their definitions could range from calculators to supercomputers. Not all computers are equal. So one must be careful in making the definition. A ball is round, but so is the Earth; and planets are not balls though both are round.

This then leads to the next level, "search." How do you search for the proper definition of an item and from this develop and understand an assertion? The inference engine would have to access the data base in a fashion that will permit a comparison of facts (objective) or assumed truths (assertive). Deduction, which is inference of facts from related information, requires a rule-based organization; this is found through the use of logic.

When a deduction or heuristic solution is obtained, it is checked by logic functions whether they are imbedded in the software or as part of any particular AI function. Logic in AI acts as the absolute boundary for a function. If the system crosses this line regardless of deduction, inference, or heuristic solution, there is a problem. Logic in relation to deduction can be referred to as the set of rules for making deductions. If all lions are cats, then all house cats are lions? (Logically, no.) Deduction is one of the most cumbersome of AI processes, but it is by far the most fun to explore. Charniak and McDermott [1985] touch on this subject on pp. 14 and 360.

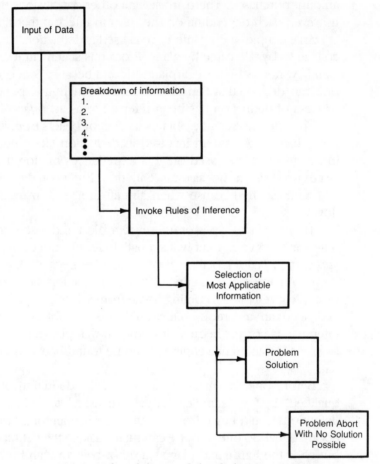

Fig. 9. AI breakdown of the deductive process.

8. Learning

Learning is the heart of AI and can be broken down into several sections: conceptual learning, inductive learning, adaptive learning, pattern classification, matching and recognition of analogies. Machine learning is currently in a fairly primitive state. Although there has been good progress in regard to heuristics and deduction, only limited success has been found in modeling learning. The basic definition of learning is "the acquisition of information in such a manner that permits its use for the resolution of future problems." Simply put, it is gaining wisdom.

The following is an example of a learning application. Suppose the Mars rover is cruising over the plains of Mars and discovers a large boulder field. The field is such that it cannot be directly traversed, so the rover must find its way through by trial and error. The rover attempts several times to cross the field through one path or another that it infers to be the best possibility. With time the rover finds a correct path and saves this information for future use (Fig. 10). This example exhibits some of the basic principles of learning.

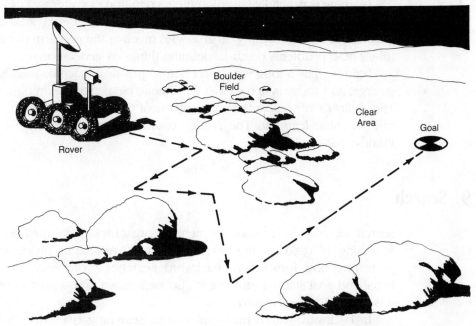

Fig. 10. The rover has to find a path to its goal.

First, similar tasks are usually done the same way unless conditions indicate that the method must be modified to produce a result. Second, actions are often taken in a trial-and-error format. Third, learning can take place in two ways: (1) success and (2) failure. The learning through success obviously occurred when the rover found a path through the boulder field. The learning through failure was equally important in that it provided data on paths that would not succeed. It is as important to learn that something does not work as it is to find out whether it does.

Machine learning has more possible representations and unproved theorems than any other area of computer science. Consequently, there is greater chance of error or insight, depending on one's point of view. In the example of the Mars rover, there are two types of learning in use: (1) trial and error, and (2) inductive reasoning. To understand this consider the following. Before the rover would attempt to cross the field, it would infer the most successful possibility. Trial and error came into play when the rover began to move through the field. This represents a learning flow.

Learning flow in heuristics involves problem identification and breakdown. In learning, extraneous data is removed from information needed for the resolution of the problem. This is referred to as a *decluttering technique*.

In learning there is no concept of good or bad data, only information that will or will not assist in problem resolution. Learning involves the assimilation of information into a format that permits a modification of the current state. By modification is meant the addition of new information.

Learning is primarily based on the recognition of patterns. These patterns are relative to past experiences, and may be considered analogies. One problem in basing learning on analogies involves the problems of the if-then rule. These problems occur in defining things as general or specialized.

Learning has a long way to go before practical machine intelligence will emerge, and today systems exist that mimic elementary learning techniques. The ability to mimic learning as in a game of tic-tac-toe is the first step toward true machine learning. The reader could profitably consult Winston and Prendergast [1984].

9. Search

Search techniques are used in memory organization and problem solving. Searching is used as the essential part of reasoning processes and is performed both forward and backward. Searches in problem solving involve initial and goal states. Searching is also performed in memory, in which case it is called a *memory search*.

In backward-search problem solving, searching is used in conjunction with guessing. In search a rule is selected for use on a problem. If the rule doesn't lead to a solution, then the steps taken in conjunction with the rule are deleted. Eventually the system will either find the appropriate rule or exhaust all possibilities. Search relies on problems broken down into two components—initial and the goal state.

The initial state describes conditions as given. The goal state implies the resolution of a problem or the development of rules to solve the problem. As an example, the initial state could be that of five trains ready to leave a station at the same time using only three tracks. The goal state would involve either developing the rules to complete this task or the resolution of the problem as a whole.

In memory searching, pattern or event similarities are investigated after the determination of the goal state. In the example of the general problem solver to be discussed in the following section, a memory search is made through a predetermined list looking for similarities of the newly discovered problem.

An additional area of search involves goal trees. Goal trees are used as a controlled method for search. Each branch of a goal tree is responsible for solving subfunctions necessary for the resolution of the whole problem (in all equations each part must be solved before the problem can progress toward solution). Goal trees are found in many areas of AI. Natural-language comprehension, deduction, and learning all utilize goal trees as search functions.

A common example of a search function is found in a tic-tac-toe game. Search is done both forward (guessing) and backward (past patterns). The game also uses goal trees as its map to lead to a solution. In search, forward is thought of as how to get to the new level, and backward as how to undo the current state. An important part of search is not to repeat sequences already attempted.

When the Mars rover was attempting to navigate a field of boulders, it used search trees to infer the most promising path. By learning whether the path was successful or not, the rover did not need to repeat the pattern. Further details are available in Charniak and McDermott [1985], pp. 257, 262, 305, 502, 510, and 615.

10. General Problem Solver

As a working example of a general problem solver a hypothetical AI system will be used that employs some of the different topics previously addressed.

It is the 35th day that NASA's Mars rover has been roaming the Martian surface. While performing its normal investigations, the rover discovers an obviously unique geological feature. As this is new to the rover, it will interpret its find as a problem. See Fig. 11. It will first begin a deductive search of a predetermined list (PDL) of interesting items to search for. During its deductive search, it compares information obtained from its discovery with definitions and conditions contained in the PDL. This list permits a step-by-step evaluation of the problem. This evaluation is performed through the use of memory organization techniques. The unique discovery does not correspond directly to any item or definition obtained through memory organization or the PDL. Therefore, an acceptable deduction cannot be produced. The discovery has now become a heuristic problem. Following the rules involved in heuristics, the rover begins to acquire all relative data about the discovery and breaks this information down into a simple list as in Chart 1.

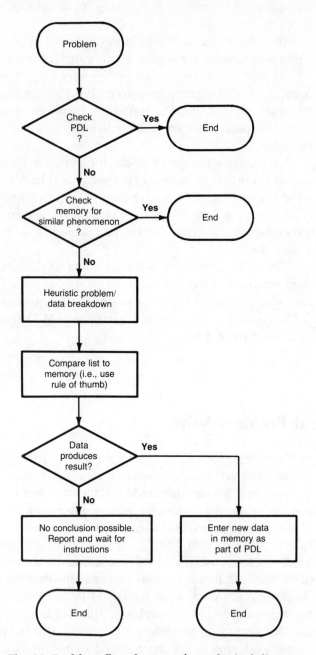

Fig. 11. Problem flow for rover's geological discovery.

Chart 1. Rover's Data About New Discovery

New Data Regarding Discovery	Possible Parallel
1. High concentrations of water vapor	Liquid or solid water
2. Evidence recent erosion	Water, wind or volcanic erosion
3. Above-normal subsurface temperature	Volcanic, thermal activity
4. New phenomenon	Never encountered by current or past missions
5. Large water concentrations	Subsurface moisture seepage, running water on surface, rapid condensation of vapor

Utilizing a rule of thumb, one can conclude that subsurface water is the most logical source of the water vapor in this area. With volcanic activity providing the needed temperature to produce liquid water on the surface and therefore surface erosion, one can also conclude that the temperature varies over time as there appears to be a cycle of erosion and frost.

Utilizing heuristic search techniques and also applying the rules of deduction, a common thread has been found and the most likely answer developed. Since the cause and the location of the discovery have now been determined, the rover has learned a new item of interest and will add this information to its list. The heuristics procedure has provided a new rover and can apply its newly learned information to future problems.

11. AI Languages

One area of artificial intelligence that does not seem to get much attention when the basics of AI are discussed is the languages the models are produced in—simply put, what computer languages to use in developing AI systems.

LISP

The most common AI language used is LISP (*list p*rocessing language). LISP utilizes symbols rather than numbers (LISP is a symbolic language). It is one of the most evolving languages in computer science. Its speed and ability to crunch information in a symbolic format makes it one of the best languages for use in AI applications. Currently the majority of AI programs are written in

LISP or a similar symbolic language. Examples are learning, natural-language comprehension (interface), expert systems problem solvers, and speech and vision experiment systems.

LISP is one of the easiest programming languages to learn. Its syntax is simple, and both LISP procedures (e.g., add, subtract) and data use the same format. LISP is divided into common and different adapted versions. As stated, LISP procedures and data are created out of a similar format: symbolic expression. In LISP a predicated argument is used to determine true or false conditions, and the words "and," "or," and "not" are used as logical expressions. LISP is one of the first languages that allow procedure names to be used as arguments.

LISP is the most well known and widely used language for AI but it is not the only one. Fortran, Assembler, Pascal, APL, and AL are some of the other languages in use to some degree in artificial intelligence. But there is another language that is now receiving a large amount of attention, as it will probably be the next major AI language; that language is Ada.

Ada

Ada is a high-level programming language developed for the Department of Defense. It is based on Pascal and is a compartmentalized language that allows "canned software" (the ability to reuse sections of code in other programs).

Ada was developed initially for embedded systems like missile guidance, and aircraft control, and as the sole major language of the four military services. Ada is named after the Countess of Lovelace because she was credited for being the world's first programmer. To an extent Ada is being thrust into the AI arena, where LISP has been the language of choice.

Almost every military system is required to utilize Ada, and NASA has announced that Ada will be the language used on the U.S. space station and all further space probes after 1994, starting with the first Mariner Mark II missions.

The decision to use Ada on the space station alone will place this language at the forefront of AI research. The U.S. Congress has tried to legislate that AI and expert systems are to be part of space station design. Even now several companies in addition to NASA field centers are conducting applications research in AI and expert systems with Ada. Some of the most promising work to date is being done by McDonnell-Douglas Astronautics Company, where an effort is underway to produce an expert knowledge-based architecture for space station control.

The task environment envisioned for the space station will include local-area networks, network interface, interface devices, mass-memory management, and display/control devices. This architecture is similar to the main system governor designed for automated factory control. The decision to use Ada marks the first time an application language was chosen before the application was designed.

Ada will most probably become one of the basics of AI as there is no doubt that Ada or a derivative of it will be one of the principal civilian and military languages used in AI and expert systems applications.

The history of Ada is unique in that it has a traceable evolution. Ada had three basic ancestors: Strawman in 1975, Woodman in 1976, and Tinman in late 1976. In 1979 the final version of Ada was completed and the Department of Defense announced that the new language would be named in honor of Augusta Ada Byron, the Countess of Lovelace (1815–1852). The language initially developed by CII Honeywell was known as Green, and during the final competition in 1978–1979 was one of four versions of Ada under consideration. The other languages were Brown, Red, and Blue.

Ada is the result of an idea to produce a common, flexible, adaptable, and long-life language for applications. This usage will eliminate the need for multilingual computer programmers and analysts.

Ada is unique to AI research or computer science as a whole because it is the first language designed for generic functions and portability. Artificial intelligence applications for the station using Ada will include operations management, fault protection, system health checks, and normal operations. With Ada comes the ability to produce a high-quality, general-purpose Ada inference engine. This ability will permit a lower cost and a more adaptable design.

To date there is no generic AI system or inference engine. But a language that allows one to modularly remove or add code as needed will reduce cost and allow massive applications. This ability alone makes Ada attractive for both civilian and military programs. An Ada inference engine or similar AI system will be able to evolve easily and on sight during the course of its life. It will allow the space station to update its AI functions in orbit during normal operation by simply uplinking new software or by receiving a disk from the next shuttle flight. This capability will cut down on operations and development costs as well as development and test times [Barnes 1983].

In Ada, as in Pascal, the language uses type and data declarations broken into four types: (1) enumeration types, (2) array types, (3) record types, and (4) pointer types. Ada and Pascal also use data declarations broken down as constants, scalars, arrays, records, and pointers. Expressions and exception handling of data are perhaps the main differences between Ada and Pascal.

As we have now discussed the two principal languages, both current (LISP) and future (Ada), of AI modeling as well as possible applications, we will now investigate a theoretical generic AI model's structure. The principal component common to all AI systems is an inference engine.

Components of an AI System

An inference engine can best be described as a gatekeeper or the ability to add or remove beliefs or data according to what is required for the solution of a problem. See Fig. 12. The second required part of an AI system is a data base, and the third is a data-base search function. A possible fourth area will be some sort of a natural-language filter also known as a *data entry translator.* Learning and deduction are also possible, but are not always required as separate functions and may be resident as parts of an inference engine.

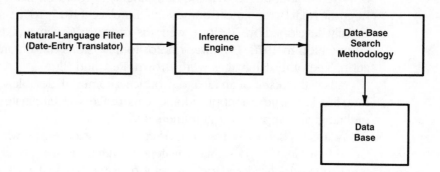

Fig. 12. AI system components.

The diagram of Fig. 13 is a crude example but gives an indication of the relationship between basic AI components. The AI languages LISP, Ada, etc., represent the stuff that future machine intelligence will be based on. The form of machine intelligence will be based in part on the methods discussed earlier and on the whole by the languages our systems are produced in.

12. Current AI Applications

In this section, we will look at four current applications of AI: the Viking Mars landers, the AEGIS weapons system, the space shuttle, and the U.S. space station.

The Viking Mars Landers

One of the first applications of AI in planetary exploration was the Viking Mars landers. They were the first planetary spacecraft to utilize basic AI techniques and they were able to act autonomously if contact with Earth was broken. These two robot stations, which were sent to Mars in 1976, had the ability to cope with certain conditions that could occur during the course of normal activity. Examples are problem resolution of sample acquisition, fault diagnosis (while the lander would take no action of its own regarding critical functions, it would collect and break down all relative data), and communications.

The Viking lander had the capability of running by itself and solving minor problems over long periods. When the last lander (Viking 1) was lost, it had been running in pseudoautonomous routine for two years, reporting to Earth once a week with pictures, weather, and related information. During the descent of Viking 2 toward Mars a failure of the orbiter/lander separation system occurred, and all contact was lost. The lander had to take its own corrective action—setting the lander aeroshield to the proper angle, adjusting for speed, following the proper sequence of the landing procedure, and, after landing, locating its orbiter. See Fig. 13. The problem in separation created such variables that without pseudo-AI applications the lander probably would not have survived atmospheric entry.

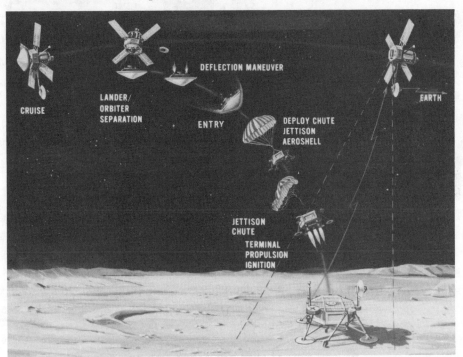

Fig. 13. An artist's conception of the landing sequence used by the Viking landers. *(Courtesy NASA)*

Viking, shown in Fig. 14, could not think for itself; no AI systems currently can, nor can they even draw conclusions from inference. Nonetheless, Viking was important. Its application of AI was very basic, but it was a start [French 1977].

Fig. 14. An engineering model of NASA's Viking lander. *(Courtesy NASA)*

The AEGIS Weapons System

A second and currently active example of AI applications is the U.S. Navy AEGIS weapons system. The AEGIS system is used on *Ticonderoga*-class heavy cruisers. See Fig. 15. The AEGIS system has the ability to locate over 300 individual targets, identify them, determine how they were launched, identify their probable targets, launch its full complement of 96 missiles in 3 minutes, and provide guidance and constant updates to destroy the aggressive systems. The purpose of AEGIS is to provide fleet defense for aircraft carrier battle groups.

Its applications of AI are in part based on its use of heuristics and scripts found as a memory organization technique and deduction. The AEGIS system is the first autonomous weapons system. With it, the only decisions that humans are required to make are (1) to engage the system or (2) interrupt operations.

Human operators could not classify, track, and destroy this large number of enemy systems fast enough to survive. The AEGIS system represents one of

Fig. 15. The U.S.S. *Ticonderoga* carries the AEGIS weapons system.
(Courtesy U.S. Navy)

the first true applications of AI as it performs its task as a separate machine-intelligence operation. To give an analogy, if there were a robot available to pick corn in the field, it would not just select an ear of a particular size, but would be able to determine if the corn was ripe, the average number of ripe ears per plant, how sweet the corn is, and what, if any, insect or disease contamination the corn may have.

The Space Shuttle

A third example of AI applications is found in the space shuttle (Fig. 16). Although the shuttle's utilization of AI is far more basic than the AEGIS system, it is the first application to a peopled spacecraft. The shuttle is too complex to be flown manually, so most functions from ascent to landing are governed by computer. The shuttle uses a voting hierarchy that requires four separate computer systems and one spare to analyze and vote on each action. The system utilized for a space shuttle general-purpose computer is a modified IBM AP-101. If there is a dissenting vote, the health of each system is checked and a full diagnosis is made of the activity because most of the shuttle's software is based on mid-70s technology and methodology. Through this voting hierarchy and a recently developed microwave landing system the shuttle is capable of landing itself from orbit [NASA 1981].

U.S. Space Station

Other near-term AI applications will be control systems, or perhaps the most significant application of AI in the short term will be the permanent U.S. space station. The station is set to be operational in the early 1990s. It will make extensive use of AI during the course of its operational life. Artificial intelligence systems will control life support, station keeping, communications between satellites and platforms, factory production, communications between satellites and even running the station untended for long periods.

Fig. 16. United States space shuttle. *(Courtesy NASA)*

In short, the first true civilian application of machine intelligence may be found on the station. The basic design of the station will consist of four manned modules (45 to 50 feet long), one logistics module, multiple docking ports and air locks, one or two handers for satellites and orbital transfer vehicles, repair facilities, platforms, and robot systems used in construction and repair. This description shows how complex the environment will be for an AI system. The AI systems on the station will be continuously evolving with the state of knowledge advances.

The environment described above for the station will become even more complex as future human-supporting modules and remote platforms are added.

An association of independent AI systems may develop with the construction of different mission modules by Japan and Europe. A materials processing facility and a bioscience lab may not require the same capabilities from an AI system. This will produce a network of independent AI systems working in conjunction with space station governor systems. See Fig. 17. This example illustrates the basic structure of a combined AI system using independent modules. This association of AI systems may pose interesting problems. What type of networking should be utilized? What type of hierarchical system should be set up? Which system has priority for power or other resources?

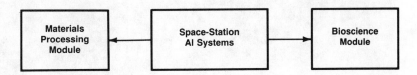

Fig. 17. Space-station AI systems must operate dissimilar facilities.

There probably will not be an AI system as complex as that described above for the station within the next 10 to 15 years. Other near-term applications of AI for the station involve generic robots that will assist the station's crew in construction and normal operations. See Fig. 18. Television-operated systems will allow astronaut crews to repair systems without venturing from the station; orbital transfer vehicles will replace and retrieve satellites in Earth orbit.

The AI applications for these systems will be similar to some found in Earth-based industries. These systems will need the ability to run untended, solve basic problems, and learn as they function.

13. Future AI Applications

The future application of AI to everyday life, industry, defense, space exploration, and medicine is a topic that can fill volumes. The first AI applications will be broken down into categories, each depending on the nature of the task (Chart 2). By this it is meant each AI capable system will be endowed with only the capabilities required to complete its task. This approach will permit a wider range of AI application utilization.

**Fig. 18. An artist's drawing of generic space robots
assisting in the construction and maintenance of the
first U.S. space station.** *(Courtesy McDonnell-Douglas Astronautics Co.)*

Chart 2. Categories of AI Applications

Category	Capability
Generic robot	Varies depending on task
Space station	Total capability
Space probe	Varies but can be total

A generic robot found in a factory may not need learning or a natural language front end, but a space station may require as great a capability as can be provided. The end product may be a basic generic robot system fitted with hardware that would vary depending on its particular task, and it could have AI capabilities "plugged in" to its general processing computer. Fig. 12 is a basic diagram of a generic AI system. With a generic AI system that is cannable (able to be based on a common inference engine and an advanced general processor) applications will be broad based. With the proper design almost every area of life will be enhanced.

Domestic Robots

To give a better impression of possible future AI applications let us consider three scenarios detailing their use. First let's consider an application close to home, at least the home of the future. Domestic robots of the type that are popularly envisioned will require extensive capabilities, vision, a natural-language front end, and learning, reasoning, and heuristic capabilities. To appreciate this, consider the environment a domestic robot would be required to function in. Picking up things on the floor, vacuuming, washing, or doing the dishes—each function is admittedly somewhat repetitive but the condition will not always be the same (objects will not always be in the same place) and new objects need to be identified, classified, and determined as to required care. Granted, at first this sounds like a relatively simple application. But under the surface the subfunctions, extremes, and other related conditions provide problems equivalent to an AI system operating in battle (including fighting off the more aggressive children in some households).

Farming Systems

The second example is on a farm in Iowa where an AI system is functioning as part of an automated harvesting and care system. The AI system is busy checking the soil pH, scanning for insects, checking the condition of the crop, and regulating water flow. In addition the system checks and controls problems. This example of an AI system is slightly more complex than a simple robot. It utilizes multiple drones, preplaced sensors, expert systems, and a central AI governor. See Fig. 19. This form of automated farming may never show up on a family farm, but this type of application can be widespread in corporate farming and large-scale harvesting.

Medical Systems

The third example is in a hospital where an AI system is performing simple surgery, the removal of a bullet. With a CAT scanning system, 3-D mapping, and the proper monitoring and control equipment, a robot surgeon could control the anesthetic, plasma and any other function or object required. Artificial intelligence systems of this type may be somewhat commonplace in the midpart of the next century. This type of AI system is far in the future but illustrates a significant type of benefit.

The General Outlook

In 20 years the reader may be hard put to find an area of his or her life that is not influenced by AI applications. Robotics will have a firm role in battles, and simple surgical procedures will be performed with AI systems. There will be automated aircraft no longer having a need for the pilot or copilot to intervene or take action unless a critical condition warrants it. Telephone and all other communication systems will be automated. The simplest way to extrapolate the future applications of AI is to look around and try to find something that could *not* benefit from some type of AI application.

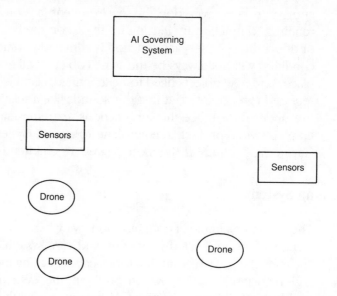

Fig. 19. Possible physical layout of an automated farming system.

14. Conclusion

The architecture of the human mind is so complex that a society that is now exploring the outer regions of the solar system is just beginning to understand the processes that allow these and all other activities to take place. Through the use of models the first systems that will emulate human intelligence will be developed.

Artificial intelligence can best be compared to early aviation: It is a bit further along than a Wright brothers flyer but not as advanced as a DC-3. As in early aviation, the most rudimentary principles and methods must be found to attain the chosen goals. In 20 years AI systems may be developing most of the software in use—controlling factories, transportation systems, and even working in construction and farming. If civilization is fortunate, many of the discoveries of tomorrow will be made by AI machines. Artificial intelligence systems may educate our children and diagnose and cure our diseases. The applications of AI are boundless, just as in the beginning of aviation. Today we learn to fly; tomorrow we will learn how to make flight work for us.

15. References

Barnes, J. G. *Programming in Ada*, New York: Addison-Wesley Publishing Co., 1983.

Charniak, E., and D. McDermott. *Introduction to Artificial Intelligence*, New York: Addison-Wesley Publishing Co., 1985.

French, B. *Viking Mission to Mars*, Washington NASA Government Printing Office, 1977.

NASA. *Space Shuttle*, Washington: NASA Government Printing Office, 1981.

Winston, P. H., and K. A. Prendergast. *The AI Business*, Cambridge, Mass.: The MIT Press, 1984, pp. 1, 249, 252, 290.

Chapter 7

Artificial Intelligence in Manufacturing

S. Patrick
Illinois State Government

1. Abstract

Artificial intelligence will play an ever-increasing role in the future of robot units in flexible manufacturing systems. This chapter reviews artificial intelligence (AI) with regard to appropriate applications and specifically the role of the expert system (or ES).

Factory applications of AI are also discussed. The factory scenario covers the interactive role of combined technologies such as machine vision, sensor technology, quality control, and cost effectiveness. Also reviewed are significant applications of AI/ES by leading manufacturers such as Ford Motor Company and Phillips. Next, decision-support systems are treated, with seven different types described. Finally, the probable future of AI/ES is envisioned.

2. Introduction

Artificial intelligence? No! What the economy needs is real intelligence. As we embark into the 21st Century, the world is faced with a new set of economic problems which are hauntingly familiar to the ones we have faced in this century. In order to compete effectively in the world marketplace, labor costs must be minimized. This is especially difficult when one compares "industrialized" nations. How can these latter nations compete effectively without decreasing the standard of living which their populaces enjoy? The answer is productivity. All of these countries, most specifically the United States, must maximize productivity throughout their markets in order to maintain the economic advantages which they have attained through the evolution of the Industrial Revolution.

Such increased productivity must be attained by improving each worker's efficiency and ultimately his or her daily output. To do this, labor must take advantage of the techniques developed by the most efficient industries; the most productive technicians, professionals, and researchers; and the optimal procedures to get a job done.

Given this as a goal, what is the mechanism to implement the objectives necessary to attain the goal of maximizing American productivity? A mechanism is needed by which experience, intuition, and knowledge can be shared so that each worker can be potentially as effective as any other worker. Artificial intelligence is such a mechanism.

3. Manufacturing

Before we explore how to develop artificial intelligence (AI) applications, we will discuss potential AI applications in the manufacturing arena. One of the first problems for which AI can be utilized is repair work. Heavy equipment, specialized machinery, conveyor systems, furnaces, etc., do not break down often, but they eventually do break down, resulting in lost productivity (which means lost "money") until they are fixed. Usually, the frequency of breakdown is such that there is little opportunity to gain local expertise in their repair. Thus, equipment operators must wait for an expert, or try vainly to find the glitch and remedy it before the expert arrives.

With a resident AI system, or more specifically an "expert system," which is a piece of software residing in a computer, the repair technicians have the opportunity to consult with an "expert" who can give them ideas as to what approaches can be taken to get the equipment fixed (Fig. 1). The software will allow the technician to describe the symptoms and then ask for assistance. It will suggest a procedure or test to be conducted and use the result to give the technician more insight into the problem.

The technician, in effect, becomes an expert in the repair of the equipment because of this software assistance. This results in less "down time," which means less lost output. Optimally, the technician will have been guided through the repair procedures with visual assistance in the form of diagrams and pictures to enhance his or her ability to locate and resolve the

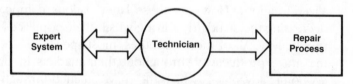

Fig. 1. Expert system for equipment repair.

problem. Is this really any different from using a repair manual? Of course it is! The technician is able to converse, albeit through typing (unless a voice interface is provided) with the software system and interact with the process. If the technician does not understand why a test is requested, or why a result is indicated, he or she can question the software as to the logic that was exercised to reach the point in question.

Granted, AI can help repair equipment in the factory. But what else can it do in a manufacturing environment? Let's consider what a manufacturing facility does. In its simplest representation, a factory has input (raw materials, parts, etc.); it transforms (shaping, cutting, molding) this input; it creates an output (TVs, ingots, computers, appliances, and the like).

4. Expert Systems

Until we can pursue a better understanding of what AI is, let us assume that AI is that combination of software and hardware that can allow a "machine" to manifest those faculties that we call knowledge, reasoning, induction, language, vision, and controlled movement of appendages (which we can call robotics). Additionally, we will call the knowledge/reasoning/induction/language capability an *expert system*. The expert system (ES) has these components: a knowledge base, an "expert" interpreter of this base, and the ability to communicate the interpretation, i.e., a user interface (Fig. 2).

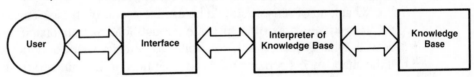

Fig. 2. Components of an expert system.

Let's consider a factory that makes intelligent controllers. The latter must have a case, keyboard (or some input device), a display (or output mechanism), a power supply, and a circuit board with electronic components (Fig. 3). To make the case, the factory needs to have plastic injection-mold facilities and the ability to trim excess to form the finished case. It would be great if the amount of trimming could be minimized, because less plastic would be wasted (Fig. 4).

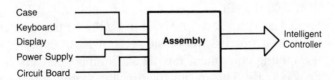

Fig. 3. Assembly process for intelligent controllers.

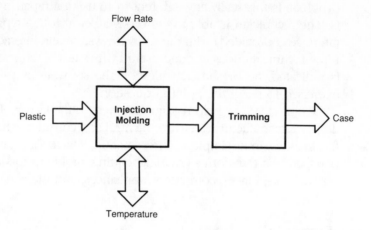

Fig. 4. Making cases for intelligent controllers.

By putting in sensors that the expert system can monitor, one can determine the temperature and rate of flow of the plastic that produces the optimal case. But, because the quality of chemicals for the plastic varies (cheap materials are used), the required rate of flow and temperature need to be varied. The expert system will monitor the resulting molded case for uniformity and quality. If there is too much waste, less plastic will be injected. Or, if there is too little plastic, more will be injected. The temperature and flow rates will be adjusted to produce an optimal case.

What kind of sensors should be used to accomplish this? Thermal, weight, and density sensors do not provide enough information. Shape is a concern as well. What is needed is the capability to perceive shape and then determine if the shape meets certain criteria (does it need to be trimmed or should it be tossed away as imperfect?). The expert system needs some form of "vision" to accomplish this. And, as we will see, for many processes, vision is a key component for the success of an AI system. In a simple form, a production line worker could look at a controller case and tell the expert system that too much plastic is being used. In a more advanced form, the expert system would "see" the problem and route the case for special trimming while adjusting the injection-mold parameters so as to use less plastic (Fig. 5).

Trimming the case can be done without robots; this type of process has been done cheaply by people for many years. But our intelligent controllers are special—the Pentagon specifications say they cannot vary in size by more than 0.0001 inch. (I don't know why either, but I don't buy $50 hammers.) Special equipment can be built to do the cutting at such close tolerances, but the cutting process will be slowed down. An expert system with "vision" can use cutting equipment rapidly and immediately check the tolerances of the finished case. This means that quality control can be performed expediently for all intelligent controller cases rather than randomly sampling some cases.

Coupling the expert system with cutting equipment and vision has resulted in a robot—a machine capable of making decisions and performing physical tasks.

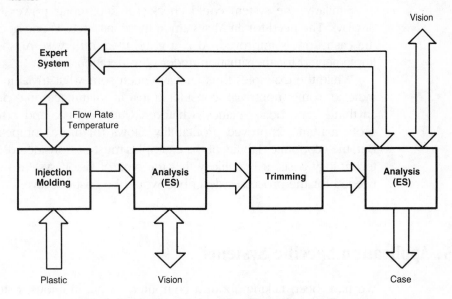

Fig. 5. Producing optimal intelligent controller cases.

So far, the AI system has been used to cut plastic costs, improve quality control, and improve efficiency by reducing manufacturing time for the intelligent controller cases. What can be done for the keyboards?

The vision system can verify that the keys have been placed in the right place and each keyboard can be tested to make sure that it functions properly. While more innovative ideas could be applied, quality control would seem the most likely AI application for the keyboards.

The circuit board has a more interesting potential. The vision system can be used to check the quality of each board and to verify the placement of components. Once the components are in place, the board can be tested for correct operation. Again the "expert" is used for quality control.

But what happens if the circuit board does not work? Usually, the board is tossed and a random sampling is made to determine if faulty components are being purchased. The cost of producing the board does not warrant human intervention to fix it. What if the expert system has the capacity for diagnosing the problem and replacing the faulty components cheaply? Waste could be reduced (i.e., throwing the faulty component away instead of the whole board) and better feedback obtained as to which components are causing failure. Is this a good idea? If 100,000 intelligent controllers a month are produced and throwaways reduced from 5% to 1% (4000 intelligent controllers are saved a month), the factory would save $2,400,000 per year if the cost is $50.00 per intelligent controller.

Of course, the expert system would be cost-effective only if it cost less than $2,400,000 per year. But, if it cost $10,000,000, it would pay for itself in just over 4 years!

Similarly, the system could check out and repair power supplies and displays. The need for an AI system in these instances is one of economics. If the cash flow is improved, AI is a good idea; otherwise AI should not be implemented for the situation under consideration.

While the examples thus far have been somewhat trivial in nature, they indicate some nontrivial considerations in manufacturing processes for anything: cars, boats, planes, whatever. Cutting waste and error improves profit margins. Improved profitability allows for more competitive pricing. But, the economic viability of the examples must be considered. With current technology costs, it is unlikely that the type of vision system that would be needed for the processes described would be cost-effective.

5. Application-Specific Systems

We have been talking about a computer, or autonomous system, that can address such aspects as machine setup variation, workpiece variation, differences in machines, the effects of temperature changes, and compensation for tool wear [Grossman 1986]. These types of systems are on the edge of realization. Computer-controlled appendages for "robots" exist now as do imaging systems. But a robot designed to weld car doors is not something one could afford to buy to paint houses. An imaging system designed to locate the hole in the car door so that a robot can place a lock in it is not effective for evaluating X-rays.

The vision technology of today is special-purpose. Rather than developing general-purpose imaging systems, one must build application-specific systems. While significant accomplishments are being made, industry does not have all the pieces necessary to provide a general-purpose robot/computer that can do all of the needed functions. That, in short, is the hang-up. Significant investment must be made to develop systems that will do tasks like those we have discussed. Many hours of programming, design, and study must be performed to create an effective system. To do this, a person called a "knowledge engineer" analyzes the tasks to be performed and develops a software implementation that allows the simulation of reasoning and the application of logic to be combined into an "expert system." This expert system has limited capability. Its knowledge is limited to a "domain" from which it can draw inferences on what action should be taken. An expert system to test the intelligent controller board will not have the ability to test an electronic watch unless it is specifically designed to do so. The imaging system that finds the hole in the car door for the lock cannot identify a coin unless it too is so designed.

These limitations will be overcome in the future as science develops better understandings of the problems involved. With faster computing ability in smaller packages, it is conceivable that the equivalent of today's fastest computers will be housed in packages that will be self-contained portable machines that can make robot systems as inexpensive as personal computers, for example.

Even with these constraints, AI has great potential now. The trick to using AI is picking implementations which will give a sufficient return on investment to justify the development costs.

Start-Up Costs

As part of implementation, management must also include within the start-up costs the training of its people and the cost of hiring consultants with expertise that its personnel might not have. In general, these costs could be quite high. Since this field is relatively new, one might surmise that the rate of failure might also be high. Since the demand for AI applications expertise is high, one may conclude that the cost of qualified consultants is high. As for training its people, management is faced with typical learning-curve difficulties and the associated delays in implementation as its people become familiar with the tools they need to use. And, of course, as soon as these in-house experts are trained, they become possible targets for recruitment outside the parent company.

Hazardous Environments

Given that high front-end costs must be paid to develop an AI system, which tasks or processes will be good candidates? First, let us consider hazardous environments. The greater the risk, the higher the cost of people. More to the point, it would be extremely desirable to keep people from being exposed to high-risk environments.

Exposure to toxic chemicals is a threat that would be nice to minimize or totally eliminate. However, many processes in the manufacturing environment require toxic chemicals. By using robots to work in the hazardous environment, the immediate threat to human life is eliminated. But this introduces new complexity into the AI system. If the robot does something "stupid" (we'll just define that to be some action that is not desirable, such as dropping potassium into the cleaning bucket instead of the chemical vat), it adds a new dimension to the software/hardware system. How are accidents prevented? How should all possible logical combinations be tested to guarantee that there are no errors?

These questions do not have simple answers. Almost everyone has had a bad encounter with a computer—an incorrect bill, a wrong address, etc. Even though the computer system was following a program that people developed, the tendency is to blame the computer. Since AI systems are also being developed by people, one might surmise that the confidence level in the infallibility of AI should not be significantly higher than for existing computer software.

An extension of AI would be an expert system that could validate the correctness of systems prior to implementing them. Such a system would be invaluable, but this would put management in an immediate quandary: *Quis custodes ipos custodes?* (Who watches the watchers?) How does one validate the correctness of the system which validates the correctness of other systems?

This also raises an interesting specter. What is the impact of ES mistakes in terms of legal liability? Since industry so far lacks ES systems on a large enough scale to make such mistakes, there does not appear to be any precedents on which to draw examples of these problems. But these situations will one day appear in the law courts. Will a manufacturer have any more or less liability because its ES caused a defective or harmful product to enter the marketplace? Will independent software developers be held liable for product inadequacies? Will manufacturers be held liable for damages resulting from the lack of adequate ES to enhance quality control? Will regulators use the ES as a means to determine if industry has met legal obligations for safety and health? These questions are not particularly simple to answer with today's technology and its current association with the legal system. We will have to wait for the results of actual cases before we know for sure, but we must keep in mind that these issues are very real and they might have a major impact on the way we do business.

Enough of philosophical discussions. There is a valuable place for AI in hazardous environments. An ES robot could repair an operating nuclear reactor. It could enter a blast furnace to modify its structure. It could make explosives or produce plutonium. Any manufacturing activity that people do could be done by a robot. But there is a catch: The robot has to do it as effectively and safely as a person. The first implementations of such robots will interact with people. Just as there is a need for people to have an expert system to consult with concerning areas where their expertise is minimal, we should anticipate that ES robots will need to consult with people when unanticipated situations are encountered.

6. ES Functions

In a more general sense, one can summarize the classes of expert systems activities as interpretation, prediction, diagnosis, design, planning, monitoring, debugging, repair, instruction, and control [Sviolka 1986]. See Fig. 6.

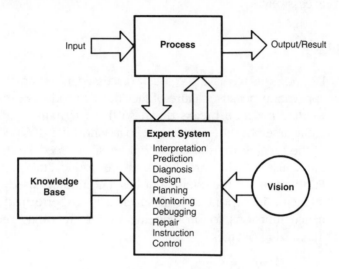

Fig. 6. Expert system activities.

Interpretation

Within the manufacturing environment, ES interpretation capabilities can be utilized to infer situations arising from the processes. For example, if an order is received for 10,000 intelligent controllers for shipment in 15 days, the ES could initiate orders for any additionally required supplies. And it could schedule equipment and the people necessary to make the intelligent controllers in the required period, or it could advise management that the current inventory is adequate and additional production is unnecessary.

Prediction

In the preceding example, the ES could predict that this extra order will require earlier maintenance of the production equipment because of the increased work load. Or, with more complex inputs in the form of economic indicators, the ES might advise that this order is the leading edge of a new demand for intelligent controllers and the factory will need new production capabilities.

Or, the ES could actually perform the functions for production line scheduling. Given a set of orders to be accomplished over some period, an ES could optimally schedule equipment, people, and supplies so as to meet order dates for a variety of products. More specifically, the ES could determine equipment setup scheduling so as to keep production lines from being idle excessively.

Diagnosis

Diagnosis, as we have previously discussed, is extremely attractive as an ES/AI application because failure of facilities or products can prove expensive. If a welding machine breaks down so that car frames cannot be attached, the entire assembly line could come to a standstill. If 100 people are idled because of the breakdown, the costs could easily exceed $1000 per hour. The faster the cause of the problem can be found, the faster it can be fixed. Furthermore, if the equipment has a computer-based control system, an ES might be incorporated in it specifically to perform diagnostic and maintenance functions to prolong the useful life of the equipment as well as minimizing outages.

Design

An expert system augmenting design has tremendous potential. Consider, for example, a technological breakthrough that would allow the intelligent controllers to run off body heat. Such a feature would significantly improve the demand of these intelligent controllers over others, but the competition could have the same strategy. Therefore, the manufacturer which can produce a body-heat–powered intelligent controller will have a competitive advantage only until the competition catches up. An ES designer could help cut down the time it takes to modify the circuitry and implement new procedures on the assembly line to get the product to market first.

Moreover, the AI system could be developed to allow prototyping various designs. With prototyping, one would be able to test our hypotheses before making a major commitment of resources to a specific plan. And a good software tool for AI would also allow prototyping the ES to determine how effective it would be in its environment for any of the beforementioned applications.

Planning

Planning has further potential for successful implementation in the manufacturing environment. Expert systems can give a factory the ability to couple manufacturing, engineering, and management skills into a system interacting with human counterparts to provide maximal potential to provide for new strategies in production, finance, research and development, marketing, distribution, and all other aspects of the plant environment. In short, management can develop planning skills that exceed the expertise of any individual in the organization.

Monitoring

Monitoring aspects of ES are an equally lucrative potential. This area includes quality control, process control, sales analysis, production control, and any other activity comprising an observable event to which someone may want to compare an expected outcome to generate a signal or report of exception. The ES can reveal that production is falling short of projected (or actual) sales, or that the intelligent controllers have too many defects.

Debugging

Debugging with an ES provides the potential of reviewing multiple solutions to resolve diagnoses of problems. The ES earlier determined that the welder must be malfunctioning. Now, the debugging ES can help determine what is wrong with the welder.

Repair

Of course, this process would not be complete without the next phase: fix it. A repair ES can help direct the technicians as to what action should be initiated to make the welder operational again. Honeywell, for example, has developed Mentor, an ES for doing preventive maintenance on large air conditioning systems. It estimates that this application can extend the life of their equipment beyond 20 years ["Honeywell High Tech" 1986].

Instruction

Inherent with the above activities is the obvious: instruction. The ES must be capable of giving instructions so that the technicians may diagnose, debug,and repair. But it has greater abilities. Through its instruction, people may be trained by their interacting with simulations of problems or situations that they might encounter on the job. By practicing with the ES, employees can sharpen skills to make them more productive. For example, the ES might instruct a trainee to determine why one of the welders was malfunctioning.

The ES could step the trainee through each of the actions needed to complete a successful repair.

Control

Finally, the ES can exercise control. Through its ability to interpret, predict, repair, and monitor, the ES can utilize the resultants of these tasks to control various parts of the manufacturing process. By knowing the probable output potential of the production facility and the projected sales levels, an ES could control the ordering of all raw materials while minimizing costs through the evaluation of economic order quantities.

7. Current ES Applications

The possibilities are impressive. Some of the preceding applications are already being used. One of these applications is real-time process control. Phillips has implemented an ES in a high-density–polyethylene plant in Houston, Texas. A further application, viewed as an offshoot of this system, includes customer service wherein the ES will aid in pinpointing the cause of customer complaints [Brooks 1986].

An ES named XCON at Digital Equipment processes order entry requests. A typical sequence can be done in two minutes as opposed to the one to two hours it took manually. Another ES, PICON™ by Lisp Machine, is being offered commercially for process control applications [Teresko 1985].

The Carnegie Group Incorporated and Ford Motor Company entered into agreements to develop diagnostic systems for Ford's Electrical & Electronics, Engine, and Parts & Service divisions. In the area of industrial maintenance, General Electric has developed an ES for locomotive service. Campbell Soup Company has an ES to diagnose malfunctions in its cooker systems [Teresko 1985].

WaXpert, an ES developed by Ex-Cell-O Compressor Components of Cleveland, diagnoses problems found in the wax injection process associated with manufacturing jet turbine components. This ES has the capability of addressing eight problem classes found in the wax injection process: air bubbles in the wax; flow lines formed in the wax pattern; flashing or wax leakage between the die halves; cavitation, the shrinkage of the wax so that the mold is not fully filled; chill damage, which is holes in the wax caused by shifting chill; nonfill, which is parts of the die which have no wax; pattern-crack, which is a breakage in the wax pattern; and poor surface, which is a general defect in the surface of the wax [Texas Instruments Data

Systems Group 1987]. Obviously, with enhanced vision, such an ES could determine the severity of these problems and correlate multiple causes of problems.

The target for an ES in such an environment is to diagnose and recommend. While knowing what the problem might be is extremely valuable, it is even more so if a recommendation accompanies the diagnosis to further improve the technician's ability to correct faults.

8. Decision-Support Systems

As one might surmise, much of what we have been discussing can fall into the realm of what is called a *decision-support system,* or DSS. A DSS is exactly what the term implies: a system for the support of decision making. Unlike some of the advanced-technology ESs we have talked about, much of the software for decision support systems exists already. An important aspect of such software is to allow nontechnical managers to converse (through typing) with the software and ask questions in normal English. Most importantly, this interaction of language is such that the ES can (and usually does) give its own explanation of the request for information so that the manager can see that the software "understands" the request and will implement it correctly.

Production Scheduling

A good example of such an application is production scheduling. While there is ample technology for utilizing linear programming to optimize usage of resources such as machines, there are numerous drawbacks because many constraints for this scheduling have nothing to do with numerical modeling. If one's best customer must have something immediately, one usually complies even when the setup costs are excessive. Generally, though, an effective system would allow for timely completion of products while minimizing low inventories of work in progress and simultaneously allowing initiation of orders with minimal advance notice. An ES can assist executives in this by providing them with analyses of the current status of all the equipment needed to produce a product or assembly. This in turn, is augmented with the optimal path for the processes to be scheduled based on the current requirements and schedules of all the equipment and resources needed to complete the task.

For example, if only one stamping press is available, the ES can give the manager a view of when he or she can most expediently obtain use of the press while minimizing any adverse effects to other assembly processes. While a person could also give us such information by utilizing Pert or Gant charts, an ES can produce the same information in a very short time frame. Thus, the manager can initiate scheduling quicker and, by inference, cheaper. But, to be efficient, such an ES must have access to data bases which give the requirements for machine setup, current schedules, job priorities, operator availability, and all of the rest of the same information that a person would need to make an effective analysis. In those cases where some information is not available, the machine's knowledge base would probably be coupled with that of a human's intuition to arrive at a desirable solution. Notably, the person would be unable to exercise this intuition with such accuracy without the hard data presented by the ES. And the ES would probably not be effective without the intuitive capabilities of an experienced person. But, the ES still could be augmented with the intuitive ability in those cases where the manager could quantify the decision processes.

Most importantly, this ES can only be as effective as the knowledge base that is built for it. If personal qualities are not a part of the data base, no inferences can be made about their effect on efficient scheduling. One of the drawbacks of the current technology found in ESs is that they have a limited repertoire of interfaces to data bases. In short, they can only retrieve data from a limited number of types of data bases. While this is not a debilitating deficiency, it does create a bottleneck when data is needed from an unsupported type. In such a situation, a conversion must be done to get the required data into the format that the ES can use.

Taxes

A second application of the intelligent DSS is taxes. One system, ExperTAX^{SM}, developed by Coopers and Lybrand, allows tax planning to be done on a personal computer [Shpilberg, Graham, and Schatz 1986]. Such systems can be used in decisions such as capital equipment acquisition and depreciation method selection.

In general, strategies can be developed to minimize the tax commitment the corporation must incur as part of its operations. Alternate strategies can be assessed to maximize benefit to the organization.

Policies and Procedures

Policies and procedures are also candidates for ES/DSS assistance. In large organizations, policies and procedures can become unwieldy volumes of manuals which are difficult to update and change. Suppose that a computer terminal replaces these books and that instead of thumbing through indices, one would simply pose a situation as a question to the ES/DSS and have it determine what organizational policies and procedures would apply. Since the "manuals" would be computer resident, changes and distribution would be much quicker. And less time would be spent by employees trying to keep their books updated. Consider, for example, someone trying to determine if it is legal to export a high-technology electronic component to some nonaligned country. With an ES/DSS knowledgeable in export rules, a decision might be found expediently rather than wading through volumes of bureaucratic gobbledygook and ultimately having to wait for a written response from the Department of Commerce.

Disaster Recovery Consultant

An excellent candidate for an ES/DSS is that of a disaster recovery consultant. In the event of a disaster, there is a reasonably high likelihood that critical planners and implementers would be unavailable as a result of the disaster. The corporation still must address bringing its facilities back into a productive mode of operation. To counter this dilemma, an ES can be developed to advise and consult with the people who must make plants operative. This ES would have a complete inventory of the equipment and processes necessary for normal operation. Additionally, the ES would have recommended procedures to address scenarios envisioned by the prior critical planners and how they would suggest approaching normalization. In effect, one could anticipate the originators of a plant being the very resource that would help establish a new plant after a disaster through the incorporation of their talents and expertise into an ES.

Data Processing Capacity Planning

A peripheral area of manufacturing is its data processing support. In order to be effective, it must maintain an adequate level of computer hardware to meet the needs of the organization. However, capacity planning for data processing equipment can be extremely complicated and require significant commitments of resources to develop effective plans. An area in which the ES may become very effective is data processing capacity planning. By developing intelligent systems to digest the performance data available on mainframes and their associated peripheral equipment, one can obtain information which will allow computer operators to be alerted to bottlenecks and performance deficiencies which might not normally be noticed. By analyzing this same data, an ES can inform managers what alternatives they can take to maximize utilization of existing capabilities and help them to plan for what resources they will need in the future. Essentially, the computer will help them plan for its own successor [Feldt 1986].

Computer Configurations

Another associated potential use for an ES is computer configuration. Given the fact that computer configurations can be very complicated, the user can find it very difficult to determine what equipment will work successfully on a particular computer or what equipment can work with other peripheral equipment. An ES can validate these configurations and even help determine the relative performance levels within the computer system. While this might seem an obvious need for large computer installations, one can also see its applicability to microcomputer environments. Which board should be bought to perform asynchronous communications? Will it work with a synchronous communications board? Will the power supply handle all the boards desired? Even sophisticated users may find it difficult to understand all aspects of their microcomputers.

Similarly, an ES can be used to configure other equipment, whether it be an air conditioning system for a building or an onboard guidance system for aircraft. Any set of equipment which has complicated interfaces or constraints could be augmented through a configuration ES assisting its users to develop valid combinations.

Labor Relations

An intriguing application for an ES/DSS would be labor relations. Consider having an ES consultant available to all managers and supervisors such that they would have instant interpretation of all aspects of current labor contracts. If nothing else, this would help to minimize grievances caused by misinterpretation of the application of these contracts. If union stewards had access to the same information, it is also conceivable that less time would be lost in the resolution of contract-related disputes. Of course, such an application would require that labor and management agree on the development of the ES and the implementation of the knowledge base.

Essentially, the goal of the ES and the DSS is to deploy expertise from the most knowledgeable people to the less knowledgeable so the latter may more effectively do their jobs.

9. The Future of AI/ES

Where is AI/ES going? Significant advances are being made in applying AI to the manufacturing arena, and more are possible. The applications we have discussed as having been implemented are limited in scope. They must be thoroughly tested to guarantee their correctness, and as much as possible, their infallibility. New advances in technology, especially in sensors, will make AI more viable to many more applications.

Machine Vision

The most promising of the new technologies is vision. With a general-purpose vision system, an ES can actually assess a situation and determine a suitable response. For example, consider a turbo-fan that has an imbalance which causes vibration. An ES with a general vision capability could watch the operating fan from the inside and determine the problem. While a remote camera facility could allow a person to do the same, a person's ability to calculate the difference in image changes would be significantly slower than a computer's.

Even more appealing is the fact that a vision system could be processing multiple images simultaneously. The ES could be assessing an infrared and ultraviolet image to determine the differences between the two. Such simultaneous processing could give new capabilities in stress analysis of certain materials as well as material identification.

Consider the problems of inferior parts. Suppose that a manufacturer receives the wrong grade of steel bolts. Current testing of such parts could be expensive, but an ES with vision, stress analysis capability, and spectrographic analysis could test incoming parts before they are used in assembly processes. This would obviously avoid expensive breakdowns and product recalls.

Applications

But where will AI/ES be used the most? Given our original premise that improved productivity is a mandate for economic survival in the next century, we must see AI/ES pervade the very fiber of manufacturing.

Large manufacturing facilities will obviously continue to be interested in applying AI to cut costs and improve quality. Anticipated returns on investment of ten to one [Kalb 1986] make AI extremely attractive for any use which appears to have potential for a successful outcome.

But the emphasis needs not to be solely on the largest industries, it must also be on the smaller concerns. Consider, for example, a clothing manufacturer. Foreign competition has the advantage because labor is cheaper. Therefore, the clothes can be made cheaper. But if the domestic manufacturer were aided by an ES that could suggest ways in which to cut cloth with less waste, and fewer people could do more cutting, cheap labor would not be the competitive edge. It is not necessary to use cheap resources, but it is necessary to use those resources more efficiently than the competition, and thereby make a product that reflects high quality at a lower price.

The same situation can be observed in other industries. The cheap manufacture of common (nonspecialty) integrated circuits becomes a function of minimizing resource costs. Cutting ICs from the original wafers can be expensive if the relative yield is not high. Specialty ES cutters can help make that yield high while performing the operation quickly. Making sure that the leads and packages are correctly assembled can also produce higher yields. People can do this function, but they are relatively slow. By having a few expensive people do the function of managing a robot ES, management can reduce production costs through increasing efficiency and quality, and minimizing defects.

Similarly, a robot ES assembling electronic equipment (such as tv's) has a high start-up cost, but the ongoing costs are minimized because a few people can do the work of many.

Does this mean that AI/ES is going to create massive unemployment? Perhaps, but I doubt it. It is more likely that it is going to create an accelerating pace of change in which the machine operator's job will be greatly affected. Instead of someone becoming an expert at assembling a tv, he or she will become an expert at running a machine that assembles 100 tv's at a time. Expert system managers will be created who will act as custodians of the ES robots and assure their quality and integrity. Jobs will be created that will start new processes that are not even imagined today.

Remote ES systems are viable because they essentially operate independently, with occasional consultation with a human counterpart. Will factories be established in the hostile environment of space? The inherent advantages are tremendous. Processes can be developed in near zero-g conditions. Total vacuum is a cheap commodity, and extraneous contamination there can be virtually eliminated. Solar furnaces can be used to develop temperatures impossible on our planet. But this same environment could be extremely dangerous for humans. Remote ESs can allow industry to take advantage of this potential, and minimize the danger by reducing the number of people necessary in the factory.

Another facet of future ES applications is microminiature assembly. Expert system robots can work on small just as well as large scales. While there are currently limits on the economic viability of miniaturization, ES robots could be developed to handle extremely small components. Consider a robot that could repair the substrate in an integrated circuit. While this would not have general applicability on the Earth's surface at present, a remote space factory could have extreme need for such repairs if replacement parts were not readily available.

Similarly, miniature ES robots could travel through fiber-optic conduits to repair broken links under the sea. Or, they could repair underground pipes and cables.

Obviously, industry is a little short on technology to accomplish these things today. A miniature ES robot traveling through a pipe would probably not have enough computing power to be useful. Therefore, some sort of communications link would have to exist to effectively control the robot and evaluate its vision from a different location. While such a capability does exist via radio control, there are inherent limitations in such a configuration that would have to be addressed before the system would achieve a high degree of reliability.

Possible Evolution

What about the future? Artificial intelligence is in its infancy. While we have discussed some of the more probable applications of AI in reference to the directions taken by current technology, there are many more areas which may be of great significance. Artificial intelligence will be integrated into many disciplines, including cognitive science, decision analysis, operations research, and control theory. Extensions of these disciplines will aid researchers in developing machine systems that will be able to learn and display more advanced capabilities of humanlike capacities. From this integration will evolve true information processing by these machines, which will be able to do improved resource allocation as well as augmenting their abilities through learning. Instead of engineers developing specific-application AI systems, the new systems will be more dynamic in nature with the ability to undertake new direction without specific instruction. The future ESs will learn from their mistakes and avoid repeating them. Moreover, one should anticipate that future AI systems will be better able to utilize imperfect information toward a reasonable outcome while allowing industry to utilize its resources (people, equipment, funds, etc.) more effectively in the pursuit of its goals. As AI is supplemented by advances in psychology and cognitive research, AI systems may become more able to perform tasks in adaptive learning, machine learning, adaptive control systems, and dynamic resource allocation [Sage 1986].

Much more effort is obviously going to be expended on human-machine interfaces to improve industry's ability to maximize the effectiveness of AI systems. Furthermore, one may expect better delineation of the tasks allocated to people and those allocated to AI systems. A logical extension of this would be that there will be better systems and processes that effectively utilize both humans and AI working as a collective unit. With the current constraints on human-machine interface, we should anticipate that much of the effort to optimize this interaction will be in the area of natural-language interfaces so that human and machine will be able to communicate effectively with each other.

As the scientific knowledge of the principles and theory of AI improves, it is almost certain that AI systems will be able to exercise judgement and more cognitive reasoning to arrive at solutions to their problem sets.

We may also expect new forms of education. Rather than allocating one human teacher to 20 or 30 students, there will be a one-on-one teaching capability with the AI system tutoring the student and the human teacher becoming an education supervisor.

As these AI applications become reliable, AI will evolve through improved software productivity and design capabilities. Prototyping software through AI will permit the development of new systems more quickly and more reliably.

To reach these outcomes, there will be significant evolutions in the representation of knowledge and the communications or presentations of it. There will be advances in group decision making which will allow AI systems to simulate collective expertise in multidisciplinary areas. As such, the ESs should provide a wider range of consultive capabilities while integrating all the expertise into each of the decision-making phases. For example, a scheduling ES might make management aware that the overtime required for a particular project will result in decreased productivity due to increased psychological strain caused by workers being away from their families excessively. As a result management might determine that it would be more effective to add people to the work force.

In summation, AI/ES is going to be firmly entrenched in future manufacturing processes. And AI will have a very positive impact on industry's economic dealings with the world marketplace. The degree to which this impact will attain is open for conjecture; but I steadfastly believe that AI is the front edge of a new industrial revolution which will take our society to new heights of wonder and sociotechnological advancement.

10. Suggested Reading

The following publications are recommended to the reader who would like further study in machine vision, natural-language systems, expert systems, and robotics.

Vision

Best, P. J., and R. C. Jain. "Three-Dimensional Object Recognition," *ACM Computing Surveys*, Vol. 17, No. 1, March 1985, pp. 75–145.

Natural-Language Systems

Biermann, A. W., Rodman, R. D., Rubin, D. C., and J. F. Heidlage. "Natural Language With Discrete Speech as a Mode for Human-to-Machine Communication," *Communications of the ACM,* Vol. 28, No. 6, June 1985, pp. 628–636.

Expert Systems

Bobrow, D. G., Mittal, S., and M. J. Stefik. "Expert Systems: Peril and Promise," *Communications of the ACM,* Vol. 29, No. 9, September 1986, pp. 880–894.

Dixon, N. R. (ed.) "Knowledge Systems," special issue of the *IBM Journal of Research and Development,* Vol. 30, No. 1, January 1986, pp. 1–124.

Robotics

Denning, P. J. (ed.) "Factory Automation and Robotics," special section of the *Communications of the ACM,* Vol. 29, No. 6, June 1986, pp. 484–522.

11. References

Brooks, K. "AI Tackles Real-Time Process Control," *Chemical Week,* Vol. 139, No. 11, September 1986, p. 38.

Feldt, T. "Can AI Relieve Mainframe Bottlenecks? *High Technology,* October 1986, pp. 58–60.

Grossman, D. D. "Opportunities for Research on Numerical Control Machining," *Communications of the ACM,* Vol. 29, No. 2, June 1986, pp. 515–522.

"Honeywell High Tech Is Aimed at Service," *Air Conditioning, Heating and Refrigeration News,* Vol. 167, February 1986, p. 1.

Kalb, B. "Facts," *Automotive Industries,* Vol. 166, November 1986, p. 96.

Sage, A. P., and W. B. Rouse. "Aiding the Human Decision Maker Through the Knowledge-Based Sciences," *IEEE Transactions on Systems, Man, and Cybernetics,* Vol. SMC-16, No. 4, July/August 1986, pp. 511–521.

Shpilberg, D., Graham, L. E., and H. Schatz. "ExperTAX: An Expert System for Corporate Tax Planning," *Expert Systems,* Vol. 3, No. 3, July 1986, pp. 136–151.

Sviolka, J. J. "Business Implications of Knowledge-Based Systems," *Data Base*, quarterly publication of the special interest group on business data processing of the Association of Computing Machinery, Vol. 17, No. 4, summer 1986, p. 16.

Teresko, J. "AI Moves Into Industrial Control Arena," *Industry Week*, Vol. 227, November 25, 1985, p. 70.

Texas Instruments Data Systems Group. *AI Interactions*, Vol. 2, No. 6, February 1987, pp. 2–3.

Chapter 8

Artificial Intelligence/ Expert Systems Scheduling in Manufacturing

K. Stonecipher
Systems Consultant

1. Abstract

One of the most important and exciting aspects of future robotics systems will be the development of decision-making capabilities. Future systems will utilize functional dynamic modules of knowledge-based systems as a means for assisting a robot in making decisions during the normal workday. The focus of this chapter is on the application of artificial intelligence/expert systems (AI/ESs) in scheduling operations in a manufacturing environment. The author believes that expert systems that schedule activities for robot workstations and also coordinate the activities of the entire plant environment will be the most initial widespread use of AI/ESs in the near future [Stonecipher 1985]. The areas discussed in terms of AI/ES schedulers (hereafter referred to as AI/ESs or schedulers) are the goals of such systems, the concepts behind such systems, the domains in the area of robot material-handling systems, workstation routing control systems, plant production control systems, plant support control systems, and plant engineering control systems. This chapter also reviews material-transport mechanisms, analyzing the plant for traffic patterns, looking at the physical and logical analysis of the plant floor, material-handling and storage systems, personnel management ordering and accounting systems, and engineering aspects of a plant environment such as design, analysis, and documentation.

2. Introduction

There is a wide variety of AI research projects that are taking place today. The following areas may incorporate AI systems:

(*a*) machine vision,
(*b*) robotics,

(*c*)   natural-language programming,

(*d*)   automatic programming,

(*e*)   game playing,

(*f*)   knowledge-based or expert systems.

The area that has shown the highest degree of commercial acceptance is that of knowledge-based or expert systems. Knowledge-based systems may be defined as the systems that use some form of computer program that can make decisions based on a set of structured facts and a dynamically ordered rule base system. Many expert systems that are currently being used are based on a system developed by Bruce G. Buchannan and Edward K. Shortliffe, both of Stanford University. The project was entitled Mycin and began in 1972. This expert system was developed for diagnosing infectious diseases and has been used as a model for most of the expert systems used today.

Rules which have been basic to the Mycin system have been defined as a knowledge-ordering structure for implementing an expert system. They can be considered a natural structure for capturing an expert's knowledge. Parameters are also a basic component of an expert system. A parameter may simply be defined as a fact. It is a thing, such as the robot itself, or an activity, such as a pick-and-place activity. It is important to note that a parameter is a clause and has a linguistic structure, i.e., the noun of the clause, the verb of the clause and an action statement of the clause [Winograd 1983].

Another important aspect of an expert system is called the *inference engine*. It may be defined as part of the expert production system that utilizes existing rules and parameters and tries to resolve or fire a rule to arrive at a conclusion. The basic structure of an inference engine uses rules of the form of IF conditions (premise conditions), THEN conditions (action conditions), and conclusions. The inference engine is also very important because it monitors or controls the execution of the parameters and the rules in the knowledge base. A good expert system is one in which the control structure can be very dynamic in terms of the execution of the rules and parameters. This is important so that as information changes the facts in the knowledge base, the system can be robust enough to incorporate those changes to produce conclusions. The impact of expert systems on robotics will be as follows. These expert systems can have rules programmed into them that can determine the type of action that the robot should take based on existing input information. At present there are no commercial robot systems that incorporate knowledge-based expert systems with industrial robots, but this technology soon will definitely affect industrial robotics. More importantly, this technology will greatly affect the workstations in the plant and the control of the entire plant production system. Specifically, robot manufacturing systems consist of a series of well-defined processes that are performed to produce a finished product. Some of the processes may be performed in a certain sequence, whereas others may be completed in several sequences.

Traditionally, assembly lines incorporating robot systems have been adequate as long as the production line produces only one product or group of products that require the same sequence of operations [Engelke, Grotian, and Scheving 1985]. The widespread use of robotics and other general-purpose, computer-controlled machines in manufacturing has resulted in facilities capable of producing a wide range of products for which different sequences of operations must be performed. To exploit the capabilities of these flexible manufacturing facilities it is necessary to be able to provide flexible expert systems to assist in the operation of the robots in the plant environment and their coordination with other workstations in the plant.

3. ES Flexible Manufacturing Scheduling Overview

For the last 30 to 35 years problems that the manufacturing system has had to deal with have not been adequately understood by the data processing or computer science personnel. This does not indicate the problems have been minuscule in any way. It does indicate that the problems that manufacturing has had were too complex for the existing computer science to cope with significantly.

There are some common factors which have been exhibited by manufacturing in the past. One is that the complexity of problems in the manufacturing environment incorporating factors such as industrial robots has been highly complex in nature. These problems in terms of manufacturing design, flow, and specifically scheduling may have been ill-defined or lacked designation of the proper constraints. In addition to this there have been a lack of standard solutions for these specific problems [Embrey 1986]. The real expertise in the past may have been an individual's "educated guesses" or "this is the way we did it in the past" approach to the particular manufacturing process. In terms of productive manufacturing this sort of philosophy did not guarantee a successful solution. Management has accepted solutions that were reasonably good as a substitute for total success in the past. The inability to use past computer science technology has given computer science offerings a less than successful track record.

With the incorporation of AI, such as the scheduler being discussed here, which can incorporate fuzzy logic and model real-world environments, comes great promise for manufacturing without retrofitting or redesigning major plants [Biegel 1986]. Another factor that the scheduler will incorporate is the capability to address factors such as increasing costs of manufacturing. Without having a tool which can incorporate expanding technologies, such as robot manipulator systems, in the overall manufacturing system, the past manufacturing solutions may not be future solutions for that system. By incorporating automation in the sense of schedulers, existing manufacturing systems can stay competitive for the flexible nature of manufacturing requirements in the future [Barkocy and Zdeblick 1982].

The AI/ES scheduler is based on the work reported by Kimemia and Gerswin [1983] regarding the on-line scheduling of a flexible manufacturing system (FMS). The flexible manufacturing system should be one that is based on a group of machines in which a family of related parts can be made simultaneously. It can consist of a set of computer-controlled machines and transportation elements, a robotics system being one of the computer-controlled machines on the plant floor. The changeover time between different operations on the plant floor at a workstation should be small compared with operation times. To be able to incorporate flexible manufacturing systems and expert systems to optimize the use of a robot will require understanding different manufacturing life cycle goals. These goals are design, building implementation and debugging, operation, modification, and end of life. Corresponding to each one of these goals, appropriate methods of manufacturing are required.

An AI/ES scheduler can be applied appropriately to the design, implementation and debugging, operation and modification phases. During systems design and modification, modeling with an AI/ES scheduler is faster and can assist in the more appropriate planning of the flow of products, information, and resources; better resource allocation; better specification of the robot production system; and better understanding of the system behavior regarding throughput, turnaround time, work in process, flexibility, and reliability. During the operation phase the AI/ES scheduler can support not only product scheduling and line control but also result in the optimal utilization of existing resources.

The key to improving techniques is a concept describing the scheduling of robot manufacturing processes in general terms. This method should allow the dynamic modeling of not only the robot workcells but all production systems such as resource flow, information flow and material flow. The structure of an AI/ES scheduler should provide for a top-down approach and incorporate some of the existing modeling functions [Kimenia 1982]. It should also be easy to understand and use by management, engineering, and plant floor personnel.

An AI/ES scheduler should be able to describe the execution of manufacturing activities in relation to manufacturing entities and manufacturing modeling functions. This capacity will allow for the establishment of goals for the AI/ES scheduler to enable it to signify phase completion. The system should also allow for specification of the structure as well as the behavior of the manufacturing system. The structure should specify which manufacturing function a system implements and how the functions are related to one another. It should also allow for descriptions being derived from less detailed ones, and vice versa.

The system can then be able to cope with a complexity of phases that are necessary in the manufacturing system, but it should also be able to minimize task goal description expenditures by adopting the level of task description accuracy needed by the user [Haines 1985]. The system should include the performance activity and integrate the flows of objects throughout the production system.

Resource Optimization

To be able to take advantage of an AI/ES scheduler there are certain requirements necessary for resource optimization. They are that the expert system should allow for a structured manufacturing description with a hierarchical modeling concept and also incorporate graphics-support structures for a broad scope of applications.

The user interface for the scheduler should provide for an interactive dialogue with a fast response and user-oriented graphics. The systems should also include a high-level modeling language to be used from a workstation incorporating extensive help functions in the software design.

System integration should be a key tool for resource optimization at all points. The AI/ES scheduler should incorporate the following:

(a) a modeling tool so that options such as color are available,

(b) interactive video (light pen or mouse),

(c) picture storage,

(d) utilization of mainframe central computing capacity for running simulation software,

(e) ability to integrate data-base information,

(f) ability to integrate information from the plant floor as well as from the existing host data base.

4. ES FMS Scheduling Concepts

In the following discussion we will break down the subject of flexible manufacturing scheduling into the following concepts: structured manufacturing, hierarchical modeling, manufacturing entities, and manufacturing functions.

Description of ES FMS

The manufacturing concept can be described as entities and classes of entities in the production system. The classes can be used to describe the execution operations of the manufacturing system such as information, material, and resources. Information exists in human- or machine-executable form. In machines such as robots, information occurs as digital as well as analog data. It is stored in a variety of media including computer systems, magnetic tape, and paper. An AI/ES scheduler should be able to receive information from its environment or users. It should be able to acquire technical information on the products being manufactured and the manufacturing processes from development engineers. The system should incorporate production planning which can generate orders and provide information to the production execution functions [Bruno and Elia 1986]. The information generated by an AI/ES scheduler as shown in Fig. 1 should also be able to be exchanged and used by other functions of the manufacturing system or even communicated to vendors outside the plant.

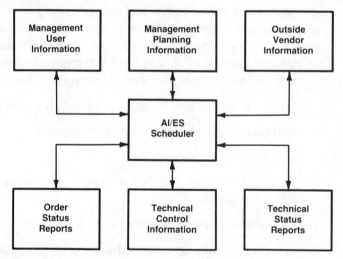

Fig. 1. AI/ES scheduler functions.

An AI/ES scheduler should be able to generate the following information or interface to existing systems that generate the following information, such as order information, order status reports, technical control information, and technical status reports, such as the status of existing robot workcells.

Orders in a manufacturing environment invoke the execution of manufacturing functions. Orders can be characterized as having attributes specifying order identity, order type, identity of related technical information, order priority, and order release date or order completion date.

Order status reports can be defined or refer to the status of existing orders and where they are in existing production systems. Orders can be in the form of acting, pending, or finished.

Technical control information should contain the data necessary for specifying the type of manufacturing function involved. There should be a direct relationship in an AI/ES scheduler between order and technical control status [Gershwin and Akella 1985]. A great deal of technical information is usually transformed into order information at some lower level subfunction. The main purpose of technical control information is to serve as a basis of generating the lower-level functions necessary for completion of the manufacturing process. It is essential to have technical control information specifically for use with robot systems for manufacturing execution. This information should also be viewed as a type of manufacturing resource. There should not be the attitude that exists today which views information as independent or an independent production factor of the actual manufacturing process [Pierson 1984]. The real goal of the AI/ES scheduler will be in being able to emphasize and manipulate scheduling information independently of the actual resources and physical nature of the plant system.

Technical status reports contain information on the present availability of entities such as robots, previous activities of a function, and reasons for unavailability of entities, specifically a robot that is in a maintenance cycle.

Material should also be viewed by the AI/ES scheduler in terms of it being a production object of the manufacturing execution function. Material should be viewed by the AI/ES scheduler to include all physical matter that enters the production system during the production process—specifically raw materials, parts/assemblies, auxiliary materials, products, and scrap material.

Resources viewed by the AI/ES scheduler should be viewed as all the nonmaterial physical means necessary to carry out the manufacturing processes. Resources can include processes, material transport, material storage, tools and fixtures; data processing resources; supply material, energy, space, and time; personnel.

Hierarchical Modeling

The flexible manufacturing system (FMS) is one in which the plant can be viewed as a hierarchy of related parts. Being able to process this mix of parts should make it possible to utilize the machines such as robots more fully on the plant floor. This is because different parts may spend different amounts of time at different machines. The incorporation of more industrial robots may vary the amount of time that a particular part may be at a robot workstation. Each part is used by some machines more heavily than others. A robot workstation may incorporate a number of functions which will make that part used at that workstation more than at other points in the plant production system. It becomes very important to be able to look at a complementary system which can be used for simultaneous production so that machines that are lightly used can be more heavily loaded than other machines, such as a robot system which may delay a part for several minutes at that workstation [Gershwin, Akella, and Choong 1984].

An AI/ES scheduler using a hierarchical modeling philosophy is able to balance several machines in terms of functional load at the same time. The problem is that such balancing is difficult when there is a wide variety of machines, a wide variety of part types, and many different assembly processes. In addition, all manufacturing systems, whether they are flexible or sequential, are subject to machine failures and repairs, material unavailability, high-priority items or batches, and personnel changes. These types of disruptive effects further complicate the optimization of the existing production system. The AI/ES scheduler because of its dynamic rule ordering structure has the ability to incorporate these real-world scenarios and still be able to come to conclusions about scheduling for a wide variety of aspects for a manufacturing system.

It should be noted that the AI/ES scheduler that we are discussing is a type of short-term scheduling process. The first phase of this project will be to prove the success of a short-term scheduler before its integration into a long-term scheduling system. The purpose of this hierarchical type of approach is to mitigate the effects of major disruptions on a manufacturing system. It should also be noted that a methodology should be used to view or review the existing production requirements that are specified for the overall production system. These production requirements should also provide initial data on the mean time between failures (MTBF) and the mean time to repair (MTTR) [Chow, MacNair, and Saver 1985].

The AI/ES scheduler can be divided or decomposed into three levels. The top level is one of evaluation and incorporation of any sort of dynamic changes by executives or engineering personnel into the manufacturing system. The middle level reviews any sort of instantaneous production rates that are necessary for the functioning of the manufacturing system. The lower level of the scheduler incorporates the two upper levels into actual part dispatch times in the production system.

Other factors that are incorporated into this hierarchical approach of the AI/ES scheduler are in terms of the transportation system, machine parameters and part data, and system loading.

The AI/ES scheduler's main features are that it can dynamically incorporate the constraints on the existing production system and provide for production losses through scheduling techniques due to a various range of failures by a building of the existing inventory. The modeling technique that has been used was developed by Kimemia and Gershwin [1983], which describes a top-level algorithm requiring the solution of a difficult partial differential equation (Bellman's equation). It is also important to note that a heuristic algorithm integrated into the AI/ES scheduler works just as appropriately as some of the numerical algorithms that have been proposed in the past.

The top-level system is an off-line system which incorporates the system configuration, the requirements of the system, and the machine parameters, such as operation time, mean time between failure, and mean time to repair. The AI/ES scheduler resolves problems in terms of integrating many changes to the system at this high executive level.

The middle level is an on-line system in which the AI/ES scheduler's main goal is to calculate short-term production rates. It integrates the statuses of existing machines, such as robot systems on the plant floor, and also evaluates the statuses of the requirements on the production system. More importantly it is constantly reviewing the parameters or facts about the statuses of the robots and other systems on the plant floor.

The next level can be referred to as the lower level, which incorporates the AI/ES scheduler to schedule times at which to dispatch parts. It reviews the status of the system in terms of part locations, and it also reviews the statuses of machines at their workstations and the transportation of parts to the appropriate workstation.

The purpose of the AI/ES scheduler in terms of a hierarchical policy is to solve problems such as when should parts (whose operation times at machines are on the order of seconds or minutes) be dispatched to a particular workstation such as a robot. It should also incorporate unreliability factors, such as mean time between failures and mean time to repair into its decision making [Capitano and Feinstein 1986].

The transportation system is reviewed in Sections 5 and 6, which cover material-transport mechanisms and plant-floor traffic patterns. Machine parameters and part data are viewed in terms of mean time between failures and mean time to repair on systems such as a robot system. The AI/ES scheduler looks at the average time a machine is available for production divided by the total time. This quantity, called *efficiency* of the machine, is further utilized in the AI/ES scheduler [Efstathiou and Rajkovic 1986].

There are other factors that should be incorporated into the AI/ES scheduler that will affect the overall conclusions by the system in terms of machine performance and part information. The system must provide for machine tool jams which can occur during operations such as an insertion process. These factors can be utilized in the AI/ES scheduler as part of the processing time rather than an actual failure of the system. Another factor to be incorporated at this point is the actual processing time and the time to move a particular part or parts in and out of a machine or workstation.

Loading is another important aspect which must be incorporated into the AI/ES scheduler. "Loading" refers to how heavily the machines in a system are being utilized. The expected utilization of a machine such as a robot can be defined as being equal to the ratio of total robot production time required to the expected machine time available. The total robot production time required is a product of the total number of parts demanded and the actual processing time. The AI/ES scheduler can also include machine utilization and any sample simulation based on the history of machine time available and repairs during a particular run. This time sequencing determines the actual amount of time that the machine, such as a robot, is available and is incorporated into the overall conclusion making by the AI/ES scheduler [Zisk 1983].

The hierarchical approach has been compared with several other simpler strategies. The hierarchical approach incorporated into an AI/ES scheduler has been found to be superior in terms of more production rules, minimizing work in process, and increasing balance of machine utilization closer to 100%.

It has been found that a hierarchical approach to plant management seems to be more robust and less affected by disruptive events. It has been shown that difference between performance on good and bad days was less than the difference for other types of linear algorithmic strategies. Most importantly, the incorporation of an AI/ES scheduler with this hierarchical approach based on J. G. Kimemia and S. B. Gershwin's paper [1983] can respond to random disruptions in the production process, and it can treat unpredictable changes in the operational states of machines such as robots and incorporate repair and failure schedules. This type of process shows a great promise in terms of its impact on manufacturing systems. To understand this process better it is important to understand the actual functions of machines such as robots in the plant floor. To do this the author has analyzed the manufacturing process in terms of functional manufacturing entities.

Manufacturing Entities

Manufacturing entities can be defined as functional units that may be found in a manufacturing production system. A manufacturing entity could be a robot workstation, a numerically controlled machine, a punch press, a loading station, etc. There are three classes that can be viewed as manufacturing entities within a plant environment. They are information entities, material entities, and resource entities.

Information Entities

Information entities can be human or a machine, such as a robot system. In robot systems information entities may be digital as well as analog. Their information can be stored in magnetic memory, magnetic tape, or paper. A manufacturing information entity receives information from the plant environment. It can accept information on products during the product developmental process. A manufacturing information entity can also use production planning information to generate orders and provide information for key management types of functions. Also, manufacturing information entities can be used to generate information for outside the plant, such as manufacturing information that may relate to vendors who supply material to a particular plant environment.

Manufacturing information entities can generate information in the form of orders, machine status information, technical control information, and personnel information. Orders that are used during the execution of a manufacturing function have attributes such as order identity, order type, identity of related technical information, order priority, order release information, or order completion dates. See Fig. 2.

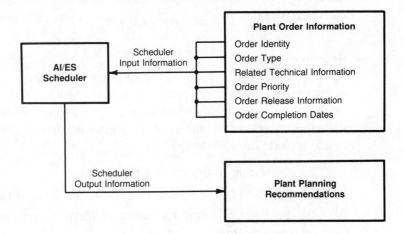

Fig. 2. Plant order information.

Technical control information is valuable during the manufacturing process. The relationship between order information and technical control information is key to an AI/ES scheduler. This technical information is going to be transformed at another level into the plant environment. The main purpose of an AI/ES scheduling system in regard to technical control is to initiate the proper sequence of events for generation of these lower-level functions. Consequently, as a resource, this technical control information is a key to the overall manufacturing process. It must be treated as independent information so that any physical constraints of resources in the plant environment can be considered independent of the logical requirements of the manufacturing information entity.

In terms of technical status information an AI/ES scheduler should provide information about the following:

(*a*) the availability of manufacturing entities,

(*b*) previous activities of that particular entity,

(*c*) any sort of information as to the unavailability of manufacturing entities in the manufacturing process,

(*d*) which entities are being used and in what requirements,

(*e*) which manufacturing entities have inappropriate types of quantity,

(*f*) which entities are being misused during the manufacturing process.

Material Entities

A manufacturing material entity should be viewed as a production object of a manufacturing system and a key to the AI/ES scheduler. Any materials that are used as physical matter that enter the production system, such as raw materials, parts, any auxiliary materials, products, and scrap metal, can be considered in this area.

Resource Entities

Resources such as the physical means to carry out part of the manufacturing entity process are another component of an AI/ES scheduler. Resources can be defined as any physical means that are used in the manufacturing process with the exception of materials. Robot workstations use resources which would include the following:

(*a*) the testing of the robot workstation,

(*b*) transport of material to and from the robot workstation,

(*c*) any sort of storage requirements for that robot workstation,

(*d*) any sort of tools and fixtures that are used by that robot workstation,

(*e*) data processing equipment such as intelligent controllers used by that robot workstation,

(*f*) energy, space, or time that is used by that robot workstation.

As regards an AI/ES scheduler this information is very important for an overall resource allocation by the scheduler to the entire plant environment.

Definitions of Manufacturing Functions

There are three basic classes of functions that are used by an AI/ES scheduler in a plant environment. These classes include workstation control, workstation execution, and workstation support.

Workstation Control

Workstation control is used by the AI/ES scheduler to model information flow in the plant environment. Examples are any sort of modifications, changes, transmissions, or quality checking of information by a robot workstation.

Workstation Execution

Workstation execution functions can be used by the AI/ES scheduler to describe material flow to and from a workstation. Examples are workstation transportation, processing, testing, and assembly of materials.

Workstation Support

Workstation support functions used by an AI/ES scheduler refer to the state of resources and can be described as a support function in the manufacturing plant environment. Examples are equipment setup schedules and provisions for feeding tools and fixtures to a robot workstation.

Overall Relationships

It is important to keep in mind that the AI/ES scheduler looks at each of these classes of manufacturing functions in its relation to the overall manufacturing object system. For example, during a manufacturing operation manufacturing entities utilize these different classes interlinked by the AI/ES scheduler for the workstation control, execution, and support functions. These classes require basic information from the AI/ES scheduler to input their start activities and what resources they have to utilize during their daily operations.

Workstation Functional Types

There are basic functional types that the AI/ES scheduler uses for the classes of workstation control, execution, and support. These classes are defined as to their functional relationship to that particular manufacturing entity. The four function types are as follows [Paul and Doukidis 1986]:

(*a*) workstation rest,

(*b*) movement,

(*c*) assembly,

(*d*) verification.

These workstation functions are important to the scheduler so that it may complete its inferencing techniques to make a complete set of activities that may be defined for that particular robot workstation.

Workstation rest activities (*a*) may be defined as the planned storage or unplanned waiting functions which may then begin in a workstation move, assembly, or verification task. The workstation rest class is viewed by the scheduler as a nonactivity even though resources may be allocated during this process.

Workstation movement (*b*) is used by the scheduler as a change of location or spatial arrangement function. Manufacturing parts may be in a transportation mode or may be being moved into a positioning orientation for the robot during the assembly process.

Workstation assembly (*c*) is the change of any sort of attributes by the robot workstation with the exception of orientation or parts positioning. The workstation assembly functional class used by the scheduler includes activities that may be the assembling or disassembling of entities of the same class. An example is the assembly of a product with any sort of subassemblies and any sort of linkage of parts assembly during the process. The scheduler also uses workstation assembly class information if any sort of disassembly is necessary for repair.

Workstation verification (*d*) is used by the scheduler in terms of comparison for any types of reference information during the manufacturing process. Each manufacturing entity, such as a robot workstation, is verified for functions such as inspection, measurement, or any sort of testing process.

Inspection is the examination of any parts or assembly parts with relationship to a specified shape identity or surface. The scheduler also views any informational entities during the workstation verification process. This is important so that a differentiation can be made between informational entities that are used during the manufacturing process and the actual manufacturing done at a particular workstation, such as a robot workstation.

Measurement looks at the attributes of a particular function such as quantity, weight, or any sort of given values for that workstation or part type. The AI/ES scheduler also reviews data files that may be measured for a specific date of origin or other parameter defined by engineering or management executives.

Workstation testing is defined as investigating how a particular product meets a functional specification defined by management or engineering. The scheduler utilizes testing as part of the workstation verification process for a manufacturing production system.

Entities and Their Functions

The scheduler is not only concerned with the classes of function in the manufacturing environment and also the functional types that are used in the manufacturing process but, more importantly, the particular connection between these entities and the functions they have to perform in the manufacturing system. The scheduler views these connections as follows:

1. The way entities may be engaged in a particular activity at a particular time. This information reviews basic entity information as to functional input/output.

2. Any sort of functional exchange entities. This information is used by the scheduler to look at precedents that may be required in the connection of entities in a manufacturing system.

3. If a hierarchy has been established for the flow between entities with the support of the particular types, the scheduler notes and gives precedence to a functional hierarchy of operations in the manufacturing environment.

The hierarchical functional requirement is important to the scheduler so that it is able to connect any sort of output entity which may be necessary by another entity workstation as a particular input. The first function is viewed as a predecessor and the second function is input to the next workstation is viewed by the AI/ES scheduler as a successor. The precedence that the scheduler takes is to view material as a functional object during the execution function. This is necessary so that the scheduler can distinguish resources and information that may be needed by multiple workstations.

The Vertical Hierarchical Functional Structure
It is also important to recognize the value of vertical hierarchical functional structure used by the scheduler. The vertical requirements may exist between a workstation entity and any sort of workstation functions that may be on a horizontal level [Dupont-Gatemand 1982]. These may be robot workstations that work in conjunction with each other but may not have a particular precedence of assembly over each other. An example would be robot workstations utilizing a scheduler that are performing a parallel operation in a manufacturing environment. A *vertical hierarchy* can be defined as a particular group of subfunctions which may be viewed as a tree structure. The scheduler must recognize that there is a unique subordination of levels that are necessary to accomplish a task.

The second important component of the vertical functional structure used by the scheduler is to be able to view the substitution of entities for subfunctions used in the manufacturing system. This information can lead to connections between functions and their subfunctions if substitutions are necessary during the manufacturing process. A complete analysis is required of the decomposition of the internal workings of a workstation or any internal functions which may be boundary functions for the next workstation. The boundary subfunctions are important to the scheduler so that if there are any superimposed functions, they are used to reallocate resources by the scheduler if any sort of repair or downtime is encountered during the manufacturing process.

These functional levels can be defined as to their order of execution utilized by the scheduler. The functions at the highest level can be viewed as *primary functions*. They determine which entities are used for the production of a particular process by the scheduler. The secondary functions utilized by the scheduler can also be viewed as execution functions. The primary functions are viewed by the scheduler as a means of representing the entire system. The resources that the scheduler uses are a key to the functionality of the entire manufacturing system. This requires that the scheduler be able to encompass a complex set of heuristically based rules to be able to represent a real-world manufacturing system.

The scheduler also has to be able to represent the subfunctions of the primary functional system. This requires the dissection of the primary functions into their subfunctional parts. If the subfunctional components of a scheduler are not adequately defined and grouped, then the entire primary function may be ill defined. Therefore, it is important that the scheduler be able to define the lowest level function or subfunction in the manufacturing system.

It is important to understand that the basic functions defined by the scheduler may be very simplistic and require only a few basic resources. This resource allocation, be it simplistic or based on very complex plant operation heuristics, is important to the overall functionality of the entire system.

The scheduler vertical structure really describes the organization of the entire functional system. The number of levels that are utilized by the scheduler should be defined in terms of the logical flow rather than the physical flow of the system [Crane and Lemoine 1977]. The logical flow utilized by the scheduler is important because it views a system in terms of logically related functions rather than the actual physical nature of the manufacturing system. Although some of the logical functions may not at present be in production in the physical system, it is important to understand logically the manufacturing system so that continual improvements can be added to the system.

It is also important for the scheduler to have a knowledge base of a logical hierarchy of levels utilized by the system so that any type of material flow or execution hierarchy can be viewed by the system from a macro level of activities that have to be performed down to the particular basic function for a workstation. This is also important so that if the plant environment is divided up into any sort of manufacturing sectors, they can be accounted for by the scheduler.

At a plant level a functional class such as workstation assembly is utilized by the scheduler as an overall production requirement. The warehousing of information is utilized by the scheduler as a rest activity. The workstation movement activity is utilized by the scheduler as an interplant requirement. The workstation verification class is utilized by the scheduler as a plant quality-control function. Also, it is important to understand that these same functions, e.g., workstation rest, movement, assembly, and verification, can be defined at a lower level.

5. ES Scheduling/Flexible Handling System Domains

The manufacturing system scheduler must be able to deal with a series of well-defined processes that are performed on a particular article to produce a finished product. These processes must be performed in a specified sequence. Other processes may be completed in a combination of sequences. To be able to take advantage of the strengths of a scheduler it is necessary to look at traffic patterns that are used in the manufacturing production system designed around these sequences of operation.

It is also important to understand how the particular transport mechanisms will work in conjunction with a scheduler to process parts and material. Assembly lines in the past have been of a very serial nature. The increasing use of robot systems and other general-purpose computer-controlled machines will result in facilities utilizing a scheduler capable of producing a wider range of products which require different series of operations to be performed. In exploiting the new flexible manufacturing facilities with the aid of a scheduler one needs to be able to take advantage of a flexible material-handling system. This is important so that the scheduler can direct the particular material-handling mechanisms to arrive at a specified sequence depending on the part being manufactured.

With the increased amount of manufacturing that is done at a particular facility the scheduler will also need to be able to handle any sort of increases in the particular routes or traffic patterns between robot workstations. The minimum number of paths between particular stations for a facility with n stations is described by the number of permutations of n things taken two at a time, assuming that (a) there is only one path from a given station to each other workstation or (b) if multiple paths exist, only one is used.

The larger the value of n, the more time consuming it is to generate the paths between particular workstations. If there happen to be multiple paths between robot workstations, the problem of generating all possible paths is further complicated. In a typical flexible manufacturing environment, all particular paths must be understood by the scheduler and any centralized computer performing other controlling operations. Any sort of changes to the particular manufacturing facility must be incorporated into the scheduler with a minimum of trouble so that the expert system will be able to redirect and redeploy the manufacturing resources as necessary.

Algorithms that have been used in the past for solving routing problems by something such as a scheduler may not be completely adequate for a real-world environment. The algorithm proposed by the scheduler should allow for components of any sort of flexible manufacturing system to make all necessary routing decisions at particular intersections without being constrained by too much of a global knowledge of the entire system. For additional background information let us discuss the possible types of material-transport mechanisms that are utilized in the plant environment today and the incorporation of routing algorithms with the AI/ES scheduler. It is important to have a survey of the various types of material-transporting mechanisms.

Material-Transport Systems

The main function of any type of material-transport system is to move objects from one particular robot workstation to another. It is also possible to assume that any sort of material that is transported may be carried on a pallet, but this may not be true in all plant environments. Material-transport mechanisms may be divided into three general categories, such as carriers, conveyors, and other material-transport systems. It is also important to note that one of the main scheduler operations is to allow for buffering at selected workstations in the plant environment. This buffering will provide a queue to assist the scheduler in minimizing the time that a particular robot workstation may be idle and waiting for work. In addition to this, workstation buffering can also provide a place for work in progress to accumulate before that particular robot workstation happens to implement it.

Types of Material-Transport Mechanisms

The types of material-transport mechanisms may be listed as power carriers, automatically guided vehicles, power-and-free conveyors, tow-cart systems, rail-guided vehicle systems, conveyors, roller conveyors, belt conveyors, air-cushion conveyors, modular conveyors, other material handlers, automatic storage/retreival systems, and stationary robot systems [Christofides 1986].

A power carrier system is one which transports material from one station to the next on some form of powered cart. This cart is usually electrically powered. Other types of vehicles can fit into this general category such as rail-guided vehicles or automatically guided vehicles (AGVs).

Automatically guided vehicles are wheeled, battery-powered carts that move in the factory system. The key component of these vehicles is an electronic control system which follows a predefined path on a floor or a photoelectric system that could be positioned on the walls in the plant. This path that is used by the AGV system may be a wire or a special paint on the floor. The wire-guided cart usually takes advantage of the emissions of a radio-frequency signal which may be tracked and also used for communication between the guided vehicle and a central computer. It is also important to note that the scheduler also plays a vital role in incorporating this real-time control information. Different types of frequencies are used to distinguish the paths and echelons used by these guided vehicles. The commands are such to speed up the movement of the cart, direct the cart to turn left or right, or even sound the horn at a particular workstation. In addition to that, the level of sophistication of some automatically guided vehicles is such that they can even recognize objects that may be in their path, such as their human counterpart, or they may contain a complete map of the plant environment and its paths through an on-board computer system. A power-and-free conveyor system is one that rides on a set of rails, or which may be on the floor suspended overhead. The carrier is driven by a chain system that is continually in motion. By discontinuing the carrier from a particular power source the carrier may stop at a particular workstation or a buffered area. This disconnection or buffering could also be done by information fed to the scheduler. This mechanical connecting and disconnecting of the carrier from the particular power source lends itself to increased mechanical functions over the long term. Also, a set of specialized skills may be necessary in the plant environment for routine maintenance of activities.

Another wheeled carrier that is used on the factory floor is the tow cart. It can be used on the floor or in an overhead situation. There are mechanical switches used to divert the tow cart to the appropriate path or from one path to another. The control of the tow cart is determined by connecting or disconnecting the tow chain speed in the system. Again, because of the highly mechanical nature of a vehicle such as this, there is an increased probability of mechanical failure over the long term. A rail-guided vehicle, on the other hand, utilizes an electric motor resident in the system. The power used for this system is from a particular supporting rail. Any type of change in the vehicle's direction is accomplished mechanically. This system also uses sensors to determine where it is and the destination or identification during an approach to a particular switching mechanism. The problem with this system is that these rails are less easily changed to incorporate a higher degree of flexibility in a plant environment than other types of design strategies.

A conveyor system is one which acts as a carrier of materials in a particular plant. Some of these conveyor systems utilize rollers, belts, air cushions, or modular conveyors. Again an important thing to remember is that with these types of fixed mechanical systems there is inherently less flexibility in terms of modification for future manufacturing processes by the plant.

Roller conveyors use power rollers to convey materials along a predetermined path. There is a wide range of mechanical switches that allow a particular part to be diverted during its movement on the plant floor. Some of these mechanisms may utilize belts which apply the appropriate amount of force on the part to divert it or lift it into another predetermined direction.

Continuous power belts are motorized by pulley systems. The problem with the belt conveyor system is that it is usually very linear or straight-line in nature. It is possible to be able to use this system to negotiate curves or turn at right angles but this is more difficult than for other carriers mentioned previously. Another factor is that usually these systems allow for the movement of material in one particular direction. If an opposite direction is needed, then the entire system must be stopped and put into an opposite setting.

Air-cushion conveyors utilize the flow of air under a particular line to propel a pallet along a particular path. These air jets can also be used to divert the pallet on a particular floor in this track system, which allows for routing control. The limitation of an air carrier or air-cushion conveyor system is in the weight of material that can be used with this system.

A modular conveyor system is one that utilizes shortened belt-powered assemblies. It also allows the use of electric motors and sensors in terms of shifting material from one point to another. The advantage of a modular conveyor system is that each of these modules may be individually controllable and thus the system is flexible to changes in the plant environment.

It should also be noted that these are not the only types of material movers that are used in a plant environment. Plants in the United States are very rich in schemes for moving material from one robot station to another. That is why with the discussion here it should be realized that these are the generic types of carriers that are utilized in a workstation environment, but there is also a wide variety of other carriers available on the market today.

An automatic storage/retrieval system is one which utilizes vertical hoists and can also move laterally in the aisles between rows of shelves. A picker mechanism is utilized to move a pallet to a particular aisle, then the choice of a particular row and shelf is noted by the computer controller and the picker may move the pallet up to its end-point placement. The automatic storage/ retrieval system has been used with success in a number of automated warehouses in the country. It allows for the automation of storage and retrieval of pallets of material or finished products to be used in a warehouse without human intervention. This lack of human intervention also means that specialized heating or cooling requirements may not be needed in that part of the plant or lighting requirements may not be necessary, because of the lack of warehouse personnel in that particular environment.

Robots should also be considered as part of a material mover. Their perfect nature of being able to pick-and-place material from one point to another has had a great deal of success with many industrial robot systems. It is also exciting that any sort of deviation between this pick-and-place path and another can easily be changed through the computer controller that is utilized at that particular workstation. There is some work being done on utilizing robot arms combined with automatic guided-vehicle systems. The problems with some of the accuracy and reliability of these particular automated characters are still being studied. In the near future automated guided vehicles will be utilized for material movement combined with a robot manipulator which is attached to the guided vehicle.

6. Analyzing Plant-Floor Traffic Patterns

Since we now have a good understanding of the type of vehicles that would be utilized by an AI/ES scheduler in relation to robot workstations in a plant environment, it is important to know the type of traffic patterns that would be utilized in terms of scheduling purposes for the scheduler. It is possible to examine three basic types of traffic patterns of increasing complexity and also to examine the common features and layouts of robot workstations in relation to these traffic patterns.

Sequential Workstation Flow Patterns

The sequential workstation flow pattern shown in Fig. 3 is the implementation of a single sequence of processes very similar to existing manufacturing systems. For example, material may be loaded into one workstation as input and removed from another workstation as output. Some buffering may be taking place in the system. The means of traveling between robot workstations may involve passing through buffering at each workstation in route. Routing is very simplistic because it is very serial in nature. This type of pattern does not take advantage of the flexibility of an FMS coupled with an AI/ES scheduler because material may have to wait at each workstation before it is used as input to that workstation or output to the next workstation. Also, if there is a problem of quality control at one of the middle workstations, then the part must have to recycle through all the workstations or require a special run to correct that existing assembly problem [Gershwin, Akella, and Choong 1985].

Cyclic Workstation Flow Patterns

The next type of traffic flow pattern can be described as a cyclic workstation flow pattern. See Fig. 4. This level of sophistication of a traffic flow pattern by our scheduler incorporates any type of serial pattern by dedicating buffers on particular spurs off a main loop type of flow control system. If any sort of carrier needs to return to the main loop after processing, it can utilize the subloop and buffering system to take advantage of the capabilities of a particular robot workstation.

It should be understood that this type of traffic pattern can take advantage of any sort of quality control checks so that errors may be buffered and recycled through a particular workstation. The scheduler can now take advantage of a more complex set of variables in terms of the routing that it has to deal with. One problem, for example, may be just the following of material in the main loop until the appropriate subloop that contains the destination is needed. For a particular carrier or pallet to go into that subloop a decision must be made by the scheduler whether it is appropriate to enter that particular subloop to utilize the functions of that particular robot workstation. The main loop can also be utilized by the scheduler as a type of secondary buffering process and can recirculate materials until they are needed by a particular robot workstation.

The overall problem of this type of pattern is that it is still necessary for a particular component to traverse a loop or visit each series of workstations

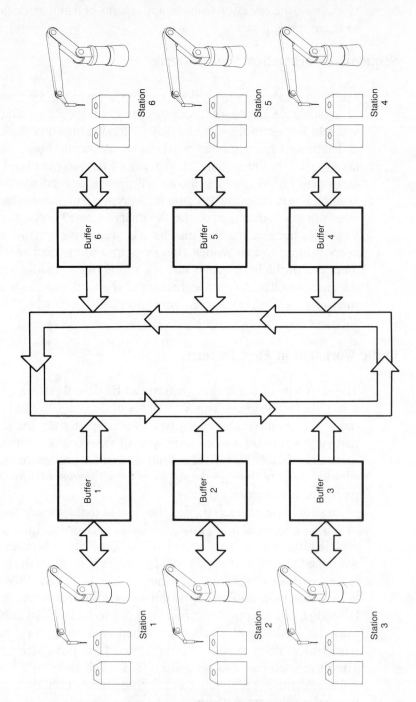

Fig. 3. Sequential workstation flow pattern.

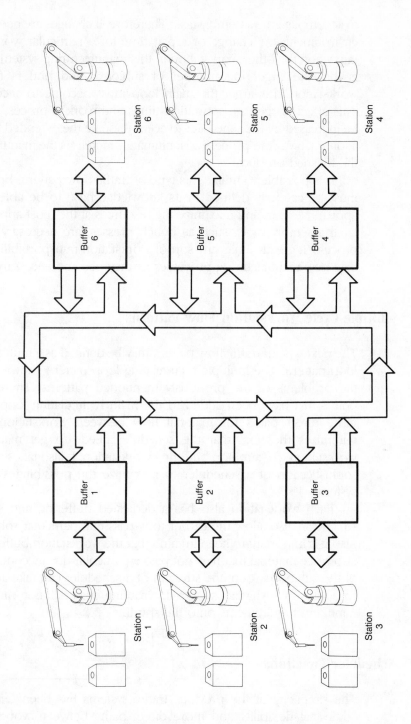

Fig. 4. Cyclic workstation flow pattern.

to accomplish the assembly task. Therefore, if changes are needed in the plant environment, the change or repair time for a particular workstation has an impact on the other workstation in this manufacturing system. Another factor is that the larger the number of subloops and buffers for a particular workstation, the larger the main loop must become to accommodate this. This affects larger transportation times and work-in-process inventory must be increased by the scheduler to accommodate the extended travel time. This additional work-in-process cost ultimately increases the manufacturing cost of the finished product.

It is possible to utilize this type of traffic flow pattern, but the scheduler must be carefully defined in its knowledge base to be able to control the appropriate part and maximize the resources at the most appropriate time. If large assembly tools, such as punch presses, are necessary in this type of process, it greatly limits any sort of workstation transportability to accommodate new manufacturing processes as they become necessary.

Multiple-Cycle Workstation Flow Patterns

The next type of traffic flow pattern may be defined as a multiple recirculating loop pattern. The multiple recirculating loop pattern shown in Fig. 5 solves the problems of the previously mentioned patterns. There are crossover points that have been added to the main recirculating loop which provide more direct paths for material flow between workstations. This further minimizes the time that the scheduler needs to get material from one workstation to a subloop buffering workstation. It also takes advantage of the sophistication of a scheduler to maximize the possibilities of the existing system.

Each workstation also has a dedicated buffering and subloop system which can also allow the carrier to bypass that particular robot workstation. Also it is important to keep in mind that the workstation buffering system can also place material that may not pass a particular quality control of a spurline of the subloop. Again, the strength of a scheduler can take advantage of this type of very dynamic system by routing material not meeting specified minimum requirements onto the spurline.

Scheduler Functions

The simplicity of the previous traffic systems has been decreased so that additional flexibility and more direct paths between workstations can be utilized with this traffic flow system. The true strengths of an AI/ES scheduler are required to handle the complex decisions necessary for the best possible

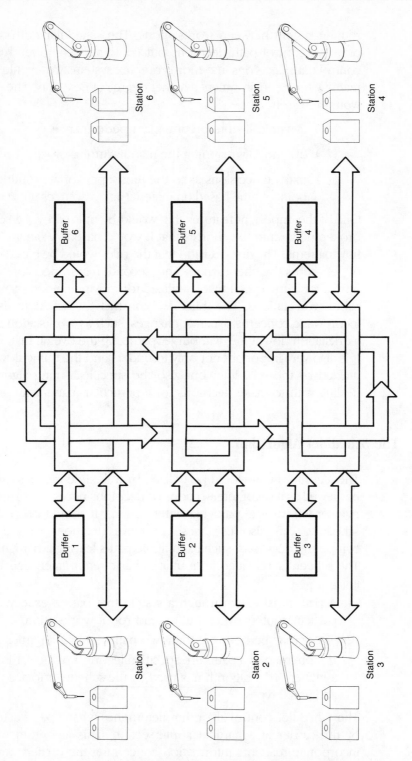

Fig. 5. Multiple-cycle workstation flow pattern.

routing system between workstations. The scheduler not only could utilize primitive control path decisions but could also compound those particular control path decisions into more complex systems that would give the overall manufacturing environment a higher degree of flexibility. The AI/ES scheduler would in essence be

(*a*) dynamically interpreting plant performance,

(*b*) dynamically mapping the manufacturing process on the plant floor,

(*c*) making decisions as to the most appropriate routing at a particular point in time based on material and resources utilized by the system.

One of the important features that would be utilized by the scheduler can be broken down into the choices that it would have to examine for these traffic flow patterns. The first decision that the rules would be based on is the choice of left turns by the carrier. The second major decision utilized by the scheduler is the speed that is utilized for moving particular material between robot workstations. The third decision that the scheduler is to be able to incorporate concerns dynamic changes, such as workstation maintenance or workstation downtime, without jeopardizing the overall manufacturing goals. It is also very important not only to understand the traffic flow patterns to be utilized by the scheduler but also the specific routing algorithms that it is dealing with to make decisions for a particular manufacturing system.

The Scheduler Algorithm

The algorithm that would be utilized by a flexible manufacturing system can be viewed as a set of intersections or decisions necessary by the scheduler for right or left turns at particular intersections. It should also be noted that the scheduler can also use these primitive decisions of right and left for compound decisions, such as multiple paths leaving a particular intersection. The scheduler rule algorithm utilizes basic requirements such as the following:

1. A path must exist through a system that passes exactly once through a particular intersection, buffer, and robot workstation.
2. There may be no more than two paths leaving a particular intersection.
3. If more than two paths are specified leaving a particular intersection, then a higher-order algorithm is used by the scheduler to accommodate these additional types.

The scheduler control algorithm determines what type of action is necessary by the carrier at a particular intersection. This algorithm must be able to incorporate real-time information concerning the carrier movements in that particular plant environment. Another advantage of the scheduler is to be able to simulate the motion of carriers at any point in time to be used to train individuals in the plant environment or assist plant managers in looking at possible future manufacturing processes and their impact on the existing manufacturing system.

One of the most important components of the utilization of routing algorithms by the scheduler is that it not only views the plant environment's physical nature but also incorporates logical-machine entities in addition to the physical workstation machines. The incorporation of a logical machine in addition to a physical machine is such that one can assign alternative logical names to logical machines to increase the flexibility of the manufacturing process flow; thus a physical machine may have multiple logical names utilized by the scheduler. This also enables the scheduler to be able to have enough flexibility in terms of incorporating scheduling algorithms in a very complex routing scheme. The key to the assessment of the most appropriate path will be the incorporation of not only physical workstation functions and addresses but also the logical nature of those workstation functions and addresses.

Another essential ingredient of the scheduler routing algorithm is to be able to determine the length of paths in the system and to assess the appropriateness of a particular path utilized or material utilized by the manufacturing system. A numbering scheme is utilized by the scheduler to look at switches or intersections on the traffic flow pattern. When a particular component proceeds through the system, the scheduler is constantly reviewing resources necessary for assembly, material necessary for assembly, and the time for switching the carrier at the appropriate moment to the appropriate logical and physical workstation address.

At any particular point the scheduler routing algorithm views a particular switch point as a choice between paths. The order of precedence in the rules is for the scheduler to look at the first switch point encountered on a path. This switch point is viewed as a first candidate if the rules decide that it is an appropriate candidate for utilization. The scheduler routing algorithm will weigh the data of the candidate intersection and its subsequent length as being the most appropriate path to route material to the appropriate workstation. If the conditions are inappropriate, then it will make the decision not to switch to that particular path.

Certainty Factors

Another important advantage of the scheduler will be the inclusion of certainty factors in the system. With certainty-factor rules not only can IF-THEN-ELSE decisions be made by the routing algorithm, but also fuzzy logic can be incorporated so that a broader range of manufacturing flow decisions for logical and physical workstations can be embedded into this system. An example of this is to switch a carrier to a particular workstation based on a number of rules indicating a cumulative positive certainty or cumulative negative certainty. This aggregated certainty of fuzzy logic takes advantage of the fact that decisions on routing made in a plant environment may not necessarily be limited to 100% purely programmatical schemes. The fuzzy logic rule system incorporates these cumulative certainty factors based on conditions occurring on the plant floor.

Changes in the Manufacturing System

The most important aspect of the scheduler routing algorithm is that its utilization in terms of routing is based on a workstation level, so that any changes to the existing manufacturing system are easily made or have very little effect on other workstations. An example would be that if additional robot workstations and buffers are added in a particular traffic pattern, they can be very easily incorporated into the scheduler by simply adding the appropriate rules based on the appropriate routing algorithm.

This allows for the scheduler to be able to incorporate new workstations very dynamically in terms of their logical and physical functions. The routing choices made by the scheduler can be made very simply by considering a particular carrier's destination in regard to the number of logical paths, or the scheduler can incorporate inferencing techniques which take advantage of fuzzy logic, which can look at making decisions based on rules. These rules are the aggregated certainty of previous decisions based on the dynamic nature of the plant at any particular point in time. Incorporating these fuzzy logic decisions by the scheduler increases the flexibility of the plant environment not just arithmetically but geometrically in the type of outputs, both short term and long term, with regard to the competitiveness of the particular plant.

7. ES Scheduling/Flexible Plant Production Control Domains

There are three major areas in a flexible plant production control system that can utilize the functions of a scheduler. These three areas are part and tool production, materials assembly, and material handling and storage. We will look at all three of these areas in relation to how a scheduler might enhance these functions that exist in factories of today.

Continuous and Discrete Manufacturing

First, it is important to understand an overview of the manufacturing process before we examine the impact of AI in terms of part and tool production. Manufacturing can be viewed as having two major categories, such as continuous manufacturing and discrete manufacturing. Continuous manufacturing may be defined in terms of something such as a chemical goods production system. This is one in which there are continuous steps that must be resolved before other steps in the manufacturing process can take place. The other type of manufacturing process is discrete manufacturing. Discrete manufacturing can be the use of mechanical assembly processes such as robotics to put together specific parts. An automobile or airplane manufacturing system is an example of the discrete manufacturing process; manufacturing such things as washing machines, stoves, or refrigerators is also discrete manufacturing. It should also be noted that discrete manufacturing, such as in the areas of electronics or electronic component assembly, is also another candidate for implementation of a scheduler. For the purposes of this discussion we will examine the impact of a scheduler in terms of the discrete manufacturing process.

Part and Tool Production

To examine the part and tool production component, a model should be discussed which looks at the overall processes in a manufacturing system. These processes consist of phases which include the part design phase, and the part process phase, and the part assembly phase.

Part Design Phase

The part design phase is one which deals with the initial design concept of the part to be manufactured. The basic ideas of the product are generated and may be developed in some sort of prototype or research-and-development testing. The constraints that are put on the product by the scheduler are many and varied in nature. It is through this ability of the scheduler in terms of part and tool production to be as flexible as possible to incorporate the real-world factors that will have an impact on the manufacturing process at this point. Initially, from product planning there begins a specific set of functions and performances in packaging of the process that will affect the manufacturing system. It is also important to note that a lot of information will come from research investigating the impact of technologies from other vendors. These considerations will be incorporated into design of the part or tool. Another factor which will affect this process is the conceptual design of the particular product. From all of these factors management and the engineering staff will establish goals specific to engineering constraints. These goals will be incorporated into the scheduler to enable this information to be passed on to other parts of the manufacturing process.

The next major component of the design phase is one which incorporates the best design of the particular part to be put into production. At this point the engineering staff examines that particular part or design concept for strengths and limitations. Any sort of constraints that have been defined in the initial concept phase are passed to the particular detail engineering phase at this point. It is hoped that concept limitations may be overcome by the engineering staff. These constraints are also ones which will be incorporated in the scheduler so appropriate resources of personnel and material can be scheduled at the most appropriate point. An example of what happens at this point would be that the list of specific features or functions that have been incorporated are now defined and analyzed into their individual parts. Also, a documentation system is set up so that specific information can be incorporated into manuals for maintenance or production assembly personnel. A detailed analysis with extensive calculations is developed to support the particular design of the part or tool to be put into production. This step also includes any sort of prototypical or test feedback data.

Another important component is the analysis for manufacturing the particular product. A detailed analysis would include not only the development of a new particular part but, just as important, the synthesis of any existing parts which could meet the requirements of the particular product. In addition to this the search would include information from the existing data base of component design or from vendors outside the corporation. The scheduler is able to incorporate the detailed product specification and pass this information on in terms of material and plant resources to the process phase.

Part Process Phase

The process phase is close to the part design phase except the focus now of the scheduler in this phase is toward the actual manufacturing production system itself. The initial step is one in which the product is now viewed from a production standpoint, and a test may be run. A number of manufacturing constraints may be extracted from this design phase. Just as important is the ability to look at resources that are available on the plant floor and also personnel and materials. The scheduler at this point plays a key role because of its ability to look at the resources of both material and personnel inside and outside the plant dynamically and incorporate these into the overall manufacturing system.

One important side aspect of this process is to provide information to management that may be translated into any sort of budgetary limitations which can be evaluated as appropriate or inappropriate in manufacturing this product. The most important aspect of this phase is one of the final checks to determine whether the tool or part to be manufactured is to be put into the final manufacturing process. The second major component of this phase is to look at incorporation of engineering testing in a prototypical manufacturing process. The functions that are incorporated by the scheduler at this phase are the availability of facilities. This would incorporate functions which would dictate whether a component of the total product or tool should be built by the existing manufacturing plant or whether this should be bought or assembled by a particular subcontractor. The scheduler also will provide information so that if the "build function" is decided upon, the ordering of materials, tooling, or parts can be planned for at this point.

A parallel function of the scheduler also incorporates whether the tools that exist in the manufacturing process can be used in series or in parallel for the design of the product at this point. This is important so that if any special tooling requests are needed, they can be noted and approved by management. Therefore the scheduler must have a working knowledge of the toolmaking that is available for the manufacturing process so that decisions can be made to utilize existing or other plant resources. Another important factor is that if a decision has to be made so that the mechanical aspect of the manufacturing process at this point needs to be restructured for any multilayered or hierarchical process, these decisions can be provided to management.

The ability of the scheduler to assist management in terms of a "build/buy" decision is very critical [Beregi 1984]. The scheduler can provide information to assist management on whether to buy a particular part in terms of the overall cost in the manufacturing process or to use existing tools or parts that are available. The scheduler can also provide information as to the appropriateness or inappropriateness of parts being manufactured within the plant. The final outcome of this particular phase should be the material assembly phase for manufacturing.

Part Assembly Phase
This phase is described at length in the following section.

Material Assembly

After the design and planning phase of a particular part or component the final process is to assemble the actual component. The scheduler at this point looks at resources of raw materials and tools necessary that have been approved specific to the production schedules of equipment, such as robot workstations, numerically controlled machines, and material-handling machines. In addition to this the scheduler also looks at inspection or testing of the finished product and incorporates these quantities into the overall schedule/material/cost requirements. The scheduler provides information specific to the best incorporation of different types of workstations in the existing plant. It also looks at the finishing phases and also the impact of existing storage requirements. The scheduler is viewing information in terms of a generalized assembly and its relation to material-handling and storage requirements.

The constraints that may affect the AI/ES scheduler at this point are incorporated and designated to management for approval. Again management has the option to view any sort of constraints provided to it by the scheduler in terms of production time and costs. The main focus of the scheduler is very specific to the actual plant floor. The previous phases were looking at the engineering or research phases of the particular product and incorporation of resources necessary at those points. The scheduler is viewing information highly specific to the existing manufacturing system and subcontractors for component parts of the existing manufacturing system. The key to success of the scheduler is its flexibility to incorporate fuzzy logic specific to actual plant-floor work scenarios.

The fuzzy logic function of the scheduler will allow designers to incorporate functions such as "Murphy's law" in expressing the reality of the actual plant floor. This fine tuning of the scheduler through fuzzy logic produces an expert system which incorporates accurate real-world outcome information to management. The incorporation of the scheduler of workers and material in previous phases may be fairly linear or arithmetical in nature. The strength of the scheduler is to incorporate fuzzy logic at this point so that inferencing can take over and provide information that is highly specific to the manufacturing system as it exists on the plant floor of a particular manufacturer [Kempf 1985].

The important component of this phase is the actual final phase of the product. If the information is not applied appropriately at this point, then the information provided to management as to actual production schedules and cost may not be very reliable. If the information provided at this point is faulty, then this also requires the reincorporation of system design or system processing phase information. This directly affects the cost and marketability of any part or tool being assembled.

Material Handling and Storage

There are many components or aspects to the whole area of material handling and storage and the impact of AI/ES systems. The area which will be discussed here is one which would incorporate a scheduler utilizing information specific to machine vision. In previous sections of this book the various aspects of machine vision have been described. There are also excellent examples described by Professors Gonzalez and Brzakovic in their chapters, which deal with the technical limitations of computer vision and its impact on industrial robots. In addition to this it is very exciting to look at the incorporation of artificial intelligence with machine vision and industrial robots. To be able to do this incorporates the dynamic analysis of the particular part of material by the machine vision and passing this information on to the robot system for appropriate handling of that material. This dynamic analysis is the key concept in the coalescence of artificial intelligence, machine vision, and robotics.

Previous discussions by Drs. Ahmed and Gonzalez and Brzakovic have provided an understanding of how machine vision works. It is important to note that a system that incorporates edge detection does not satisfy the requirement of future industrial robot machine-vision systems. The incorporation of edge detection into an expert system to recognize a particular part or material to be handled is the goal of research and a requirement of future manufacturing processes. It should also be noted that just being able to identify a particular component is less important than the recognition of the component and how it is dealt with by the robot system. The ability of a robot machine-vision system to use two-dimensional images with edge detection is providing guidance to robot and monitoring processes today. The ability to incorporate analysis of parts or components in the manufacturing system will be necessary in the future. The ability to view parts and components the way human beings do is the goal of existing machine vision research today. The problems in the past have involved the massive requirements of computational power necessary to fulfill these objectives.

Not only the ability to view parts in terms of a three-dimensional scene but, more importantly, to be able to incorporate an analysis of that information and direct the particular robot during this process are most important. The latter capability requires a number of different transformation algorithms to represent images at multiple resolution layers. Also, it becomes necessary to be able to filter any sort of images so that the computational problems of constraints in the past can be eliminated. To accomplish this it is necessary to view images as data structures which may be dissected or connected specific to the requirements of the robot workstation. To do this dissection or connection is known as *incorporating shape primitives.*

Shape primitives use expert systems to dissect or assemble images as is deemed necessary for that particular workstation. In addition to this, there may be multiple types of input which must be utilized by the shape-analyzing ES and matched during a dynamic analysis process.

The shape-analyzing ES can use a variety of algorithms which incorporate the structure of three-dimensional surfaces. Each shape-analyzing ES will be taught an initial representation of a particular component in terms of its shape, structure, and composition. This will enable the ES to use this information to base other conclusions about the processes in the workstation.

In the material-handling and storage processes there will be a hierarchy of expert systems that will be utilized by the robot workstation. We have discussed the role of the scheduler for the overall control of the plant floor and specific control of the robot workstation. Another component of the AI/ES scheduler will be utilized to be able to incorporate appropriate representations of a part as observed from the machine vision system into its overall planning algorithm. An example of this would be that the texture information observed by the expert system will provide information to the robot in terms of surface edge location, robot orientation, and weight information in terms of shading information. In addition to this, the ES vision systems would be able to incorporate information in terms of shading specific to strengths of the part or component being moved. For example, the shading or surface texture of a block of metal moving down an assembly process would be totally different from the shading and structure of a piece of plastic moving down the assembly line. This information is critical for a robot vision system that can grasp metal pieces and use them appropriately and differentiate them, by means of weight and structure, from weaker materials, such as plastics or woods.

To accomplish this the ES would look at a previous or abbreviated template of that particular component and also incorporate information such as shading information. From this the machine vision AI system is able to determine whether the shape is the correct one and it can also look at the relationship between the light and the orientation of the shape and provide this information to the robot manipulator. These actions are based on some very sophisticated physical and geometric rules. They incorporate features such as the optics of surface lumination and reflectance and intensity measurements by the AI machine vision system.

A modular form of a machine vision design philosophy is also very important. With the ability to incorporate different types of modules of machine vision AI systems that can discriminate features such as texture, color, or shading, a system is able to perform a wide variety of functions. When new part shapes are to be used by a particular robot-workstation machine-vision system with a modular design, a particular module with software may be added to that AI machine-vision system. If particular modules become obsolete, then the software for those modules can be deleted from the AI machine-vision system. The different types of modules will provide the constraint analysis and also hardware and software requirements and processing requirements necessary for the AI machine-vision system.

In addition to this the modules can be incorporated into the AI/ES scheduler because varying amounts of time are necessary for the processing of a robot workstation, depending on the particular component being viewed by the machine vision system. This timing information can then be included in the overall production schedule for that particular robot workstation.

Another important component of the material-handling ES is one that will incorporate *composite modeling*. Composite modeling is the ability of the machine vision ES to determine the component parts of any structure that it is working with; it graphically dissects or breaks the part being handled into its component parts. The ability of the AI machine-vision system to incorporate composite modeling is very important to the functions of the robot workstation.

The composite model may be information that is contained in a particular data base at some point. For example, the composite model may have been developed on a CAD/CAM system during the initial product development phase. The composite model formed by the machine vision ES will be utilized for analysis of particular points for information provided to the robot. For example, if a composite model indicates a weakness of the structure of the particular part to be picked or placed by the robot, then this information is conveyed to the robot manipulator so that the end effector is placed at the strongest point of the particular part to be picked up. In another example, it is possible for the AI machine vision composite modeling system to know about a particular stress point of the component being worked on by the robot manipulator. It then provides information so that if the end effector on the robot is equipped with a tactile sensing device, the sensing of the pressure of the gripper is such that it does not overpressurize the part that is picked up.

One of the particular problems of a composite modeler in terms of an AI machine-vision system on the workstation is the processing power. If during the assembly process the ES needs information specific to a component model, then how might this then have an impact on the overall production rates of that particular robot workstation? If composite modeling requirements slow down the overall production time of that particular workstation, then composite modeling is a detriment more than an asset to the ES for that robot workstation.

If on the other hand a composite model may be utilized in the AI machine-vision robot workstation, then this could add to overall workstation production speed. For example, if a composite model of a particular part being assembled is used, rather than the entire machine vision image, then this requires less processing power in the analysis and subsequent orientation of the robot arm for that particular part. Specifically, an abbreviated image such as might be provided through a composite model might be used for ES vision and robot orientation rather than the actual visual image. In this sense, the visual image may be used as only a template-matching or verification scheme to determine that the proper part is being used.

Another aspect of a material-handling AI machine vision is in dimensional conversion. For example, if a machine vision system utilizes a simple two-dimensional input, then a module of an AI machine-vision system could convert this to a three-dimensional perception. The ability of the AI machine vision system to make this conversion could also help to alleviate some of the computational problems that have been encountered in past machine vision systems. The ability of the AI machine vision system to unify its perception of a particular object to provide orientation information to the robot manipulator might also help to keep the workstation at production-line speed requirements. Again, as mentioned previously, if the AI machine vision system computations take great amounts of time, then this negates the value of incorporating AI machine vision at a robot workstation.

The abilities of different modules of an AI machine vision system could bring to bare certain heuristics. Also, rules or heuristics might be incorporated which could fill in information necessary for the robot without extensive computation of the actual visual image itself. For example, if an abbreviated image is supplied by the machine vision system and an ES module fills in the necessary information for robot orientation and handling, then production-line speed requirements could be met.

Also, image preconceptions might be utilized to reduce computational time necessary for the AI machine vision system. For example, if an AI machine vision module has incorporated into it or has been "taught" a preconception or template of a particular part, then the machine vision system would only be utilized to deal with the taught template.

One theory of development in terms of teaching machines to understand or learn surfaces and relationships is one which extrapolates from a two-dimensional system or image. The basic image is defined as the $2\frac{1}{2}$-dimension or "sketch" stage. Thus an ES module is able to understand a three-dimensional image from a limited amount of input information such as a $2\frac{1}{2}$-dimension image. The strengths of this design philosophy again are such that the reduction of processing time necessary by the AI machine vision system results in a better throughput time for the overall robot workstation. This overall throughput or the preconceived or $2\frac{1}{2}$-dimension requirements of AI machine vision modules is information that would be incorporated into the AI/ES scheduler so that overall workstation and plant flow requirements will be appropriately designated.

The ability of the AI/ES scheduler to incorporate features such as part and tool production, material assembly, and material handling and storage is specific to a hierarchy of AI modules that are necessary for the functioning of the robot system vision workstation. This hierarchy of ES modules enables the workstation to be able to deal with a wide and changing variety of functions necessary for that particular workstation. Also, this design philosophy of modularization of functions of AI systems enables the existing processing hardware to swap modules as necessary for the requirements of that workstation at any point during the manufacturing day. Modularization of ESs would also enable the knowledge engineers, who might need to change any particular module, to substitute modules, perform the necessary maintenance on the rules for that particular module, and place those back into a production mode without jeopardizing the functionality of that particular robot workstation.

For example, if a module specific to the assembly of a radio for an automobile needed rules that were updated, then that module could be modified and tested by the knowledge engineers with their particular processor. When the knowledge engineers find that the inference making of their new rules was performing appropriately, then they could substitute this module for the module that was currently operating at that particular workstation.

Just as exciting is the transfer of new AI modules over existing data communication lines. If necessary, a diskette could be exchanged between the knowledge engineering development and testing group and the particular robot workstation to be upgraded. This exchange would require a minimum necessary amount of time for the actual upgrading of that robot workstation for the new component or radio that is going to be used. This ability to make changes in a short amount of time is a critical component of true flexibility in the manufacturing systems of the future.

The AI/ES scheduler could also be defined to incorporate any sort of changes necessary at robot workstations and resources necessary during that time of workstation program modification. In the past where a retooling of a particular manufacturing system dictated the closing down of particular plants, now through the resources provided through a scheduler any plant closings would be unnecessary. The allocation of resource functions could be redirected if a particular robot workstation needed to be reprogrammed. This reprogramming could take a minimal amount of time and could cause only the loss of minutes of production as compared with the loss of weeks in production that has occurred in the past. The scheduler can also redirect necessary resources and material, combined with the buffering of robot workstations, so that there is no loss in overall production of the entire system. This ability will assist in keeping production costs to their minimum requirements.

8. ES Scheduler/Flexible Plant-Support Control Domains

Many times in the past it has been noted that without the proper engineering or maintenance activities on the machines that we deal with today their active life is greatly shortened. For example, with microprocessors being used to control automobile engines a higher level of sophistication and maintenance requirements is needed to deal with this increased complexity. Without the ability to maintain and diagnose problems in a production system that accepts the philosophy of ever-increasing complexity of machines and their interrelationships, the competitiveness of that particular manufacturing facility will decline. It is a fact that workstations with robots also require an increased level of sophistication and support by engineering and maintenance personnel.

The scarcity of large amounts of robotics engineers and diagnosticians or troubleshooters is something that is not unique to industrial robots. The large number of machines that are currently being used on the plant floor, such as numerically controlled machines and other computer controlled devices, require an increased number of highly skilled diagnostic or engineering personnel. To meet the needs of these higher levels of skills just in the area of machine maintenance and machine diagnostics will require the incorpo- ration of AI/ES systems. The ability to accurately and rapidly diagnose problems in a plant environment translates directly into lower overall production costs.

Malfunctions that may be electrical or mechanical for a robot workstation not only may cause a loss of money for the manufacturing system, but also may result in loss of life by a robot manipulator arm striking a worker. In addition to this, without the proper maintenance schedule on robot work- stations the overall functions of that workstation will decrease, the cost of the component being manufactured will increase, and customer dissatisfaction will also increase as will returned material.

Accurate and rapid diagnosis, and maintenance or prevention of faults by a particular robot workstation, are key ingredients of the success of that robot workstation in the future. The problem is that to accurately and quickly diagnose a problem at a machine workstation on the plant floor may require a skill that is extremely difficult and/or expensive to acquire. See Chart 1.

Chart 1. Machine Diagnosis Problem Set

1. Understand the normal machine functions
2. Understand the failed component and symptoms
3. Acquire a working knowledge about the failed equipment through questions and information
4. Synthesize the failed equipment operation and failure preconditions
5. Specify conclusions and additional testing

The problems of machine diagnosis are difficult because of the vast amount of experience that may be required depending on the complexity of the machine being diagnosed. First, an individual must understand how that machine functions normally. Specifically, an individual who has a robot engineer must have a working knowledge of the functioning of electronics, servomechanisms, and computer controllers. Second, an expert diagnostician requires information about the component that has failed and the symptoms surrounding the failure of that particular component. This again requires an understanding and practical background in the basic equipment and the kinds of different failures that can occur and preconditions for the failure of that equipment. Third, a working knowledge must be acquired of the types of information or questions to be asked about the failed piece of equipment. For example, if a robot manipulator stops during its normal operation, should questions be asked about the power being used by that robot workstation, or about the pneumatic equipment being used by that robot workstation, or about the hydraulics that are being used by that robot manipulator? Without a good understanding of the appropriate questions to ask, the amount of time to diagnose a problem is greatly extended, which results in increasing the amount of time the piece of equipment is not productive. Fourth, an expert diagnostician has the ability to synthesize the previous information and mentally represent what brought about the particular failure of the equipment, which component failed, and what the preconditions were for the failure of that particular component. This is important because to diagnose the failure of a robot workstation requires that additional information be used to determine if the precondition for failure could be repeated in the future. This knowledge will enable the maintenance personnel to avoid these particular preconditions or look for these preconditions in the future. The final and most important ability of the diagnostician is to be able to specify conclusions as to the problem and suggest tests to get additional information if necessary to confirm or deny that particular conclusion. For example, if information is supplied specific to the preconditions and actual failure of the robot workstation, is this information adequate so that an expert can diagnose the actual problem of the robot workstation? Or is there not enough information being provided to diagnose the problem adequately and recommend a solution? Or is there an inadequate amount of information being provided so that tests might be recommended to provide the minimal amount of information necessary to recommend the appropriate solution to the problem?

Gathering diagnostic data and interpreting it may have to be repeated many times. It is also important to keep in mind that each time the diagnostician provides tests, negative as well as positive information might be obtained specific to those tests. This negative information also defines specific types of tests necessary to be performed so that a minimum amount of positive information may be supplied to diagnose and correct a particular problem in the manufacturing environment. When all the appropriate questions and positive as well as negative diagnostic information have been provided, then the maintenance diagnostician is able to recommend an appropriate solution for a replaced or failed component.

The problem is very obvious in that the expertise required to become a good diagnostician is at a premium. Also, it is important to keep in mind that good diagnosticians or troubleshooters may have been promoted so that they are not directly involved in machine maintenance as they were in the past. This further limits the amount of expertise that is necessary or available to do machine diagnostics and troubleshooting in the plant. The compounded problem is that when these individuals are promoted, their ability to stay current on diagnosis and troubleshooting of equipment may also be deterred.

The option that is available to address problems such as this is through an AI/ES to assist in the area of plant-support control domains. An AI/ES provides a way of preserving the expertise of an equipment diagnostician. An AI/ES also provides a very consistent methodology of diagnosing and troubleshooting a problem of a piece of equipment on the plant floor. Using an AI/ES to do diagnosis and troubleshooting also greatly extends this function to a larger number of people than was previously available. In addition to this the incorporation of an AI/ES scheduler can provide insights into the amount of time necessary for a particular maintenance or repair activity and its impact on the overall production system. The scheduler can incorporate information from the machine diagnostic ES scheduler and redirect plant resources as appropriate to minimize any sort of deterrents to the overall production schedule. The key feature of the AI diagnostics system is the expertise extracted from diagnostic technicians and incorporated into an ES. This enables that particular machine diagnostician to provide advice and also teach individuals that may not have that much expertise in machine problem diagnosis and machine repair requirements.

The ever-increasing complexity and sophistication of not just the plant but the plant field-support system has been increasing despite the incorporation of automatic testing equipment. It has been noted that some of the automatic equipment tests that have been predesigned in a particular system require a high level of interpretation. The messages that are displayed by automatic test equipment require an expertise that may not be available in a local plant environment. In addition to this, some of the tests that may be performed during an automatic testing process may not be sophisticated enough with respect to the actual specific nature of the problem. For example, research has indicated that troubleshooting and retesting of sophisticated aircraft equipment such as the F16 can consume 50% or more of total worker-hours spent for repair. Test design and test automation comprise an engineering discipline in its own right. The level of sophistication necessary to design test equipment which incorporates a wide range of tests is very difficult in nature to obtain. Much of the information concerning automatic testing equipment has stemmed from confidentiality factors based on a history of failed components or parts. The problem has been that these automatic tests, which are designed into the systems, are related to individual components rather than overall system design. Also, there could be an underlying strategy for the use of specific tests, in terms of verification and isolation of faults, which may incorporate a higher level of expertise than is available.

One important concept in the arena of testing for maintenance activities is dependency modeling. Dependency modeling is the understanding of a system, such as a robot manipulator system, and checking the higher-order dependencies that are built into the system. This proceeds from a simple to a complex dependency relationship. The important thing to keep in mind with dependency modeling is that different components may have different life cycles. For example, a robot system on the plant floor consists of a computer controller and the actual manipulator itself. The manipulator servomotors might require one maintenance cycle per time frame as compared with the smaller number of cycles time frame on the electric components of the computer controller. That is why this complex relationship for one machine out on the plant floor must be coordinated by a scheduler. The large number of complex machines that are on the plant floor with their highly complex components makes it necessary to have a system to assist plant maintenance personnel in this function.

The general study of dependency relationships of systems looks at the way that the system is built. For example, there are certain components that are dependent for input data information so that they can perform their particular function. A servomotor must receive a command from the computer controller before it can move to a particular point which in turn moves the manipulator system. If there is a problem in the proper functioning of the data communication lines going to the computer controller because they have not been maintained appropriately, then this will lead to workstation downtime. The scheduler can incorporate the large amount of mathematical algorithms in order to identify these particular dependencies at the workstation level. A broad range of measures can then be recommended by the scheduler to isolate or utilize preventative maintenance on particular components at the robot workstation. Ambiguities will arise if the particular hierarchy of component dependency is ill-structured for a particular workstation. This will also result in a difficulty in isolating components during a particular fault.

The main function of the scheduler in the arena of facilities engineering maintenance is in fault isolation. Fault isolation means finding the component that may have failed in that particular robot workstation. When a particular fault strategy has been decided on by the maintenance personnel, the scheduler can take this information to buffer or reschedule work at that particular robot workstation if necessary. Also important is the fact that there may be multiple faults at a particular workstation. Again, the scheduler incorporates the algorithms of multiple faults at a single workstation or multiple faults at multiple workstations and provides expertise and assisting management in minimizing the amount of lost production time and maximizing existing resources.

The actual machine fault algorithm that the scheduler utilizes is specific to the search strategy that the maintenance personnel must utilize for a particular fault. The search strategies are algorithms that can occur in single or multiple instances. It is important that the scheduler not only understand these search strategies but, just as important, be able to compound these search strategies if multiple faults have been determined at one or more workstations.

In the arena of facilities engineering and maintenance the scheduler must incorporate an ordered structure for testing and fault resolution. This ordered structure is documented by the scheduler and then incorporated into the overall system. This forces the facilities engineering and maintenance person-nel to designate the particular sequence of tests and components in a hierarchy so as to be able to incorporate this information into the scheduler. This ordering of the fault hierarchy is a key to the scheduler and also in minimizing the amount of fault scheduling that has to occur at a particular workstation.

The next important concept that the scheduler embodies in regard to facilities engineering and maintenance is in utilizing the fault information that has been previously designated. It is important to note the quantity, amount, or type of information that is being utilized in the fault isolation strategy. This quality, amount, or type of information will indicate to the scheduler the state of the robot manipulator system while it is in a particular test mode. The understanding of not only the hierarchy but specifically of the quality, amount, and type of fault problems assists the scheduler in further refining the scheduling requirements for the other workstations during production in the plant.

The fact that the information may vary from one particular workstation to another is noted. For this reason again it is very important to have a scheduler that can incorporate a wide variety of rule bases to accommodate the broad range of faults that may occur at a particular workstation. Without this ability to deal with a wide variety of problems, the scheduler would give information only about the faults at a particular workstation with and accuracy of 40% or less. Without good information put into the algorithms of this component of the scheduler the outcome will be inappropriate in terms of information provided to management or plant maintenance personnel.

The fault isolation process is also dependent on the outcome of that isolation. The scheduler should also incorporate information in terms of balancing content so that when a test outcome has been obtained the redeployment of resources at this point can then occur. The scheduler can take information in fault content resolution and redirect and redeploy resources in the plant environment on successful completion of appropriate tests. The complexity of this system comes about because fault isolation may not be as linear in the real-world plant environment as discussed here. That is why a strong rule base for fault resolution is important to acknowledge to the scheduler the correction of the problem for resource deployment.

Another important component of the scheduler module which uses fault isolation is weighting information. There is a wide variety of tests and failure rates and test times that will be utilized by the scheduler. It is very important that there be a weighting system in terms of certainty factors and fuzzy logic, which are used by the scheduler. For example, there are some fault tests that are extremely complicated or lengthy in nature. Other fault tests may be costly, whereas some tests may be extremely simple to perform. The ability to attach a weight in terms of certainty factors and aggregated certainty factors to the type of testing performed is a critical component of the algorithms utilized by the AI/ES scheduler.

Some weighting schemes have been developed which review factors such as the expense of the test being performed. The test expense can be defined as a value that can be inversely proportional to the test frequency. The AI/ES scheduler weighting factors are specific to such factors as test time, mean time between failures, plan costs, and maintenance costs.

The time of test activity examines the value of information inversely proportional to the time required to perform a test. The data from the mean time between failures test is inversely proportional to the probability of test failure.

The plan costs are those costs that have been predetermined by the vendor for particular repair activities.

Routine maintenance costs are those costs which have been defined by the vendor for maintenance at regular intervals on a particular system or components.

These weighting factors can be incorporated by the scheduler and may be generalized to a wide variety of machines on the plant floor. Each of these weighting systems will provide the scheduler with more information that can be incorporated into its rule base. With these factors and the other factors mentioned previously in regards to fault hierarchy with specific goals, this information can minimize the fault isolation scenario for facilities engineering and maintenance personnel and provide information to management in terms of scheduling as to the minimal expected time for fault resolution.

The scheduler will actually develop a fault hierarchy incorporating these features which will be utilized in the rule base. Not only will it look at primary fault isolation hierarchy but a broad variety of conditions in testing requirements for components or complete systems on the plant floor. This information is incorporated into the scheduler by means of symptoms that are entered for the failing component. As a result of this the scheduler incorporates the hierarchical fault isolation algorithms, weighting algorithms, and testing requirements to provide information to management in terms of the overall fault time for that particular workstation and, more importantly, information on how to reallocate resources. Another factor incorporated into the scheduler is in regard to the test equipment necessary for the particular problem. The scheduler contains rules that identify whether testing equipment is available on the machine and the time requirement to use those built-in functions. When test equipment has to be brought to a particular workstation the scheduler can also include information on the times necessary for moving the equipment, checking the equipment, and hooking it up to the robot workstation for testing.

After the initial symptom has been fed into the scheduler it begins to weigh certainty factors to optimize the particular fault-isolation diagnostics and repair times.

Another important component of the scheduler for facilities engineering and maintenance occurs when a particular symptom has been determined inappropriate by the maintenance personnel. The additional times for repair based on a new diagnostic procedure are immediately incorporated into the system. The scheduler will try and infer all the information specific to that particular diagnostic procedure for that particular robot workstation. It will also use checks and provide information about its inferencing conclusions. If this information is inappropriate or out of a specific range, human intervention in terms of overriding this information can be incorporated into the scheduler.

At the conclusion of the successful diagnosis of a component failure for a particular workstation, the scheduler will also have information in the rule base about specific components or groups of components that might need to be replaced. With this information the scheduler can determine how long it might take to replace the component. It can then project when the robot system can be put back on line. The ability of the scheduler to incorporate information such as component failures and replacements is also very critical in terms of scheduling requirements in a plant environment. The ability to incorporate component failure requirements and component replacement requirements also begs of the capability to update these as the equipment is upgraded. There is a new-entity integration facility in the scheduler so that the plant maintenance personnel can provide information to the scheduler about new or changed component incorporation. With this information the scheduler can update the necessary information that may have an impact on its overall algorithms as regards fault isolation and repair for that workstation. Another important aspect is that a component that may have been incorporated in the scheduler as faulty can be designated in the form of a report for future reference and analysis by management. Also, the projected times and actual times that have been utilized by the scheduler can also be included in a report format. This information can be utilized by management to determine appropriate or inappropriate vendor support for the robot workstations, numerically controlled machines, CNC machines, or other machines in terms of their performance on the plant floor. It also provides a log as to the service times at which vendors provide service on the plant floor for any failed component at workstation.

The information that is supplied by the scheduler in an error report is the following:

(a) the specific workstation that suffers the fault,

(b) the component by symptom that occurred at that particular workstation, (*c*) the mean time between failures,

(*d*) the initial time of fault at the workstation,

(*e*) the time of fault repair and on-line introduction of the robot on the workline,

(*f*) the identification of the specific failure,

(*g*) the probability of future failure based on past failure information.

Information of this nature is extremely critical in industries such as the aerospace industry. For example, information specific to aircraft avionics and failure rates is very critical for planning purposes by aircraft manufacturers. In addition, this information provides valuable data on equipment performance that can be utilized by military and civilian pilot personnel.

It is also interesting to note that the scheduler can be set up to differentiate field information that may be provided on a component as compared with information that may have been gathered at a central site. The information may be specific to different environments of plant floors. This information provided through the scheduler in the maintenance and engineering component or module can assist managers in looking at the varying requirements of different types of plant environments in the field compared with a centralized location.

Fuzzy logic theory is excellent for expressing states in real-world events. Real-world events, especially in the area of financial management specific to a scheduler, are not simply true or false conditions. The fuzzy logic incorporated into the scheduler is extremely important in creating models that are used in the daily activities of financial management or accounting.

A key module of the scheduler would be specific to asset and liability management for a particular corporation. The goals of the scheduler in this arena are as follows:

(*a*) increase net interest margins,

(*b*) minimize specific variability in terms of interest,

(*c*) avoid short-term inability of a corporation to meet its cash obligations.

The problem has been that asset and liability management is very human-intensive. In some cases the models that have been utilized to simulate different strategies are not flexible enough or dynamic enough to keep up with events in the business world. These models have also been based on general financial market planning whereas a company's financial states, goals, and production constraints may not fit into these existing models.

Another fact to keep in mind is that when individuals have been working with this process it may become an extremely lengthy one. In some cases individuals may take weeks to generate information from raw data utilizing a specific model to come up with a recommended management strategy. As a result of this companies may have to operate in a multiple week strategy review mode to be able to have information specific to financial modeling. In utilizing the scheduler for financial management the time involved in terms of planning utilizing models can be reduced drastically. In addition to this the scheduler with a financial planning module is able to consider a broader range of alternatives and risk scenarios, and it can do this very consistently and in less time. This reduction in time constraints with very consistent results will provide a company with the ability to become more competitive and more flexible to deal with future markets as they evolve.

The specific components of the scheduler for asset and liability financial management first involves the incorporation of some existing models. The models may contain information specific to interest rates, the financial position of the company, securities, and tax regulations. The models in the past have used ways incorporating how they might best utilize interest rates for different types of notes.

The key component of the scheduler is to be able to incorporate models which look at the behavior of interest rates such as rising, falling, or static. In addition to this the scheduler incorporates algorithms that look at future interest rates and also past customer buying situations. Another important component of the scheduler for financial management that it includes rules specific to certain state or federal regulations. The key concept here is that the scheduler is able to look at any sort of conflicts that may be developed in terms of management requirements to the system. With conflicts this information is fed back to the manager using the scheduler so that additional information can be gathered from the manager so that the scheduler can arrive at a final goal. The system incorporates some raw financial market data and information specific to the company itself to utilize these in its rule base. In addition the scheduler will incorporate marketing, competition, and customer information to arrive at the best financial management plan to suggest. The strength of the system is its ability to interface to existing management and analysts and to provide information specific to scheduling.

9. AI/ES Decision-Support Systems

One of the main components of the AI/ES scheduler is the decision-support system (DSS). The DSS component of the AI/ES scheduler is an interactive, computer-based system that utilizes rules and or models combined with an informational knowledge base. By comparison, an expert system, or ES, is a program that includes a knowledge base containing an expert's knowledge for a particular domain. It also contains a reasoning mechanism for inferring from the knowledge base. In addition to this, an ES contains an explanation and justification function which provides the user of the knowledge base with details of the reasoning process.

The major characteristics of this DDS module are the following:

1. It aids the user in resolving unstructured or semistructured problems.
2. It possesses an interactive search facility.
3. It incorporates an Englishlike dialogue between itself and the user.

There have been some classification systems used for decision-support systems in the past. These categories are

(a) retrieving single items of information,

(b) proposing decisions,

(c) making decisions,

(d) estimating consequences of decisions,

(e) proposing prespecified data into reports,

(f) providing a mechanism for ad hoc data analysis.

The data-support system component of the AI/ES scheduler incorporates information specific to proposing decisions and estimating consequences of proposed decisions. It is the feeling of the developer that anything beyond these components would incorporate an option that would not be cost-effective for the commercial community.

The objective of the AI/ES DSS component is to support the manager or individual on the plant floor in making decisions. The problems that the DSS encompasses are complex in the sense that it has to work with a more structured and narrow domain, such as the existing expert systems function. As a result AI/ES DSS is more suitable for dealing with unique and changing situations. The other modules of AI/ES DSS deal with more repetitive problem areas, such as robot malfunctions and diagnosis. Decision making can be viewed as having the following processes:

(a) specifying objectives or probabilities,

(b) retrieval of information,

(c) generation of decision alternatives,

(d) inferring consequences of decisions,

(e) assimilating verbal or graphical information,

(f) evaluation of sets of consequences,

(g) explanation and implementation of decisions.

Natural-Language Understanding

One of the most important subcomponents of the AI/ES DSS is its natural-language understanding system. During the past few years there has been a growing tendency to make computers easier to operate for people outside the mainstream of computing. There have been innovations such as mice for microcomputers and touch-sensitive screens. It holds, therefore, that research and developmental engineers are sensitive to implementing systems in which naive users will be able to use natural language when they are utilizing the computer.

The use of natural language is an information-processing activity of great complexity. Having computers with this ability has long been a goal of research in AI. The primary goals of this research are (*a*) to understand human communication, and (*b*) to create machines with humanlike communication [Winograd 1983].

The initial goal pursued has helped us understand ourselves better. Although we are experts in the use of natural language, we have only a rudimentary understanding of the mental processes involved. More research is needed to gain clear insights into the elemental dynamic components of the mind, which may also enable us to be better communicators, educators, and better designers of computer-human interaction.

The second goal is an engineering one, which is to create machines that can communicate with people in a language with which they are already comfortable. There is a small segment of the population, computer programmers, who feel at ease in communicating with computers. The ability of engineers to make machines that understand natural language could make it possible for virtually anyone to be able to make use of computational systems.

At present a strong language barrier exists between human and machine. Not having computers talking as we do, and our discussing things that are not understood by our computers, has hindered the advanced use of computers. The attempts to make computers able to understand humans comes in the two forms of natural-language understanding, or processing, and speech recognition. These two research goals, which may be closely related, may also be very difficult to achieve. The primary task of natural language processing and/or understanding systems is to have the computer respond appropriately to something in English or other natural human languages. The main goal of speech recognition is to have the computer act as an interface and understand information that is given in the form of speech.

To gain a better understanding of this subcomponent of AI/ES DSS, let us discuss the specific functions of the submodule. In being able to understand information we transform it from one specific representation to a second. In terms of natural-language understanding we need to view this as transforming source information to target information. The transformation is a form of cognitive mapping that exists between the two information components. The target representation is specific or appropriate to the task being performed at that time. Natural languages are used in such a wide range of situations that no limited domain of understanding is able to encompass them all. In being able to build the AI/ES DSS natural-language understanding subcomponent, one of the first requirements is the precise definitions of the specific domain that the system will have to understand and the target information. These are specific to the manufacturing environment and can be divided into subareas specific to workstations, plants, or group plant activities. Being able to represent these subdomains will make the process of the natural-language understanding much easier to define.

It should be noted that there are wide variations for natural language understanding systems that may be specific to the application in which they are used. For the majority the underlying methodology is in analyzing the specific sentence. The system performs a syntactic analysis (with reference to a plant information dictionary) on a sentence, by checking word sequences against the language's rules and transforming linear sequences of words into meaningful phrases. The system performs a semantic analysis which helps to resolve ambiguity and to build the final semantic representation. A cognitive mapping is made between the syntactic structures and the objects in the task domain. Structures for which no representation can be found are rejected.

One of the problems encountered is the fuzzy boundaries between the syntactic and semantic analyses. Through a system of domain-specific analysis it is possible to be able to eliminate the unstructured nature of links between these two analyses. It has been noted that syntactic rules must be applied to sentence analysis to complete a syntactical tree before any type of further analysis can be done.

The natural-language understanding system subcomponent of the AI/ES DSS consists of the user describing a problem, specifying an action(s) that the main entity will move to after a specific action. This eliminates any need for information queueing, which could be a detriment to existing data processing architectures. The system utilizes models which take logic paths or actions. This logic path or action ability eliminates any sort of queueing activity. By eliminating the queues, the various phases of user-machine interaction become simpler and the model is enabled to react accordingly.

In model validation the client and the knowledge engineer have provided an Englishlike description which is familiar to them both. The description consists of information about entities, such as robots, and the workstations in which they work and activities they have to perform. The system also provides for alternative ways of representing the information cycle of entities and activities performed at the robot workstation. It is important to understand in problem description that information is exchanged before a successful understanding process has taken place. The AI/ES DSS natural-language understanding subcomponent incorporates a debugging facility which helps the user make changes to systems that may have already been or are partly described.

Because this is an interactive system, special concern has been given to try to prevent meaningless information in the human-machine dialog. The system also incorporates a classification based on natural-language part and discrete-event simulation domains. Boundaries have been put on the system so that if in the interaction individuals violate those boundaries, the system is capable of parsing the proposed statement, describing the mistake, and asking the user to try again. It also identifies wrong answers or misleading answers given by the user. The system is used in the initial consultation with the end user phase so that it is of fundamental importance to the entire AI/ES scheduler. It also is able to point out or elaborate mistakes and gaps in the user's understanding of the problem. These mistakes can vary from a description of a wrong entity, such as the incorrect robot workstation to be used in a specific plant operation, to an incomplete understanding of what the robot does at a particular workstation.

10. AI/ES Scheduler Applications Outside the Plant

Let's look at an example of the use of the entire AI/ES scheduler concerning scheduling systems outside the plant environment. This would involve a manufacturing environment where there is outbound transportation supplying customers from distribution centers. This information shows flexibility not only using the AI/ES scheduler for in-plant manufacturing processes but also for outbound processes. The culmination of events of a plant involving robots and other sophisticated equipment is the distribution of these products. The final step in this distribution involves supplying products from distribution centers to customers. This distribution function, often referred to as *outbound transportation,* is the most costly single item in a distribution chain. It is costly because individual customer orders must be handled and supplied separately, and this involves economies of scale to provide bulk handling and transportation of goods. The largest single amount of funds spent involved with this is that for transportation. The outbound transportation functions are of increasing importance also because fuel prices are constantly leading general inflation costs.

Vehicle Routing and Scheduling

Vehicle routing and scheduling have in the past been considered tactical distribution tools. They have been concerned entirely with outbound transportation and their objectives were to perform well-specified functions of supplying customer demands from distribution centers using a given fleet. The past objectives have traditionally been to perform the function optimally—which has often been translated to mean the distance travelled or time spent was to be minimized. The preceding traditional view of the role of vehicle routing assumes that decisions which specify the vehicle routing problems have already been made exogenously. Chart 2 shows the AI/ES scheduler vehicle routing functional components. The decisions include the following:

1. Geographic size of area served supplied specific to each distribution depot.
2. Decisions have already been made as to whether

   (*a*) certain large orders in a depot region (i.e. orders above a given size) are to be made direct from the plants, in order to avoid double handling, and
   (*b*) certain small orders, or remote areas within the depot regionalism, are subcontracted to a common carrier.

3. The vehicle fleet size and mix of vehicles which are available at each depot is known and given.
4. The level of service to be provided to customers is already decided on. This immediately implies that:

   (*a*) the frequency of delivery to customers has been specified, and
   (*b*) the time delay between receipt of an order and delivery of the corresponding product is specified (or at least some average and/or maximum delay is specified).

Chart 2. AI/ES Scheduler Vehicle Routing Functional Components

1. Geographic size specific to distribution depot
2. Size-specific order filling; small-lot subcontracting
3. Vehicle fleet size availability
4. Service level provided; delivery frequency; special-order delay reduction

It is clear that the vehicle routing problem defined after these decisions are made is quite arbitrary. Indeed, considering the size of outbound transportation costs in relation to total distribution costs it is clear that any decision involving items 1 through 3 above may be also arbitrary at best. It is therefore important to be able to have a system such as the AI/ES scheduler, which can provide accurate and realistic computational models of depot-to-customer distribution functions and assist in making the kind of strategic decisions mentioned above and in minimizing distribution costs.

The AI/ES scheduler vehicle routing and scheduling provides tactical and operational ways for daily (or weekly) routing of vehicles in order to supply customers from distribution centers at minimum cost. These packages also provide the means by which strategic questions of the types raised earlier can be answered. In the sense that they are operational they possess advantages such that they give a good representation of real costs involved and provide a workable cost-minimizing distribution plan once the strategic decisions are made.

The packages show distribution managers how to minimize the distance travelled, and the time taken, and which vehicles are to be used. They entail assumptions not stated but implicitly considered. For example, it is assumed that customers should be supplied. (In the case where customer deliveries may be delayed, it is assumed that a sufficient number of customers are supplied so that deliveries postponed until the next period, along with new orders received in that period, do not continue to increase so that it becomes impossible to maintain the required level of service.) The main objectives of the AI/ES scheduler are to

(a) maximize priority of customers' routes,

(b) minimize the number or cost of vehicles used,

(c) minimize the distance travelled and/or time spent in making deliveries.

Vehicle routing packages can determine the best size of vehicles automatically by making use of vehicle cost or priorities. However, additional sensitivity results can be obtained if the vehicle size to be considered is defined exogenously by the user (either by size or mix of sizes); in practice it often turns out that using a vehicle slightly larger than the minimum-cost size required has advantages that outweigh the slight increase in both capital and operating costs. Clearly the effect of changes and service level on the other costs, namely, inbound transportation costs, inventory carrying costs, etc., must be computed before an overall distribution figure is obtained. These costs are much simpler to compute, and once this is done the AI/ES scheduler provides a seven-day service level (including two days spent on order processing).

The Vehicle Fleet

In addition the AI/ES scheduler examines the optimum size and constitution of the vehicle fleet including such factors as customer service level, variability of demand, geographical characteristics of a depot region, and characteristics of order sizes. In the case where a variability of demand is high, the AI/ES scheduler is also able to compute the desirability of hired vehicles during peak demand periods for either short-term or long-term hire. Even in cases where seasonality in demand pattern is not pronounced, however, it may be profitable to operate hired vehicles on certain routes depending on the terms that may be obtained. For example, if the terms involve a fixed charge and a variable charge for distance traveled, it may be profitable to operate a hired vehicle on a very long route—if the fixed charge is high and the variable charge is low—or operate the hired vehicle on a short route with a high load in the reverse case.

The objective of the AI/ES scheduler is not just to find an optimal vehicle size but to decrease the number of vehicles on hire by improving the utilization of vehicles owned. The analysis taken by the AI/ES scheduler is typical of that followed in other studies optimizing vehicle fleet size by running a simulation of vehicle routing packages on a large number of existing delivery cases using historical data. In this instance only vehicles at the depot are assumed to be available (i.e., no new vehicles can be considered).

Customer Area Service

The final major function of the AI/ES scheduler routing module is to look at profitability for the customer within a depot region to be supplied in a different manner from the rest of that region. This is achieved by utilizing a module that produces area-change proposals and a vehicle routing package that evaluates these proposals in an operation mode.

The AI/ES scheduler defines exact boundary-separation regions of two neighboring distribution centers. The proposals produced by the AI/ES scheduler involve the transfer of a small customer area from the area of one depot to that of the next. The resulting configuration is then evaluated by running a vehicle routing submodel on the modified depot regions using historical demand data. The initial delineation of depot is usually done by considering only direct distance, travel times, and associated costs, from the area to the distribution centers. However, real routing costs are more highly complex and depend not only on the above measures, but also on the density of customers in neighboring areas, vehicle capabilities, etc. Thus the AI/ES scheduler evaluation uses the real operation mode—by means of a vehicle routing package model—that can produce appreciable changes to the depot regions and a corresponding appreciable reduction in distribution cost. The AI/ES scheduler is able to examine any shift in customer areas from one depot to another, and this may lead to modified inbound transportation factors as well. The total change costs are evaluated before the reallocation of the customer area is made. Because outbound costs are much higher than the inbound costs, usually a reduction in outbound costs will also lead to a reduction in total transportation costs.

It has been suggested that the ability of outbound transportation costs to be handled by the AI/ES scheduler in addition to overall plant scheduling can reduce two of the largest cost items in an entire plant system. An area which is not currently a major component on the development side of the AI/ES scheduler is that of specific customer service shifts. It has been shown, however, that the AI/ES scheduler can provide an operational distribution tool for in-plant or inbound scheduling systems as well as outbound distribution systems which can most effectively be used in strategic distribution planning within and outside a plant environment. This will result in a high degree of cost savings and efficiency for the overall manufacturing system.

It is evident from the positions presented in this chapter that the incorporation of AI in manufacturing will take place at both the robot workstation level and the global operation level inside and outside of the plant. This similarity of structure will enhance the overall productivity of the plant operation.

Through such AI systems as an AI/ES scheduler many operations of the flexible manufacturing systems of tomorrow will become realities. It should also be noted that the growth to flexible manufacturing systems will not be an overnight conversion through completely redesigned plants but a gradual change by plant managers and designers incorporating more and more technological options such as machine vision and AI to increase manufacturing productivity.

11. Conclusions

In this chapter we have examined the use of AI/ESs in two areas. One is where an AI system acts as a scheduler in a plant environment. The second is where an AI system is used as a scheduler for shipping routes outside the plant.

From these two examples it should be evident that the impact of AI, specificially the ES, will be broad in its scope. The strength of AI combined with robot systems is in its ability to move both technologies toward a truly flexible manufacturing system. One tool such as an AI scheduler could be able to manage functions ranging from robot maintenance schedules to vehicle routing schedules for delivery of manufactured items.

In the future, AI will enter into the plant environment as specialized knowledge bases. In time these will be combined or coordinated through higher knowledge bases. There will be a hierarachy of knowledge bases just as there is at present a hierarchy of automated control in the plant.

The key to the successful implementation and growth of robots, machine vision, and AI will be the focus of management being on the long-term goals of the corporation or organization. The technological options such as machine vision, AI, and robots are additional tools available to increase plant productivity today and in the future. It is most important that management take a planned approach for the intelligent integration of these systems into their existing plants. New technologies will not solve the problems facing manufacturing today. New technologies will not make manufacturing more competitive or give a competitive edge to one corporation over another. It is through the integration of new technologies such as AI, machine vision, and robotics that a corporation will be helped to achieve its long-term goals.

12. References

Barkocy, B. E., and W. J. Zdeblick. "A Knowledge-Based System for Machine Operation Planning," *The Carbide and Tool Journal,* July–August, 1982, pp. 25–30.

Beigel, J. E. "The Future of Artificial Intelligence (AI) in Manufacturing," *Industrial Engineering Computing,* 1986, pp. 276–280.

Beregi, W. E. "Architecture Prototyping in the Software Engineering Environment," *IBM Systems Journal,* Vol. 23, 1984, pp. 4–18.

Bruno, G., Elia, A., and P. Laface, "A Rule-Based System to Schedule Production," *IEEE Computer,* July, 1986, pp. 32–39.

Capitano, J. L., and J. H. Feinstein. "Environmental Stress Screening (ESS) Demonstrates Its Value in the Field," *Proceedings of the Annual Reliability and Maintainability Symposium,* 1986.

Chow, W.-M., MacNair, E. A., and C. H. Sauer. "Analysis of Manufacturing Systems by the Research Queueing Package," *IBM Journal of and Research Development,* Vol. 29, 1985, pp. 330–342.

Christofides, N. "Uses of a Vehicle Routing and Scheduling System in Strategic Distribution Planning," *Computer Assisted Decision Making,* New York: Elsevier Science Publishing (North-Holland), 1986.

Crane, M. A., and A. J. Lemoine. *An Introduction to the Generative Method for Simulation Analysis,* New York: Springer-Verlag, 1977.

Dupont-Gatelmand, C. "A Survey of Flexible Manufacturing Systems," *Journal of Manufacturing Systems,* Vol. 1, No. 1, 1982, pp. 1–6.

Efstathiou, J., Rajkovic, V., and M. Bohanec. "Expert Systems and Rule Based Decision Support Systems," *Computer Assisted Decision Making,* New York: Elsevier Science Publishing (North-Holland), 1986.

Efstathiou, J., and E. H. Mamdani. "Expert Systems and How They Are Applied to Industrial Decision Making," *Computer Assisted Decision Making,* New York: Elsevier Science Publishing (North-Holland), 1986.

Embrey, D. E. "Approaches to Aiding and Training Operators' Diagnoses in Abnormal Situations," *Chemistry and Industry,* July 1986, pp. 454–459.

Engelke, H., Grotrian, J., Scheuing, C., Scmackpfeffer, A., Schwarz, W., Solf, B., and J. Tomann. "Integrated Manufacturing Modeling System," *IBM Journal of Research and Development,* Vol. 29, No. 4, July 1985.

Gershwin, S. B., Akella, R., and Y. F. Choong. "Short-Term Production Scheduling of an Automated Manufacturing Facility," *IBM Journal of Research and Development,* Vol. 29, No. 4, July 1985.

———."Short Term Production Scheduling of an Automated Manufacturing Facility," LIDS-FR-1356, Laboratory for Information and Decision Systems, Massachusetts Institute of Technology, Cambridge, Mass., 1984.

Haines, L. C. "An Algorithm for Carrier Routing in a Flexible Material-Handling System," *IBM Journal of Research and Development,* Vol. 29, No. 4, July 1985.

Kempf, K. G. "Manufacturing and Artificial Intelligence," *Robotics 1,* New York: Elsevier Science Publishing (North-Holland), 1985, pp. 13–25.

Kimemia, J. G. "Hierarchical Control of Production in Flexible Manufacturing System," LIDS-TH-1215, Laboratory for Information and Decision Systems, Massachusetts Institute of Technology, Cambridge, Mass., 1982.

Kimemia, J. G., and S. B. Gershwin. "An Algorithm for the Computer Control of Production in Flexible Manufacturing Systems," *IEEE Transactions on Systems, Man, and Cybernetics,* Vol. SMC-13, No. 15, December 1983, pp. 353–362.

Mullee W. R., and D. B. Porter. "Process-Chart Procedures," *Industrial Engineering Handbook,* New York: McGraw-Hill, 1963.

Niwa, K. "A Knowledge-Based Human Computer Cooperative System for Ill-Structured Management Domains," *IEEE Transactions on Systems, Man, and Cybernetics,* Vol. SMC-16, No. 3, May/June 1986.

Paul, R. J., and G. I. Doukidis. "Further Developments in Use of Artificial Intelligence Techniques Which Formulate Simulation Problems," *Journal of the Operational Research Society,* Vol. 37, No. 8, 1986, pp. 787–810.

Pierson, R. A. "Adapting Horizontal Material Handling Systems to Flexible Manufacturing Setups," *Industrial Engineering,* Vol. 16, No. 3, 1984, pp. 62–71.

Stonecipher, K. *Industrial Robotics: A Handbook of Automated System Design,* Indianapolis: Hayden Book Co., 1985.

Winograd, T. *Language as a Cognitive Process,* Vol. I, *Syntax,* Reading, Mass.: Addison-Wesley, 1983.

Zisk, B. I. "Flexibility Is Key to Automated Material Transport System for Manufacturing Cells," *Industrial Engineering,* Vol. 15, No. 11, 1983, pp. 58–61.

Glossary

a/d converter   A device that converts an analog signal into a digital voltage for use in data communications equipment.

abbreviated image   A computer-edited image provided through a composite model which can be used for expert system vision and robot orientation.

absolute accuracy   This type of accuracy is closely associated with electric servomotor systems. It is the exactness of a robot manipulator system. It is used as a measure of the engineering design of a robot system and is used to determine the calibration of a robot.

absolute orientation   The ability of a robot system to position itself exactly in regard to a fixed point.

absolute target position   The exact position of a robot after the completion of a command in respect to a given point.

accuracy   In robotics, the ability of a robot system to make precise movements. Combined with repeatability and reliability, it gives an indication of the engineering design of a robot.

accuracy error   In robotics, the physical factors which account for the inability of a robot system to successfully complete a function such as a pick-and-place operation.

acoustic ranging   A sensor used in industrial robot that is based on directing the movements of a robot by a a sonic feedback system.

acrylic plate   A component of a CCD camera used in the digitation of a visual image from a lens.

actuators   The means of movement of an industrial robot. It consists of three different types, i.e., hydraulic, pneumatic, and electric-servo systems.

Ada   Ada is a high-level programming language developed for the use by the Department of Defense.

adaptive controllers   A microcontroller system that adjusts to physical factors such as the load that the robot is lifting or carrying, the known drift of the servo systems, or the inertia of the arm carrying a load. These factors could be in feet, inches, or millimeters.

adjacent positions   Coordinates used to determine the maximum cycle speed of a robot manipulator in moving from one point to the next point.

advantage-disadvantage equation   The measure of cost of a visual imaging system weighing the strength of the technology used against the cost of the technology.

AEGIS weapons system   The AEGIS system is able to identify, track, intercept, and destroy 96 targets in 3 minutes, all without human intervention. It is used by the United States Navy on attack-class ships.

AML   A Manufacturing Language, the high-level control language developed by IBM for use with their industrial robots. The language was developed by David Goldssman of the IBM Corporation.

angle-side-angle   A formula of trigonometry used to calculate a range in computing a relative orientation.

anode   In machine vision, a component of a camera which attracts electrodes and is used in the picture tube of a visual system.

arm links   The component of a robot system which gives the robot its shape and reach. It supports the end effector and is attached by joints.

arm solution   The ability to convert the digitized end-effector tool position back to a set of servomotor joint positions.

arm subassembly   A component which may consist of three to four degrees of freedom of movement, which will position the end effector at a specific coordinate of the workpiece.

armature link   A term for the arm links of an industrial robot which can be numbered from the base of reference where "joint 1" is the joint which is connected between the armature link and the supporting base.

array   In visual imaging systems, a term used which corresponds to a binary representation of an image. Usually it is assumed that 0s correspond to background pixels and 1s to object pixels.

artificial intelligence   The ability of an automated system to emulate human cognition based on inference-making techniques of predefined facts and rules.

assembly operation   In robotics, the functions necessary for a robot to assemble the component parts of a workpiece.

automatic guided vehicles   A type of material-transport mechanism including power carriers, automatically guided vehicles, power-and-free conveyors, tow-cart systems, and rail-guided systems.

automatic storage/retrieval systems   An automated system used in the warehousing of material.

automation   The use of machines as tools to assist a factory in achieving a manufacturing goal.

autonomous system   A system programmed to perform a fixed set of predefined functions in a predefined sequence.

autonomous weapons system   A system developed for the military such as the AEGIS system. The only decisions humans are required to make are (1) to engage the system, or (2) to override the machine interpretations of a battle strategy.

backlash   The physical nature of a robot manipulator to move unexpectedly for a short amount of time.

batch production   The production of an item in large amounts for a single manufacturing process. It can also refer to the submission of multiple programs to be executed by a computer in a predefined sequence.

binary image processor   A microprocessor used in visual imaging systems that uses a processor to provide information about the silhouette of an object.

binary images   A binary representation of a picture digitized by a camera into a sequence of 0s and 1s. A binary image is the basis for interpretation by a computer system for image identification.

binocular vision   The use of multiple cameras to not only determine a visual image but add depth to the image.

boundary tracking   The ability of a visual imaging system to determine the outline for description and measurement.

buffering   The ability of a system to hold the creation of a task until an appropriate predetermined time. Buffering prevents systems from being overloaded because of processing restrictions.

cabling system   A cable used to prevent damage to a robot end effector in the event of the end effector breaking away from the robot joint. It attaches the end effector to the robot joint.

CAD/CAM   The abbreviation for computer-aided design/computer-aided manufacturing, which is the utilization of a computer to electronically design entities (CAD) or assist in the manufacturing management process (CAM).

calibration   The setting of a robot to predefined points to check the accuracy, reliability, and repeatability of a robot. It is used to check for positional errors of the robot which may develop over time.

camera rangefinder   The ability of a vision system to calculate a distance.

Cartesian coordinate plan   The mathematical orientation of a robot in terms of an X, Y, and Z perspective. This type of nomenclature is used to communicate to the robot controller the positions of objects in the workstation.

Cartesian robot   A robot that has joints which move in Cartesian coordinates.

CCD   The abreviation for charge-coupled device. This is one major component of a visual imaging system.

CCD matrix   An integrated circuit used to digitize visual information.

certainty factors   A mathematical algorithm used by the inference engine in an expert system. Certainty factors are based on inferential statistics and are used by an ES inference engine.

chain codes   An algorithm used to represent a boundary-connected sequence of straight-line segments of specified length and direction. This is used in visual imaging systems.

characteristic lines   The orthogonal lines to gradient lines in a model-free method which assist in the determination of the surface of an image.

chessboard distance   The distance between adjacent pixels in a machine vision system.

circuit boards   The hardware of an electronic system of a robot where the individual electronic parts are connected to a predefined circuitry.

clock signals   The electronic signals in a microprocessor cycle.

closed boundary   A boundary defined in a visual imaging system to be used for the analysis of the visual input.

closed-loop system   In robotics, an electric-servo system which uses direct-current stepping motors with microcomputers for control and feedback.

clutching   A component of a robot used so that acceleration and deceleration of the servomotors are minimized with high load factors.

CNC   Computer numerically controlled machines used in plants for drilling, milling, and grinding operations.

compliance   The ability of the manipulator wrist sockets and end effector to accommodate certain forces or loads that may arise between the contact of the end effector with a workpiece.

compliant motion   A robot-motion servocontrol strategy which includes force, position servoing, compliant motions, visual servoing, and other sensor-directed servo processes.

conditional movement   If an object's position is not exactly known and it must be grasped, this conditional movement or supervised movement can be used to center the end effector accurately.

connected conponent   In a visual imaging system, the points at which pixels are connected to each other.

connectivity   In a visual imaging system, the concept used in establishing the boundaries of object and components.

conscience of the process   Logical deduction can be referred to as the conscience of the process.

constants   Ada and Pascal use data declarations broken down as constants, scalars, arrays, records, and pointers. This breakdown is a structure of the language to assist in the definition and manipulation of data for an AI system.

control hierarchy   A control strategy for a robot unit composed of a minicomputer acting as a master controller, and a microcontroller in the robot unit acts as subcontroller in this type of control hierarchy.

convex deficiency   In visual recognition systems, convex deficiency is the difference set $H - S$, where H is the convex hull of set S.

convex hull   In machine vision, a set of image points that can be used to understand the boundary which encloses a solid region.

conveyors   A category of material-transport mechanisms. A conveyor is used to transport materials or products from one workstation to another workstation.

cooperative method   A design method that incorporates information not based on models of a biological nature. An example is the photometric stereo method.

coordinate frames   A machine vision technique used in the orientation of a robot based on the X and Y coordinates identified by the camera.

coordinates   Mathematical points used in the orientation of a robot system with a machine vision system. These points can be described using Cartesian coordinates, those points in an X, Y, Z plan system which give the robot its orientation in relation to a workpiece.

curvature   Curvature is defined as the rate of change of slope. In general, it is difficult to obtain reliable measures of curvature at a point in a digital boundary because these boundaries may tend to overlap.

curve-fit procedures   In machine vision a mathematical procedure, such as least squares, to locate an object in a minimal amount of time in order to orient a robot to act on the workpiece.

cycle speed   The time required for a robot to perform a function and return to a starting position. An example would be a pick-and-place function with the cycle speed being the time to return to start position of the robot.

cylindrical coordinates   One of four basic motion definition categories: (1) Cartesian coordinates, (2) cylindrical coordinates, (3) spherical or polar coordinates, and (4) revolute or articular coordinates. It is the use of two linear coordinates and one rotary axis, such as a rotation on a z-axis plane.

data declarations   In Ada, like Pascal, the language uses type and data declarations broken into four types: (1) enumeration types, (2) array types, (3) record types, (4) pointer types. Ada and Pascal also use data declarations broken down as constants, and scalar, array, record, and polar pointers.

data dictionaries   The critical parts of NLC systems are (1) NLC front ends (filters), (2) data dictionaries, (3) search functions, and (4) comparison types, and (4) pointer types. Data dictionaries contain information specific to the AI domain being used.

data entry translator   In AI/natural-language processing, a natural-language filtering system.

data-base query language   The basic definition of natural-language comprehension (NLC) is "the translation of natural language into a data-base query system." A data-base query language is software that analyzes the structure of language and matches it with a predefined data-base identifier.

decluttering techniques   In AI, this is the removal of extraneous data from information needed for the resolution of the problem.

deduction   Deduction is the inference of facts from premises by the rules of logic.

degrees of freedom   In robotics, the amount of movement available to a robot system. This is usually six degrees of freedom and indicates the flexibility of the robot.

descriptors   An aspect of machine vision which forms the basis for dimensioned analysis, and the choice of descriptors for a given application is strongly influenced by the type of dimensioning one wishes to examine.

detents   Detents consist of two or more structural elements that are held in position with respect to one another by a spring-loaded mechanism.

diagnosis   In AI, an extremely attractive AI/ES application because failure of facilities or products can prove time-consuming and expensive to a company.

digital boundary   An area of machine vision that can be approximated with arbitrary accuracy by a polygonal boundary.

displacements   Along with rotational changes and movement, displacements may impinge on the total force performance of the robot system. The extraneous movements of a robot that adversely affect the performance of the system.

domains   A term used in AI to designate the area of influence of the knowledge base. It can roughly be equated with multiple interrelated application areas.

drift   Drift is the outcome of the mechanical subcomponent inaccuracies and also such factors as aging, temperature factors, and loading factors on a robot.

dynamic motion   In robotics, an approach in robot control which incorporates dynamic motion equations which are nonlinear and which are affected by external factors such as inertial stresses placed on the robot system.

eccentricity of the boundary   The ratio of the major to minor axis in a machine vision system.

edge detection   In a machine vision system, the analysis of the system to identify the visual boundary of a workpiece. This method is invaluable in orienting the robot to work with the workpiece.

eigenvectors   The principal axes of a region are the eigenvectors of the covariance matrix obtained by using the pixels within the region as random variables. In machine vision it is a method of robot orientation.

elastic membrane   A component of a machine vision system that is used in object light/dark and boundary detection.

electron beam   In machine vision one of the components that produces the video signal. The electron beam is the stream of electrons which is formed into a video image.

embedded system   Ada was developed initially for embedded systems, such as missile guidance and aircraft control, and as the sole major language of the four services. A software system that can coexist and interface with an existing high-level language such as Ada.

enabled system   A software system that acts as a front end to existing high-level languages such as Ada, COBOL, and FORTRAN. It is used in AI systems as an intelligent front end to existing programs.

end effector   A component of a robot that adapts the end of the robot arm to a specific function. Different functions require different end effectors. For example, a pick-and-place end effector is designed differently from a spray-painting end effector. End effectors have been referred to as grippers but this is only one type of end effector.

equivalence relation   A relation in machine vision satisfying a certain set of properties is called an equivalence relation. An important property of equivalence relations is that if R is an equivalence relation on a set A, then it is possible to divide A into k disjoint subsets called equivalence classes.

Euclidean distances   In machine vision the Euclidean distance between points $p = (x, y)$ and $q = (s, t)$ is defined as

$$D_e(p, q) = [(x - s)^2 + (y - t)^2]^{1/2}$$

It is used to determine distance measurements.

expert systems   An area of AI which uses inference-making algorithms to simulate human problem solving. The original expert systems are based on Mycin, developed by Bruce G. Buchannan and Edward K. Shortliffe, both of Stanford University.

factoring system   The AI system used to determine repeatability and absolute accuracy incorporating an algorithm to determine an absolute target position.

fault hierarchy   A method in an AI/ES to isolate machine errors or faults and prioritize them into an appropriate schedule for repair.

fault isolation   The main function of the scheduler in the arena of facilities engineering maintenance is in fault isolation. Fault isolation represents finding the component may have failed and reporting this to an AI system for the appropriate action.

faults   Error conditions or states that may occur in a robot system or other electromechanical devices found in a plant.

feedback loop   In robot control, an electronic system used to indicate a successful completion of the task of the end effector of a robot through sensors placed in the robot's end effector.

fiber optics   A data communications medium for transmitting data over fiber strands with light rather than electrical current as the carrier signal. The advantages of fiber optics are in the amount of data signals carried or wide bandwidth, low loss, small size, EM noise immunity, low cost, and the speed of operation with a very low transmission error ratio.

filament   In a machine vision system a component that is used to heat the cathode of a vidicon.

filter   In a machine vision system, a part used to screen unnecessary parts of an image to be analyzed. Also, filters are software used in natural-language systems to screen parts of information to be analyzed.

flexible manufacturing system   The flexible manufacturing system (FMS) is based on related machine functions which can continuously operate with product changes or workstation downtime either eliminated or not adversely affecting the overall work schedule.

floating-point binary accuracy   Accuracy or exactness used in robot control. The higher the binary accuracy, the more consistent the robot accuracy and reliability.

FLOPS   The acronym for floating-point operations per second. It is used as a rough measure of computer performance.

FMS   *See* flexible manufacturing system.

focal length   Used in machine vision in analyzing 3-D space and its projections. The most frequently required parameter is the position of the center of projection, i.e., the focal length.

force   Some mechanisms may utilize belts which apply the appropriate amount of force or pressure on the part to divert it or lift it into another predetermined workstation. Also, the measure of mechanical contact of a robot end effector as for example measured with a sensor.

force sensors   A type of robot sensor that can give useful information only if the robot tools are in contact with the workpiece being used with the robot.

Fourier transform   A mathematical formula used in machine vision to compute the one-dimensional discrete transform, to obtain an image's spectrum.

frames   A robot system is composed of rigid frames called links which are connected by revolute or prismatic joints.

fuzzy logic   A method used in AI which uses certainty-factor algorithms for inferring a conclusion based on an inexact reasoning process.

galvanometer-operating mirror   A mode of operation used in stationary lasar scanners incorporating a mirror controlled by a galvanometer to scan at any rate over any part of a field.

geometric distortion   Geometric distortion, which is used in machine vision, results from scanning a rectangular area from an electron beam that should be scanning a section of a sphere.

goal state   In AI problem solving, the use of search in problem solving is divided into initial and goal states. The goal state is the state which the AI system is programmed to achieve.

goal trees   Goal trees are used as a controlled method for search. Each branch of a goal tree is responsible for solving subfunctions necessary for the resolution of the whole reasoning process.

grasping   A robot function utilizing a tool to hold a workpiece. The arm subassembly may consist of three to four degrees of freedom of movement necessary to perform this function.

gray level   A measurement in machine vision systems for analyzing the varying degrees of light/dark contrast in an electronic image. Gray level is a critical measure in image boundary definitions for robot orientation.

gray-scale transformations   A method of image modification, along with gray-level corrections, which compensates for the nonuniformity of sensitivity of sensors.

gray values   A simple measure used as region descriptors, which include the mean and median of the gray levels, the minimum and maximum gray values, and the number of pixels with values above and below a given threshold.

gripper   *See* end effector.

gross motion   The overall motion of a robot system as in a transfer operation.

guarded move   The use of sensor information or other conditional events as a control strategy for a robot system. An example is the control of the overpressurization of the end effector of a robot for extraction positioning functions.

hander   A software control program for space station orbital maneuvering vehicles.

hand-held trainer   A manual control system for programming a robot to perform a sequence of operations.

heuristics   In an AI system, rules that may be simplistic or based on very complex plant operations. Heuristics are important to the overall functionality of the system.

hierarchical conceptual servo   A method of robot control which has been discussed as a method of interfacing sensors to a manipulation sequence based on a logical hierarchy of control.

histogram flattening   Histogram flattening is used to reduce the frequency of very numerous intensity values and HSD coordinates: hue (color: blue, orange, etc.), saturation (grayness of color), density (overall brightness of color).

ICAM   A study funded by the U.S. Air Force regarding integrated computer-aided manufacturing. It gives excellent recommendations regarding the examination and integration of robots in manufacturing.

IF-THEN-ELSE   One of the language structures used in the definition of rules in AI. IF a state of a parameter is ⟨ premise statement ⟩ THEN ⟨ action statement or parameter ⟩.

illumination   The light falling on a surface, such as a workpiece used in machine vision.

illuminators   There are two types of visual sensing systems: illuminators and light sensors. Illuminators can be single-point sources.

image analysis   Image analysis is accomplished by identifying regions and boundaries, or edges. Edges represent boundaries where two pieces come together.

image irradiance equation   The equation identifies the interface in which the surface reflectance replaced by the image intensity, i.e., an equation of the form

$$i(x, y) = R(r, q)$$

is called the image irradiance equation.

image processing   Image processing can be used to extract weak data signals from noise, i.e. where the signal-to-noise ratio is very low. It is a design philosophy of machine vision analysis.

image subset   Two or more images that are part of a larger image. Image subsets are used in the analysis of an image.

imbedded sensors   Sensors used in a robot placed in a component such as the end effector to be used in tactile sensing.

inbound costs   The costs incurred by a plant for operations.

inductive reasoning   A type of learning such as trial and error, that is used as a model in AI for autonomous vehicle research. Before the autonomous vehicle would attempt to cross the field, it would deduce the most successful possibility. Trial and error come into play when the rover begins to move through the field.

inference engine   The basic function of an inference engine is using rules of the form of IF conditions (premise conditions); THEN conditions (action conditions); and conclusions. The inference engine is also very important because it monitors or controls the execution of the parameters and the rules in the knowledge base.

integrated circuit   In machine vision the CCD matrix is an integrated circuit, or collection of electronic circuits on a single planar board.

interactive dialogue   The user interface for an AI/ES should provide for an interactive dialogue with a fast response and user-oriented graphics. An interactive dialogue maintains a high degree of interaction with a human operator.

interface   In a machine vision system the area common to the overlapping boundaries of specific pixel groups or sets.

inverse kinematic method   An inverse kinematic method can be used to obtain the position and orientation of the end effector of a robot. In this case the particular position and orientation of an end effector is to be translated into a particular position and orientation so that the robot can be placed in a specific position to grasp an object.

Jacobian matrix   An algorithm used in robot control for motion positioning and or rotation.

joint axes   A joint which is established at the connection point of two armature links.

knowledge-based   Knowledge-based systems may be defined as systems which use computer programming to replicate human logic and to make decisions based on a set of structured facts.

knowledge engineers   Knowledge engineers are the developers and maintainers of the knowledge base. In AI/ESs the knowledge engineers who might need to change any particular module would have the ability to substitute modules, perform the necessary maintenance on the rules for that particular module, and place those rules back into a dynamically ordered rule-based system.

Lagrange-Euler Method   A method for simulation of robot kinematics and dynamics mathematically.

Lambertian surface   A perfectly diffusing surface used in machine vision models of irregular surface analysis.

laser scanner   In machine vision, an electronic device that provides a very intense coherent light which is then reflected and analyzed.

LED   An infrared light-emitting diode, used in machine vision. Once the part is in the grasp position between the two fingers of the gripper, the infrared beam is broken, indicating to the robot controller the commencement of the gripper closure function.

lens distortion   The amount of variation of the actual image and its reflectance through a lens. This is used as a measure of lens quality in machine vision systems.

light sensors   There are two types of visual sensing systems: illuminators and light sensors. Light sensors can require a certain amount of light to effect an image which results from the combination of illuminator intensity and sensitivity of the sensor.

linear axes   Cartesian coordinates are those which may be defined by three orthogonal linear axes. Cylindrical coordinates are the use of two linear axes, such as x and y axes and one rotary axis, such as a rotation about the z axis.

linear imaging devices (LID)   A device which performs a single scan and is very useful for sensing objects that are moving relative to the camera.

linear variable-differential transformer (LVDT)   In robotics, the LVDT uses sensor information such as from an optical digital encoder on servomotors and assists the robot with orientation.

linear voltage differential   The voltage difference used in tactile sensing devices.

linear voltage differential transformer (LVDT)   A robot sensor based on voltage flux resulting from force sensing structures in the end effector.

linkages   The mechanical components of a robot which transfer motion in a desired manner, such as linkages, gears, and beam lengths. The linkage structure can affect the accuracy of the robot positioning and is analyzed so that algorithms can be developed and programmed into the controller.

LIPS   In AI applications, LIPS (logical inferences per second) are a rough measure of the inferring speed of the system.

LISP   An acronym for list processing. It is a high-level language used in the development of AI systems.

load factors   The loads or weights that are placed on a robot manipulator. It is important to break up or segment an operation into two or more positions when the particular trajectory of the manipulator arm is being used at its maximum point.

loading   Loading is another important aspect which must be incorporated into the AI/ES scheduler. Loading refers to how heavily the machines in a system are being utilized.

local noise   In image processing of electronic signals, local noise is unnecessary pixels that are not productive to the analysis of the image and are screened out by a software filtering method.

logical flow   The analysis of a domain in AI to identify the logical hierarchy of the knowledge base.

logical selection   The selection of alternatives in decision making in AI based on logical conclusions.

logistics module   In the AI utilized on the planned U.S. space station, the basic design of the station will consist of four manned modules (45 to 50 ft long), one logistics module, multiple docking ports and air locks, and one to two handers for satellites and orbital vehicles. The logistics module will be the "command" or control center for the space station.

low-resolution feedback transducer   Resolution of the wrist-joint training is very difficult. To overcome problems of control in this area, vendors have utilized what is called a low-resolution feedback transducer in the wrist joint. This transducer supplies a controller with feedback information which is specific to the orientation and load factors of the end effector.

machine-readable translators   Natural-language processing utilizes information into relative applications such as (1) information breakdown, (2) transmission, (3) natural-language filter or machine-readable translator, (4) input and utilization.

magnetic sensors   Noncontacting sensors include optical, acoustic-ranging, vision, and magnetic sensors. Magnetic sensors are also called magnetic-field proximity sensors and use the attraction or repulsion of magnetic field as a feedback system for robot control.

major universal   A method of positioning for robot control based on gross and fine movements of a manipulator. Minor universal accuracy factors may occur from the major universal range to the number of feet of accuracy within the positioning of the robot manipulator.

manipulator systems   The integration of servomotors, joints, links, and end effector to form the "arm" of the robot.

MAT   The skeleton of a region may be defined via the medial-axis transformation (MAT) proposed by Blum. The MAT of a region R with border B is as follows. For each point p in R, we find its closest neighbor in B.

matches   In machine vision, the ability to correctly identify images based on the comparison of pixel patterns.

material handler   A type of robot system. *See* material handling. It is included with conveyors, air-cushion conveyors, modular conveyors, other material handlers, automatic storage/retrieval systems, and stationary robot systems.

material handling   A function that has been used to define a type of robot system. It is also included with workstation-routing control systems, plant-production control systems, and plant-support control systems.

mating operations   A robot function that can be broken down into transfer operations, contact operations such as grasping, insertions, and other mating operations.

mean time between failure   The average amount of time between machine failures. A measure of machine performance in a plant environment.

mean time to repair (MTTR) The average amount of time before the successful repair activities have been completed. It can be used as a measure of machine performance in a plant environment.

measure of correlation A mathematical algorithm used in matching techniques for a machine vision system.

mechanical fuses Mechanical fuses are used as a robot safety feature because they are easily replaced and inexpensive.These fuses take the form of shearing pins that will break when there is excessive force applied at the robot's wrist. There may also be a small degree of "give" in the mechanical fuse.

medial-axis transformation (MAT) A skeletal region proposed by Blum for boundary representation in machine vision systems.

memory search In AI, searching for rules to attain a goal is performed forward and backward. Searching performed in memory is called a memory search.

Mentor An AI system developed by Honeywell for doing preventive maintenance on large air-conditioning systems. Honeywell estimates that this can extend the life of their equipment beyond 20 years.

microcomputer controller A component of a robot system that controls the movements and sequencing of robot movements through the use of a microcomputer.

minor local The types of accuracy needed in a total robot system can be described as universal, minor universal, major local, and minor local. Minor local involves the least amount of gross movement and is usually an adjustment before the function goal is completed such as a grasping operation.

minor universal accuracy The minor universal is a robot control flow for minor robot movement control before a minor local control movement is performed. *See* minor local.

MIPS The abbreviation for million of instructions per second. MIPS is used as a rough estimate of overall computer performance.

modeling techniques A simulation of an event or function, such as a real-world event. Modeling techniques are developed to be programmed into robots to help them perform a wide variety of functions.

moments In robotics, a description of robot-arm motions with respect to fixed reference point coordinate systems without the impact of forces or moments that may cause motion.

motion sequences Motion sequences are the movements that the robot has to execute in order to achieve the desired assembly task. They are examined by viewing the motions on a graphical screen from different viewing angles to check for collisions.

motion strategies Robot positions are obviously required with tailored sensor-based motion or movement strategies to ensure assembly accomplishment. An overall design for control of a robot system.

nanosecond One thousand-millionth (10^{-9}) of a second.

National Television Standards Committee (NTSC) A regulatory committee which specifies standards for color television.

natural-language filter A component of a natural-language processing system which can be broken down into relative AI applications as follows: (1) information breakdown, (2) transmission, (3) natural-language filter or machine-readable translator, (4) input and utilization.

natural-language processing Computer system processing that is based on rules and can analyze statements given in a nonsyntactical format.

NLC The abbreviation for natural-language comprehension. *Also see* natural-language processing.

nonlinear differential equations In robotics, mathematical formulas used in the computation of the most efficient robot control sequencing.

normalize In machine vision the use of an algorithm in the reduction of a list of coordinates for the control of robot movements. Normalizing positions can also reduce the number of command increments necessary to perform a wide variety of functions.

NTPM Normalized Texture Property Map (NTPM). This map, used in machine vision systems, encodes the observed effects of the surface orientation on a particular texture property.

numerically controlled machines A manufacturing entity that is controlled by the insertion of numerical data at some point.

object and assertions There are two types of inferences used in AI: object and assertion. Object inference relies on facts (I know it's a ball; balls are round). Assertion is based on supposition (I believe this to be true because the evidence indicates such).

occluding points Points that are used in machine vision systems so that points and shadows can be excluded for the image analysis process.

on-line system monitor A computer-based system which receives information on the assembly process on the plant floor and provides information on successful assemblies and any assembly error conditions.

optical tactile sensor A sensor utilizing a CCD imaging array integrated circuit combined with an acrylic plate and lens for image focus.

Optomation A vision system developed by General Electric.

orientation The position of an entity in relation to an external entity. A machine vision system combined with an AI system can position a robot in relation to parts in its workplace.

orthogonal directions A direction is orthogonal to another direction if the directions are at right angles to each other.

orthographic projection Planar geometric projections are called perspective projections or orthographic projections if they are projected at right angles to a specified plane.

oscillations In robotics, vibrations found in a robot hydraulic system as a result of a rapid stopping function in regard to picking up a particular tool. Through software control a settling time can be programmed in so that these types of oscillations associated with hydraulic systems can be allowed for.

pairwise adjacency In machine vision, using a matrix of components in an image. Pairwise adjacency is a means of examining the image for connected components.

parabolic mirror The most common modes of operation in machine vision through the use of laser scanners are (1) the revolving mirror, (2) the parabolic mirror, and (3) the galvanometer-operated mirror.

parallax In machine vision, an apparent displacement of a point P due to not only the location of P but also the characteristics of the two cameras that generate I_1 (image 1) and I_2 (image 2). Cameras are generally modeled as pinhole lenses. Thus the image formation process is modeled using the methods of this nature used to receive data, e.g., from a number of camera cells, until enough data is available for parallel processing.

parameters In AI, parameters are facts used in the inferring process. The basic function of an inference engine is using rules and paramaters.

part slippage In, robotics before a transfer movement is executed, for example, the end effector will rotate the part in order to minimize the part slippage during gross motion.

pattern recognition The ability of a machine vision system to identify regular figures for robot orientation.

PE ratio An abbreviation for proportional-error ratio used in robot control. For example, if the robot is in a stable state, the PE ratio equals zero. If the robot needs to move forward a number of degrees, then the PE ratio increases.

perimeter polygons   The polygonal approximation problem is illustrated by discussing a method proposed by Sklansky, Chazin, and Hansen for finding minimum-perimeter polygons. The procedure is used as a method of image identification used in machine vision.

persistence   The tendency for an image to remain on the phospor surface of the vidicon. The persistency of the phosphors maintains the image long enough for a complete scan.

pick-and-place activity   A robot function for the picking up of a workpiece and placing the workpiece in a programmed location.

pixel binary value   An aid to the particular visual scheme involved, this information is a binary representation of a visual image necessary for processing the image by computer.

pixel grouping   One of a number of functions that are used in image analysis for machine vision, such as image smoothing, edge detection, thresholding, template matching and segmentation.

pixel image   A numeric representation for an image usually designated in a matrix format such as a 256×256-pixel image. This is directly related to the computer storage requirements for a machine vision image.

planar geometric projections   A technique for projecting a 3-D scene onto a 2-D image. Most frequently, the image formation processes are modeled by planar geometric projections wherein the projection of a point P (in a 3-D scene) is a point on a 2-D representation.

planar set   In machine vision, a representation of an image based on a predefined boundary. For example, if we consider an object region as a planar set, a great deal can be said in general about the shape of the region by analyzing its convex hull and its convex deficiency.

pointers   Pointers are used to link data together in a program. A function of software in a high-level language such as Ada and Pascal, in which data declarations are broken down as constants, scalars, arrays, records, and pointers.

polar coordinates   A means of defining robot motion. Industrial robots use four basic motion definition categories: (1) Cartesian coordinates, (2) cylindrical coordinates, (3) spherical or polar coordinates, and (4) revolute or articular coordinates. The polar coordinate is specific to the vertical plane of the robot.

polygonal approximation   Adjacent points define a segment in the polygon. In practice, the goal of a polygonal approximation is to capture the "essence" of the boundary shape with the fewest possible polygonal segments.

positional accuracy   Robot gear backdriving will affect the positional accuracy, or exactness of the robot to position itself to a specified target point. With high payloads there is also an associated beam deflection. Beam deflection can also affect the robot's positional accuracy.

position servoing A certain kind of sensor-directed condition. Examples of this strategy include compliant motions, visual servoing, and other sensor-directed servo processes. The servoing is based on a Cartesian coordinate system relative to the position of a workpiece on the robot.

postconditions In robot motion planning, the state that the robot is in after the execution of a movement or function. A robot operation can possess a certain set of preconditions to achieve a certain set of postconditions. The task of the planner is then to satisfy these conditions subject to the constraints imposed by the design of the robot, the limitations of the workstation, or the constraints of the workpiece.

power carriers The types of material-handling mechanisms may be defined as power carriers, automatically guided vehicles, power and free conveyors, tow-cart systems, rail-guided vehicle systems, conveyors, roller conveyors, belt conveyors, air-cushion conveyors, modular conveyors, other material handlers, automatic storage/retrieval systems, and stationary robot systems.

power and free conveyors *See* power carriers.

preloaded springs Preloaded springs are the springs that act in conjunction with the safety system of a wrist assembly of a robot system so that any force acting on it in any direction on the end effector will separate the end effector from the wrist in a breakaway action.

preconditions In robotics, the preliminary state of the components of a robot system prior to component failure. This term is used in understanding equipment preventative maintenance requirements, the experimental background of the basic equipment, the range of different failures that can occur, and preconditions for the failure of that equipment.

prismatic A type of robot manipulator system joint. The joints can be described as either sliding or prismatic. Sliding joints are designated with an "S" and prismatic joints are designated with a "P." Rotary joints can also be described with an "R." This shorthand can be utilized to simulate robot movements prior to execution for analysis.

probability theory In machine vision, a mathematical tool used in the determination of reflectance and/or illumination of an image.

proportional-error ratio *See* PE ratio.

quality control A plant function which could be assisted by an AI/ES to determine if the product being produced meets minimum predefined criteria before it is approved for distribution.

rail-guided system   A type of material-handling robot found in a plant that moves material from one workstation to another. It is guided or directed by wires which are placed in the floor of the plant and which are connected to a computer controller.

reaction forces   Robot movement torques, or reaction forces, coming from a function such as drilling or twisting of the manipulator in regard to a specific object.

real-time process control   A computer-controlled system in a plant that uses machine data information immediately to direct predefined activities. An expert system can control plant activities in real-time process or actual event-time mode to take advantage of information or machine events as they occur.

recognition algorithm   A recognition algorithm is implemented in vision software by adding conditional statements inside the while loop in the search routine.

reflective component   In machine vision, the workpiece from which illuminated light is reflected to be viewed by a camera for analysis.

reflective-link inertia   The inertia or energy that can negatively affect a robot link. Robot reflective-link inertia has to be compensated for in the design of the robot system to assist the robot in maintaining positional accuracy.

relative orientation   Relative orientation determines the transformation between coordinate systems of two cameras in order to determine the actual position of the target.

reliability   In robotics, the factor in a robot system that is used as a measure of machine performance. It is the ability of a robot system to consistently perform a series of functions accurately over time.

repeatability   A measure of robot performace. Repeatability is the ability of a robot to perform a function or series of functions in the same sequence over a period of time.

resample   An approach frequently used to circumvent the problems of image boundary definition in image analysis is to "resample" the boundary by selecting a larger grid spacing. Then, as the boundary is traversed, a boundary point is assigned to each node of a large grid, depending on the proximity of the original boundary to that node.

resolved motionally control system   A type of robot motion control model such as RMCS, or resolved motionally control system, and the CMAC, or cerebral model articulation control.

retooling   The restructuring of the resources of a plant, i.e., machines, plant layout, scheduling, to produce a different product. In the past a retooling or refitting of a particular manufacturing system dictated the closing down of particular plants.

revolute coordinates   One type of the four robot motion categories: (1) Cartesian coordinates, (2) cylindrical coordinates, (3) spherical or polar coordinates, and (4) revolute or articular coordinates. Revolute coordinates are the coordinates of the revolution of a joint such as the wrist in terms of a 360° orientation.

revolving mirror   In laser scanners for machine vision the most common modes of operation are (1) the revolving mirror, (2) the parabolic mirror, and (3) the galvanometer-operating mirror. The revolving mirror deflects light scanned by the laser scanner.

rigid frames   A robot system is composed of rigid frames called links which are connected by revolute or prismatic joints. Each joint-link pair combines to constitute one degree of freedom.

rigidity   The main design considerations for actuators are as follows: rigidity, absolute accuracy, size and shape of the work volume, load-handling capacity, and microprocessor-control considerations. Rigidity is the stiffness of the robot links which must be accounted for by the robot controller to determine robot positional accuracy.

RMCS   Two types of models that have been proposed are the RMCS, or resolved motionally control system, and the CMAC, or cerebral model articulation control. *See* resolved motionally control system.

robust assembly   A robot assembly operation that is able to perform a wide range of operations and handle a wide variety of error and fault conditions is said to be robust.

rotary joints   A rotary joint is one which has the ability to rotate around a given axis in varying degrees of a 360° orientation. Rotary joints can be designated by an "R." The shorthand utilized can then describe a particular configuration from the base of the manipulator to the end effector attach point.

rotational changes   Rotational changes, displacements, or movement may affect the total force performance of the mechanical subassemblies of a robot system. A rotational change is a change of force on the manipulator rotating around a joint axis.

rounding errors   A design problem of robot motion control is rounding errors whereby the microprocessor, because of its internal architecture, will begin to round off numbers in making the translations between the real-world and the servomotor joint positions. These rounding factors will affect the absolute accuracy of the robot targeting.

rules   One of the basic constructs of an expert system. A rule consists of clauses that can be conditional or action oriented. A conditional clause is located on an "if" condition on the left-hand side of the rule. An action clause is located on the "then" or right-hand side of the rule.

saturation   In machine vision, saturation is the purity or grayness of a color.

scalar   Ada and Pascal use data declarations broken down as constants, scalars, arrays, records, and pointers. In Ada scalar values are used as primitive values to develop new object values. Some examples are integer numeric literals, real numeric literals, enumeration literals, character strings, and character values.

scaling values   Values used in robot motion control to adapt Cartesian coordinates to real-world targeting positions.

scanning   In machine vision, the programmed examination of a row or column of pixels by a computer for analysis.

search   In AI, a software component of an AI system used to identify and acquire information from the system knowledge base or data base.

segmentation   An algorithm used in machine vision to identify component parts of an entire area for analysis.

sensor-based motion strategies   Robot sensors used to detect real-time errors in the part and tool positions are obviously required with tailored sensor-based motion strategies to ensure assembly accomplishment. Sensor-based motion strategies are a broad category of sensing devices used to provide feedback information for motion control.

sensors   In machine vision and robot control, devices used to provide feedback information for orientation.

sequential workstation flow pattern   The implementation of a single sequence of processes very similar to existing manufacturing systems that are used today. For example, material may be loaded into one workstation as input and removed from another workstation as output without any sophisticated material buffering scheme to compensate for workstation overproduction or underproduction.

servo process   If the faces of the workpiece boundary are known, and if the orientation of the part can be determined from this information, an accurate, centered grasp can be found. This is a servo process.

settling   A condition of robot motion control which can be programmed into the robot controller so that oscillations associated with hydraulic systems can be overcome. Also referred to as settling time.

shading   The amount of light/dark contrast that can indicate the surface texture or depth of a workpiece being analyzed by a machine vision system.

shape number A gross measure of the shape of a boundary of a workpiece which may be obtained by computation.

signal processor A microprocessor used to process or analyze digitized visual images.

signature A signature is a one-dimensional functional representation of a boundary. There are a number of ways to generate signatures. One of the simplest is to plot the distance from the centroid to the boundary as a function of angle.

skeletonizing algorithm A mathematical formula used in machine vision to determine the minimal boundary of an image to be analyzed.

sketch image An abbreviated visual image that is an extraction of a two-dimensional image.

sketch stage The ability of an expert system module to be able to understand a three-dimensional image from a limited amount of input information such as has been defined as a 2½-dimension image. This concept is such that a minimum amount of input data is expanded by the computer system for a three-dimensional representation.

sliding joints Sliding joints are joints that can be extended along a specific X or Y plane.

smoothing A process that is used in machine vision processing and is necessary so that surfaces, or regions, can be uniquely identified. After smoothing, adjacent pixels within a region will have equal or very close values.

spatial resolution Spatial resolution, combined with repeatability and compliance, is used in robot motion positioning accuracy. It is the accurate targeting of the robot in relation to the workpiece located in an area of the workstation.

spherical coordinates *See* polar coordinates.

state A condition an entity such as a robot, workstation, electronic component, etc., is found in at a particular point in time.

stops Stops are points in a sequence of robot motions that indicate a change of motion or speed of the robot after the designed subsequence termination point or stop. A robot's activities contain a series of stops between movements.

structured light system This is a model used in machine vision combined with binocular vision which is applicable to many types of environments, and has been used extensively in interpretation of aerial images, autonomous vehicle guidance, and robotics.

subfunction A great deal of technical information is usually transformed into ordered information at some lower-level function, or subfunction. The main purpose of technical control information is to serve as a basis of generating the lower-level functions necessary for completion of the robot movement.

subloop   In robotics, a plant-floor trafficking system used to take advantage of the workstation buffering system. This traffic pattern can take advantage of quality control checks so that production rejects may be buffered and recycled through a particular workstation for correction or final rejection.

supposition   A design consideration of AI used along with assertion for logical inferring techniques. Assertion is based on supposition (I believe this to be true because the evidence indicates such). An inference driver makes the distinction or supposition for objects not explicitly mentioned such as in the above example "such IS TRUE."

symbolic error analysis package   This is a hardware/software system used to propagate errors through a motion sequence and is used to check generated plans. These plans are checked in terms of whether they satsify the required error constraints.

tactile array sensors   A feedback system used in robot end effectors to sense the grasping of an object. This type of system allows only the appropriate pressure to be used by the end effector for a particular workpiece.

tactile sensing device   A device utilized by a robot system as a feedback mechanism for the force applied by the end effector/gripper used in precision guided assembly operations.

teach pendant   A manual robot programming system or a hand-held trainer. With a hand-held trainer or teach pendant, the user or trainer moves the robot through a series of desired motions.

teleoperator system   A robot system which is controlled by a human operator. Teleoperated systems such as the ones proposed to be used on the U.S. space station will allow the astronaut crew to repair systems without venturing from the inside of the station.

template   In machine vision, a binary representation of an object used to match machine vision information by a computer.

template matching   Visual templates are used to identify and orient the robot to the workpiece moving on a conveyor line. A template matching scheme or verification scheme is used for proper part or component matching.

termination phase   The final phase of a robot motion sequence. In an insertion process, the force sensor monitors a sharp change as the workpiece makes contact. It would therefore be appropriate to utilize a force sensor to monitor the termination phase of the insertion.

texture In robotics, the representation of the surface of an object necessary for the proper grasping operation by a robot gripper.

thermal sensors Robot sensors used in noncontacting operations used if information about an object is necessary before robot contact.

thinning Shape representation in machine vision system is often accomplished by obtaining the skeleton of the region via a thinning (also called skeletonizing) algorithm. Thinning procedures play a central role in a broad range of problems in image processing, ranging from automated inspection of printed circuit boards to counting of asbestos fibers in air filters. *See* skeletonizing algorithm.

three-dimensioned Refers to an image structure of depth, breadth, and height necessary for robot orientation to a workpiece in a workstation. Understanding the structure of a 3-D environment requires carrying out tasks such as measurement of scene depth, assessment of relative positioning of objects, and 3-D object recognition.

thresholding Thresholding is a procedure used to obtain a binary image such that a characteristic function $b(x, y)$ is 0 for all image points corresponding to the background and 1 for points on the image being analyzed.

throughput The amount of time required to produce a product at a workstation. Throughput is used as a measure of not only computer speed but also workstation operational time.

tool tip In robotics, the point that is used as a contact point between the robot end effector and the workpiece. Robot orientation is critical for the positioning of the tool because inaccuracies at this point can cause workstation production drops or workstation stoppage.

topology Simply defined, topology in machine vision is the study of properties of a figure which are unaffected by any deformation, as long as there is no tearing or joining of the figure (these are sometimes called rubber-sheet distortions).

torques Compliance can be defined as the displacement of the end-effector tool relative to external forces (or torques) that may be applied to it. These torques or reaction forces come from a function such as drilling or twisting of the manipulator with respect to a specific object.

tow cart A plant material handling device that transports material from one workstation to another by using a tow cable.

traffic flow pattern The flow of material or products in a plant. Traffic flow analysis is very important to maximize the resources for the proper functioning of a plant.

transitive closure In machine vision, pixel matrix relationships can be grouped into implied relational sets. This algorithmic relational grouping is called transitive closure.

transfer operation   The movement of material to or within a workstation. A robot motion sequence can be broken down into transfer operations, contact operations such as grasping, insertions and other mating operations.

turnaround time   The amount of time taken by a cycle of robot operations. Factors that affect plant operations are throughput, turnaround time, work in process, flexibility, and reliability.

two-phase clock   In machine vision, an electronic device used in the timing operations for the sequencing of microcoded events in a CCD device used for image processing.

ultrasonic ranging system   A robot sensing device used when physical contact by the robot is not possible. Used as a safety feature in robot workstations to avoid any unexpected intrusion into the work area by human workers.

unit vector   In machine vision, a measurement used to determine distances accurately for robot control.

universal accuracy   The types of accuracy needed in a total robot system can be described as universal, minor universal, major local, and minor local. Universal accuracy considerations are factors that may occur at any accuracy point within the reach of the total robot manipulator.

variance   A mathematical formula used in determining the boundaries of shapes. Variances are used with averaging techniques to correctly identify the shape of an object in a machine vision system.

vector cross-referencing table   The Newton-Euler vector formulation uses vector cross-referencing tables. These tables involve dynamic equations which exclude the dynamics of control devices and gear friction. These equations deal with each one of the armature links in an independent entity in the overall motion control of the robot.

velocity forces   Forces affecting the control of a robot. In a robot motion planning operation, the type of end effector that is being used, the orientation of the end effector in regard to a specific function such as drilling, and any type of velocity forces that are being applied to the total system must be accounted for by the controller software. Velocity forces can adversely affect the targeting and positioning of the robot if they are incorrectly calculated.

vertical functions   A hierarchy of functions in the overall operation of a plant. Vertical functions are used by an AI scheduling system to determine the prioritization of operations in a plant and also any substitutions that may become necessary in the event of a workstation problem.

via points   A method by which robots can be trained to perform a task by breaking the task into a series of movements to fixed points. These fixed or via points can be orientation points from which the robot moves to other fixed or via points.

vidicon   A camera tube which incorporates a raster scanning by electron beam system to charge photoconductive materials stored on the inner surface of the tube.

visual servoing   A servo process which represents a position or a force goal, also representing a logical or a sensor-directed condition. Examples of this strategy include force, position servoing, compliant motions, and other sensor-directed servo movements.

VLSIC processors   The abbreviation for very large scale integrated circuits, with very high speed, high data throughput rates. The demands of machine vision combined with AI require processor power of this caliber.

VPL   VPL (Visual Programming Language) was used for setting up the image processing macros which the General Electric Optomation system executes.

wire-guided cart   A material-handling cart which usually takes advantage of a radio-frequency signal through a wire placed in the plant floor. The movement of the robot is checked by its orientation to the guide wire.

work in process   A term used to designate the production or assembly of material in a plant.

workstation downtime   The amount of time a workstation machine, such as a robot, is under repair or out of the production mode.

workstation rest activities   Workstation rest activities may be defined as the planned storage or unplanned waiting functions which may then be followed by in a workstation move, assembly, or verification task.

world coordinates   The coordinate plane of the workstation rather than points relative to the position of the robot.

X and Y coordinates   *See* Cartesian coordinates.

XCON   An expert system at Digital Equipment Corp. which processes order entry requests. A typical sequence can be done in two minutes as opposed to the one to two hours it took manually.

Index

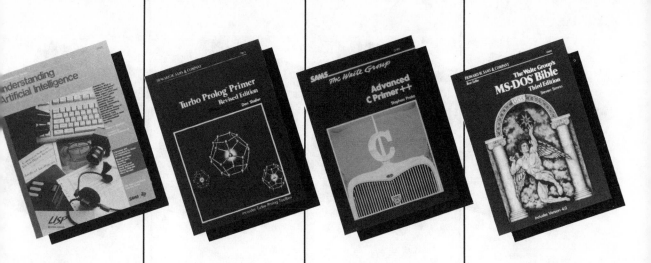

Understanding Expert Systems

Louis E. Frenzel, Jr.

This book explains how an expert system can function like an expert or intelligent consultant and answer questions, solve problems, and help make decisions.

This new Understanding Series title is suited for the technically inclined professional or manager interested in artificial intelligence and its subset, expert systems.

With the self-instructional format, readers can gain an understanding of expert systems, how they work, where they are used, and how to develop them. The material is completely illustrated, clear, concise, and application oriented. It also has marginal notes and review questions and answers.

Topics covered include:

- Expert Systems: The Big Picture
- Types of Expert Systems
- Applications of Expert Systems
- Knowledge Representation and Search
- How Expert Systems Work
- Expert System Development Tools
- How to Develop an Expert System
- References: Expert System Tool Vendors, AI Language Vendors, Publications, Glossary, and Quiz Answers

288 Pages, 7 x 9, Softbound
ISBN: 0-672-27065-X
No. 27065, $17.95

The Waite Group's MS-DOS® Developer's Guide Second Edition

John Angermeyer and Kevin Jaeger

This new and expanded developer's guide covers the MS-DOS and PC-DOS™ operating systems up to Version 3.3, concentrating on techniques for developing application programs as well as memory resident programs and device drivers. The book is aimed at the serious programmer, developer, or "power user" with a significant understanding of MS-DOS.

Topics covered include:

- Structured Programming
- Program and Memory Management in the MS-DOS Environment
- TSRs
- EMS
- Real-Time Programming Under MS-DOS
- Installable Device Drivers
- Writing Programs for the Intel 8087/80287 Math Coprocessor
- LANs and MS-DOS
- Programming the Serial Port
- Programming the EGA and VGA
- Disk Layout and File Recovery Information
- Recovering Data Lost in Memory
- Differences Between MS-DOS Versions
- High-Level Languages
- Debugging

600 Pages, 7½ x 9¾, Softbound
ISBN: 0-672-22630-8
No. 22630, $24.95

C Programmer's Guide to Serial Communications

Joe Campbell

This book offers a comprehensive examination and unprecedented dissection of asynchronous serial communications. Written for C programmers and technically advanced users, it contains both a theoretical discussion of communications concepts and a practical approach to program design for the IBM® PC and Kaypro environments.

Topics covered include:

- The ASCII Character Set
- Fundamentals of Asynchronous Technology
- Errors and Error Detection
- Information Transfer
- Modems and Modem Control
- The UART—A Conceptual Model
- Real-World Hardware: Two UARTs
- The Hayes Smartmodem
- Designing a Basic Serial I/O Library
- Portability Considerations
- Timing Functions
- Functions for Baud Rate and Data Format
- RS-232 Control
- Formatted Input and Output
- Smartmodem Programming
- XMODEM File Transfers
- CRC Calculations
- Interrupts

672 Pages, 7½ x 9¾, Softbound
ISBN: 0-672-22584-0
No. 22584, $26.95

Tricks of the MS-DOS® Masters

John Angermeyer, Rich Fahringer, Kevin Jaeger, and Dan Shafer, The Waite Group

This title provides the personal user (not necessarily the programmer or software developer) with a wealth of advanced tips about the operating system and tricks for using it most successfully.

Also included are advanced tips on using popular software packages such as WordStar® .

Topics covered include:

- Secrets of the Batch File Command Language
- Secrets of Pipes, Filters, and Redirection
- Secrets of Tree-Structured Directories
- Discovering Secrets: A Debugger Tutorial
- Secrets of DOS Commands
- Secrets of Files
- Secrets of Free and Low-Cost Software
- Secrets of Add-on Software, Boards, and Mass Storage
- Secrets of System Configuration
- Secrets of Data Encryption

568 Pages, 7½ x 9¾, Softbound
ISBN: 0-672-22525-5
No. 22525, $24.95